COMPREHENSIVE BIOCHEMISTRY

SOLE DISTRIBUTORS FOR THE UNITED STATES AND CANADA:
AMERICAN ELSEVIER PUBLISHING COMPANY, INC.
52, VANDERBILT AVENUE, NEW YORK 17, N.Y.

SOLE DISTRIBUTORS FOR GREAT BRITAIN:
ELSEVIER PUBLISHING COMPANY LIMITED
12B, RIPPLESIDE COMMERCIAL ESTATE
RIPPLE ROAD, BARKING, ESSEX

Library of Congress Catalog Card Number 62–10359

With 30 illustrations and 36 tables

COMPREHENSIVE BIOCHEMISTRY

COMPREHENSIVE
BIOCHEMISTRY

SECTION I (VOLUMES 1–4)
PHYSICO-CHEMICAL AND ORGANIC ASPECTS
OF BIOCHEMISTRY

SECTION II (VOLUMES 5–11)
CHEMISTRY OF BIOLOGICAL COMPOUNDS

SECTION III
BIOCHEMICAL REACTION MECHANISMS

SECTION IV
METABOLISM

SECTION V
CHEMICAL BIOLOGY

GENERAL INDEX

COMPREHENSIVE BIOCHEMISTRY

EDITED BY

MARCEL FLORKIN

Professor of Biochemistry, University of Liège (Belgium)

AND

ELMER H. STOTZ

Professor of Biochemistry, University of Rochester, School of Medicine and Dentistry, Rochester, N.Y. (U.S.A.)

VOLUME 8

PROTEINS (PART 2)

AND

NUCLEIC ACIDS

ELSEVIER PUBLISHING COMPANY

AMSTERDAM · LONDON · NEW YORK

1963

CONTRIBUTORS TO THIS VOLUME

ROGER ACHER
Professor of Biochemistry, Faculty of Science, University of Paris,
96 Boulevard Raspail, Paris VI (France)

OTTO K. BEHRENS, Ph.D.
The Lilly Research Laboratories, Eli Lilly and Company,
Indianapolis 6, Ind. (U.S.A.)

ENZO BOERI*, M.D., Ph.D.
Professor of Physiology, University of Ferrara (Italy)

WILLIAM W. BROMER, Ph.D.
The Lilly Research Laboratories, Eli Lilly and Company,
Indianapolis 6, Ind. (U.S.A.)

D. M. BROWN, Ph.D. (Cantab.)
University Chemical Laboratory, Lensfield Road, Cambridge (Great Britain)

JAMES D. COOMBES, B.Sc., Ph.D.
Lecturer in Biophysics, Biophysics Department, King's College,
Strand, London W.C. 2 (Great Britain)

ALFRED GOTTSCHALK, M.D. (Bonn), D.Sc. (Melbourne)
Fellow of the Australian Academy of Science, Australian National University.
Department of Microbiology, P.O.Box 641, Canberra, A.C.T. (Australia)

FRANK R. N. GURD, M.Sc., Ph.D.
Professor of Biochemistry, Indiana University School of Medicine,
1100 West Michigan Street, Indianapolis 7, Ind. (U.S.A.)

R. G. HUNTSMAN, M.B. (Cambridge), M.R.C.P.
Chemical Pathologist, Memorial Hospital, Peterborough, Northants. (Great Britain)

H. LEHMANN, M.D. (Basel), Sc.D. (Cambridge), M.R.C.P., F.R.I.C.
Reader in Chemical Pathology, St. Bartholomew's Hospital, London, E.C. 1
(Great Britain)

CHOH HAO LI, Ph.D., M.D. h.c.
Professor of Biochemistry, Professor of Experimental Endocrinology;
Director, Hormone Research Laboratory, University of California,
Berkeley and San Francisco, Calif. (U.S.A.)

---

* deceased.

RAYMOND MICHEL, D.Sc.
Professor of Biochemistry, Medical School of Dijon (France)

HOWARD RASMUSSEN, M.D., PH.D.
Department of Biochemistry, University of Wisconsin, Madison, Wis. (U.S.A.)

JEAN ROCHE, D.Sc.
Professor of General and Comparative Biochemistry, Collège de France,
Place Marcellin-Berthelot, Paris (France)

T. L. V. ULBRICHT, B.Sc., PH.D.
Twyford Laboratories, Twyford Abbey Road, London, N.W.10 (Great Britain)

M. H. F. WILKINS, M.A., PH.D., F.R.S.
Medical Research Council, Biophysics Research Unit, Biophysics
Department, King's College, Strand, London, W.C. 2 (Great Britain)

G. R. WILKINSON, B.Sc., PH.D. (LONDON)
Reader in Physics, Physics Department, King's College, Strand,
London, W.C. 2 (Great Britain)

GENERAL PREFACE

The Editors are keenly aware that the literature of Biochemistry is already very large, in fact so widespread that it is increasingly difficult to assemble the most pertinent material in a given area. Beyond the ordinary textbook the subject matter of the rapidly expanding knowledge of biochemistry is spread among innumerable journals, monographs, and series of reviews. The Editors believe that there is a real place for an advanced treatise in biochemistry which assembles the principal areas of the subject in a single set of books.

It would be ideal if an individual or small group of biochemists could produce such an advanced treatise, and within the time to keep reasonably abreast of rapid advances, but this is at least difficult if not impossible. Instead, the Editors with the advice of the Advisory Board, have assembled what they consider the best possible sequence of chapters written by competent authors; they must take the responsibility for inevitable gaps of subject matter and duplication which may result from this procedure.

Most evident to the modern biochemist, apart from the body of knowledge of the chemistry and metabolism of biological substances, is the extent to which he must draw from recent concepts of physical and organic chemistry, and in turn project into the vast field of biology. Thus in the organization of Comprehensive Biochemistry, the middle three sections, Chemistry of Biological Compounds, Biochemical Reaction Mechanisms, and Metabolism may be considered classical biochemistry, while the first and last sections provide selected material on the origins and projections of the subject.

It is hoped that sub-division of the sections into bound volumes will not only be convenient, but will find favour among students concerned with specialized areas, and will permit easier future revisions of the individual volumes. Toward the latter end particularly, the Editors will welcome all comments in their effort to produce a useful and efficient source of biochemical knowledge.

Liège/Rochester

M. FLORKIN
E. H. STOTZ

PREFACE TO SECTION II

(VOLUMES 5-11)

Section II on the Chemistry of Biological Compounds deals with the organic and physical chemistry of the major organic constituents of living material. A general understanding of organic and physical chemistry is presumed, but the reader will find the special topics in Section I of value in the fuller understanding of several parts of Section II. The Editors have made special effort to include a sound treatment of the important biological high polymers, including sections on their shape and physical properties. A number of substances peculiar to plants, certain isoprenoids, flavonoids, tannins, lignins, and plant hormones, often omitted from textbooks of biochemistry, are included. Nevertheless, it is inevitable that some omissions, hopefully minor ones, have occurred. The only intentional omission is the chemistry of the coenzymes and certain components of biological oxidation, which will be covered in connection with their function in Section III.

The previous policy of dividing the section into smaller volumes has been continued, resulting in seven volumes for Section II. Two of the volumes each contain a complete area, namely Carbohydrates (Volume 5) and Sterols, Bile Acids and Steroids (Volume 10). Comments from readers will be appreciated by the Editors and be most helpful for possible future revisions.

Liège/Rochester

M. FLORKIN
E. H. STOTZ

CONTENTS

VOLUME 8

Part A

PROTEINS (Part 2)

Chapter I. Conjugated Proteins

Section a. Lipoproteins

by FRANK R.N. GURD

Chapter I. Conjugated Proteins

Section b. Glycoproteins and Glycopeptides

by ALFRED GOTTSCHALK

Chapter II. Peptide and Protein Hormones
Section b. Parathyroid Hormone
by HOWARD RASMUSSEN, p. 93

Chapter II. Peptide and Protein Hormones
Section c. Adenohypophyseal Hormones
by CHOH HAO LI

Chapter II. Peptide and Protein Hormones
Section d. Neurohypophyseal Hormones
by ROGER ACHER

Chapter II. Peptide and Protein Hormones

Section e. Insulin and Glucagon

by WILLIAM W. BROMER AND OTTO K. BEHRENS

Part B
NUCLEIC ACIDS

Chapter III. Chemistry of the Nucleic Acids
Section a. Introduction, p. 155
by D. M. BROWN AND T.L.V. ULBRICHT

Chapter III. Chemistry of the Nucleic Acids
Section b. Nucleic Acid Bases and Nucleosides
by T.L.V. ULBRICHT

A. Chemical Constitution of the Nucleic Acid Bases

B. Chemical Constitution of the Nucleosides

Chapter III. Chemistry of the Nucleic Acids
Section c. Nucleotides and Polynucleotides
by D.M. BROWN

Chapter IV. Physical Properties of the Nucleic Acids
Section a. The Three-Dimensional Configuration of the DNA Molecule
by M. H. F. WILKINS

Chapter IV. Physical Properties of the Nucleic Acids
Section b. Solution Properties
by JAMES D. COOMBES

Chapter IV. Physical Properties of the Nucleic Acids
Section c. Spectroscopic Properties
by G. R. WILKINSON

Volume 8

Part A

PROTEINS (PART 2)

Chapter I

Conjugated Proteins

Section a

Lipoproteins

FRANK R. N. GURD

Department of Biochemistry, Indiana University School of Medicine,
Indianapolis, Ind. (U.S.A.)

1. Introduction

Most of the lipids in healthy cells, with the exception of those specialized for the storage of triglyceride, differ in two important ways from isolated preparations of lipids. First, these lipids are highly dispersed. Second, they are not readily extracted by treatment with good lipid solvents such as diethyl ether, unless the tissues are treated drastically with more polar organic solvents or else are hydrolyzed. These properties appear to depend on association of the lipids with proteins.

In the application of procedures for the isolation of individual proteins from mixtures such as blood plasma it has been found possible to isolate lipid–protein complexes containing rather regular proportions of various lipids and proteins. The complexes isolated from plasma have the solubility characteristics of proteins, and therefore are called *lipoproteins*. Other tissues, notably brain, have yielded complexes of lipids and proteins which have the solubility properties of lipids, and so have been called *proteolipids*. Of special interest are the observations that the particulate fractions separated from cells, such as mitochondria and microsomes, contain large quantities of lipids, especially phospholipids. The separation of individual enzymes or sets of enzymes from these intracellular structures has been accomplished by methods that disrupt or remove the lipid moieties.

Lipids and proteins ordinarily combine with each other by association of similar types of functional groups in the two classes of compounds, such as the non-polar, hydrophobic residues of the fatty acid moieties of lipids and the similar residues of certain of the side-chain groups of proteins. Polar or charged groups may be involved in other interactions, but primary covalent linkages do not seem to be responsible for the association. The interactions between lipids and proteins thus appear to have much in common with the interactions between small molecules and proteins or between substrates and enzymes where it is recognized that the tightness and specificity of binding depend to a large extent on steric arrangement. The strong binding of lipids to proteins may depend on the same factors of closeness of fit, multiple attachment, and matching of polarity that are recognized to determine the combination of substrates, inhibitors, and coenzymes with enzymes.

Many lipoproteins contain so much lipid that the number of lipid molecules involved in the complexes is comparable to or greater than the number of protein side chains that could possibly be available for association with the lipid molecules. In such cases the stabilization of the complexes cannot be due solely to lipid–protein interactions but lipid–lipid interactions have to be considered as well. In other cases only a few lipid molecules may be combined per molecule of protein, and it may be possible to interpret the binding in terms of individual sites on the surface of the protein, each composed of some appropriate arrangement or cluster of several side-chain groups of the amino acid residues.

For a specific detailing of the non-polar, polar and charged structures in lipids and proteins the reader is referred elsewhere in this treatise. The most important types of potential interactions will be summarized here. Because lipid–protein interactions must be thought of as competing thermodynamically with interactions between one lipid molecule and another or between one structure in a protein and another, it is important to consider all three types of potential interaction before turning to a discussion of the naturally-occurring lipoprotein systems.

With the exception of the hydrocarbons such as the carotenes, lipids share with proteins the property of containing both polar and non-polar structures. In polar structures atoms of widely different electronegativity are bonded to each other, and the shared pairs of electrons tend to be distorted from a symmetrical distribution. For example, the O—H bond in a hydroxyl group or in water is polarized so that the region of the O atom contains a net negative charge and that of the H atom a net positive charge. The grouping is said to be polar.

Polar molecules tend to attract each other. In water, for example, each O atom tends to attract an H atom in each of two neighboring water molecules at the same time as its own pair of H atoms is attracted to two other water molecules. The polar interactions between water molecules are especially effective in causing the molecules to associate with each other because the small size of the H atom allows it to serve as a bridge in a compact structure. The individual water molecules are linked together by bridges of the form O—H $\cdots$ O where the longer linkage denoted by the dotted line denotes the weaker intermolecular linkage.

Charged groups bearing a full formal charge interact very strongly indeed with other such highly polar groups as well as with the formally uncharged polar groups discussed above. Ions attract and repel each other over appreciable distances, and also attract and orient polar molecules or groups.

Non-polar structures such as aliphatic hydrocarbons have symmetrical distributions of bonding electrons. They are polarized permanently to only a slight extent if any and are attracted to each other by rather weak forces operative over very short distances. The attraction of polar molecules for each other is such that in a polar environment the non-polar molecules or groups tend to be squeezed together to allow the greatest amount of mutual interaction between polar groups. In an aqueous environment part of the driving force favoring the segregation of non-polar molecules or groups seems to be due to the tendency of the latter molecules when interspersed with water molecules to favor the development of a more ordered water structure in their neighborhood. The driving force for the segregation thus depends in part on an entropy effect.

2. Lipid–lipid interactions

The lipids may be arranged in a spectrum according to their relative balance between non-polar and polar properties. The most predominantly non-polar lipids such as the carotenoids, triglycerides, cholesterol and cholesterol esters contain so few polar groups that they tend to separate from an aqueous medium and show very little solubility in water. Finely divided droplets of pure triglyceride in water tend to coalesce spontaneously and form a separate phase with the smallest possible interface between triglyceride and water. Even though these compounds are very insoluble in water, any molecules which do come into contact with water will tend to orient so that their polar parts, *e.g.* the hydroxyl group in cholesterol, will be able to interact with the water molecules.

The more polar lipids, such as phospholipids and fatty acid salts, have relatively large polar moieties containing groups bearing formal charges. Polar moieties of this kind have such a high affinity for water and resist being buried in a non-polar environment to such an extent that they tend to remain at all times in a polar environment. For the alkali soaps this tendency is reflected in the formation of micelles in which the fatty acid anions are aligned for the most part in double layers with the carboxyl groups projecting into the water and the hydrocarbon chains intermingling with each other. The positively charged counter-ions, *e.g.* Na^+, K^+, are restrained to the vicinity of the relatively fixed carboxyl groups. Various overall shapes may be taken by the micelles, ranging from large flat double sheets to aggregates so compact that they are nearly spherical. Such micelles are in equilibrium with single soap molecules. The micelles owe their stability to the segregation and mutual affinity of the closely packed hydrocarbon chains which balances the tendency of the charged carboxyl groups in the aqueous interface to repel each other.

When mixed with water, many preparations of phospholipids tend to form sheets of double layers of molecules oriented so that the hydrocarbon chains of the fatty acid moieties of the two layers are intermingled and the polar parts protrude on either side into the aqueous environment. These structures form spontaneously and are very similar to the soap micelles except that the sheets of double layers are not often interrupted and usually curve round on themselves to form balloon-like structures or canals. These structures are called myelinic figures. Usually many double layers are found wrapped together with a characteristic and quite constant spacing between double layers depending upon the particular phospholipid preparation and the nature and concentration of ions in the medium. Apparently the concentration of single phospholipid molecules free in the aqueous medium is very low.

Both the membrane-like phospholipid structures and the soap micelles are able to accommodate more than one type of molecule. For example, a certain amount of cholesterol can be incorporated in the phospholipid without destroying the ability to form myelinic figures, although the physical properties may be altered somewhat. Similarly, long-chain alcohols or hydrocarbons may be incorporated into soap micelles.

3. Protein–protein interactions

The interactions of different groups in a protein with each other to maintain the native structure of the protein involve all the factors responsible for the association of lipid molecules with each other, such as association of non-polar moieties and interactions between polar groups. The distribution of non-polar moieties in proteins, represented by the side chains of alanine, valine, leucine and isoleucine in particular, is probably less regular than the arrangement of non-polar moieties in a lipid double layer. Nevertheless, it is probable that the non-polar side chains are segregated into pools in the structure of most proteins. The completeness of this segregation will depend on other factors, such as the sequence and folding of the polypeptide chains and the forces stabilizing the native configuration. Often the native configuration can be disrupted simply by spreading the protein molecule at an air–water or oil–water interface. In either case the non-polar side chains presumably project out of the aqueous phase and the polar side chains into it. The native, curved and probably irregular polar–non-polar interfaces are replaced by a more regular interface in the spread molecule. Usually the spread protein molecule is found to have a thickness corresponding to the thickness of only one polypeptide chain. The studies with surface films bring out the common polar–non-polar duality of proteins and lipids.

4. Lipid–protein interactions

The association of lipids with proteins may be considered in two categories. In the first the lipid molecules are bound to distinct sites on the protein molecule. In the second the protein combines with lipid molecules which are themselves associated in some way in films, micelles or emulsions. Examples of the first kind of interaction are provided by the binding of fatty acid anions by serum albumin and the binding of small quantities of detergents by several kinds of proteins. Serum albumin has been equilibrated with known low concentrations of various fatty acid salts and the binding has been interpreted in terms of two sites which bind most strongly, five sites of intermediate affinity, and perhaps twenty sites of lesser affinity. Affinity for the stronger sites increased steadily over the series laurate, myristate, palmitate, stearate and oleate.

Various studies have been made of the interaction of proteins with mono-molecular layers of lipids such as cholesterol and stearic acid spread on the aqueous protein solutions. Other investigations have dealt with the inter-

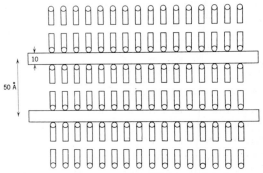

Fig. 1. Diagram of bimolecular lipid leaflets with intercalated monomolecular layers of protein.

action of dissolved proteins with droplets of hydrocarbons emulsified in water and stabilized with added detergents. Studies of this sort have confirmed that proteins can interact with lipids that are themselves associated.

Perhaps the most interesting study of the interaction of a protein with associated lipids was performed by Palmer, Schmitt and Chargaff[1]. Mixtures of histone or globin with preparations of phosphatidyl ethanolamine (probably containing phosphatidyl serine) were studied by X-ray diffraction to determine the spacings of the double layers or bimolecular leaflets. In the absence of added protein or water the phospholipid was found to be oriented in bimolecular leaflets with an identity period of 43.8 Å in the direction perpendicular to the planes of the leaflets. In the presence of histone the period increased by 13–15 Å, and of globin by 7–9 Å. The phospholipid spacings would increase more than two-fold on the addition of water, but in the presence of histone the uptake was very sparing so that the identity period increased on wetting by only 5–10 Å. The components therefore appeared to be fixed to each other. The attractive forces were taken to be between the positively charged histone molecules and the charged moieties of the phospholipids bearing net negative charges. The phospholipid and protein in the complexes were taken to be arranged according to the scheme shown in Fig. 1. The thickness of the protein layer is characteristic of a spread unimolecular layer. This layer is sandwiched between bimolecular lipid layers.

5. Some naturally-occurring lipoprotein systems

The foregoing description of the types of association that may be observed between lipids and proteins gives an idea of the variety of lipid–protein complexes that may be met in nature. The least polar lipids, such as the triglycerides, may be expected to form spherical droplets as in an emulsion, possibly covered by a film of more polar lipids or proteins or both together. The most polar lipids, such as fatty acids, lysophosphatides and some steroids may act as single small molecules reacting discretely with sites in the protein. The very plentiful lipids of intermediate polarity, such as phospholipids, tend to associate with similar lipid molecules and also to interact with non-polar and polar residues in proteins. They tend to form bimolecular aggregates in membranous structures which may interact with protein molecules. Some possible examples of these types of association phenomena in naturally-occurring lipoprotein systems will now be discussed.

Lipids occur as complex mixtures whose composition may vary according to the metabolic state of the organism. The fatty acid composition of the lipids in lipoprotein complexes is not rigidly fixed, and any preparation of lipoprotein complexes is likely to represent a family of closely related complexes whose composition with respect at least to fatty acids varies somewhat from particle to particle. In general too little is known about the detailed composition of lipoproteins for the descriptions to go beyond assignment to class (e.g. triglyceride, phospholipid).

In the discussion to follow, the plasma lipoproteins are considered first, followed by the association of lipids with certain structural elements in the cell. Lastly, the proteolipids are discussed briefly.

(a) Lipoproteins in blood plasma

(i) Isolation

It has been known for many years that the lipids in blood plasma are precipitated along with proteins and can be brought back into clear solution when the proteins are redissolved. In 1929, Macheboeuf[2] reported the isolation from horse serum of an albumin-like substance containing reproducible proportions of phospholipids, cholesterol esters and proteins. The substance was isolated by ammonium sulfate fractionation with repeated precipitation near pH 3.8 followed by resolution at higher pH. Some of the lipids in horse serum are associated with other protein fractions.

Systematic studies of the fractionation of human plasma at low temperatures in ethanol–water mixtures undertaken by Cohn et al.[3] led to the description of two major lipoprotein components. From their electrophoretic behavior they are called α- and β-lipoproteins. The α-lipoproteins are more soluble than the β-lipoproteins in the presence of alcohol or of high concentrations of salts, but in physiological saline solution even the β-lipoproteins can be prepared in concentrations greater than 10%. A third major class should be added, consisting of the serum albumin–fatty acid complexes which were not initially recognized as physiologically important lipoprotein complexes. By comparison with the α- and β-lipoproteins, however, albumin is relatively lipid-poor.

The most generally useful method of separating lipoproteins is by flotation in the ultracentrifuge. Due to their high content of lipids the plasma lipoproteins have a lower density than that of the lipid-poor proteins. If the density of the medium is sufficiently increased by the addition of salts, sucrose or heavy water the lipoproteins will be caused to move centripetally in the ultracentrifuge cell while the lipid-poor proteins continue to sediment normally.

Two general procedures have been used for isolation of lipoproteins according to density. First, by making stepwise increases in the density of the medium after each of a succession of ultracentrifugations, it is possible to take off a series of fractions each of which has in turn been floated to the upper part of the centrifuge tube. Second, by varying the concentration of solute according to depth in the centrifuge tube it is possible to establish a density gradient within which the different classes of lipoproteins distribute themselves into layers which can be harvested separately. Both procedures have been used successfully. The density gradient technique has some advantages when it is desirable to limit the number of manipulations to which the lipoproteins are exposed.

Ultracentrifugation in a medium of homogeneous density is useful not only as a procedure for isolation of lipoproteins, but has been applied in the analytical ultracentrifuge to their characterization. Flotation is opposite in sign to the usual direction of sedimentation. It is common to use the notation S_f to denote the rate of flotation in Svedberg units under certain arbitrary conditions, namely, in a unit centrifugal field when the lipoprotein is suspended in an aqueous sodium chloride solution of density 1.063 at 26°. The rate of flotation is determined by (1) the difference in density between the medium and the lipoprotein complex, (2) the particle weight, and (3) a shape factor. Since the densities of lipoprotein complexes cover a considerable range, it

TABLE I

COMPOSITION OF THE MAJOR PLASMA LIPOPROTEINS[4]

Average per cent values taken from Oncley[5-7]

Normal concentration in plasma (mg/100 ml)	Peptide	Phospholipid	Cholesterol		Triglyceride	NEFA	Carotenoid present	N-Terminal amino acid		Approximate S_f class
			Alcohol	Ester				Major	Minor	
Chylomicrons										
100–250	2	7	2	6	83		Lutein	Ser, Thr	Asp	> 40
Lipoproteins, density 0.98										
130–200	9	18	7	15	50	1	Lutein	Ser, Thr	Asp, Glu	~10–40
Lipoproteins, density 1.035										
210–400	21	22	8	38	10	1	α-Carotene, lycopene, lutein	Glu	Thr, Ser	~3–
Lipoproteins, density 1.09										
50–130	33	29	7	23	8		Lutein, β-carotene, lycopene	Asp	Ser, Thr	
Lipoproteins, density 1.14										
290–400	57	21	3	14	5		Lutein, β-carotene, lycopene	Asp	Ser, Thr	

is unwise to look upon S_f values as an indication of particle weight even though it appears from other measurements that particle weight does indeed show a general upward trend with increasing S_f. It should be recognized that certain lipoproteins, mainly the α-lipoproteins, have densities above 1.063 and would show negative values of S_f. For these lipoproteins it is sometimes the practice to use a more dense standard medium in which flotation rates can be observed.

(ii) Composition

The compositions of the major human plasma lipoprotein classes are summarized in Table I. The classes considered range from the chylomicrons, the triglyceride-rich droplets which are large enough to be detected with the ultramicroscope, to the most dense lipoproteins of molecular weight near 175,000. The serum albumin–fatty acid complexes are omitted from Table I. The values for peptide, phospholipid, cholesterol, triglyceride and non-esterified fatty acid (NEFA) are percentages. The types of carotenoid known to be present are indicated, as are the major and minor N-terminal amino acids recognized in the polypeptide moieties. Lastly, the approximate S_f classes are indicated. It is obvious from the spreading of the S_f values that none of these classes contains homogeneous complexes. Oncley *et al.*[8] have shown that variations in composition and density within each class appear to be continuous but that all fractions separable from a given class have much greater similarity to each other than to fractions separable from any other class.

(iii) Stability

The stability of the plasma lipoproteins may be considered in terms of (*1*) factors affecting stability during handling, and (*2*) the maintenance of discrete structures under physiological conditions. Lipoproteins are readily damaged by the common denaturing conditions such as heat, extremes of pH and frothing. They are also susceptible to damage in the lipid moiety due to autoxidation and possibly hydrolysis. Autoxidation is retarded by agents such as ethylenediaminetetraacetate that complex with metal ions, notably cupric ion, and such agents should always be present during purification or handling of the purified lipoproteins. Autoxidation is usually accompanied by changes in the visible and ultraviolet absorption spectra. Aging of lipoprotein preparations often results in release of fatty acids which remain bound to the lipoproteins and alter their electrophoretic mobility. The change in mobility may be minimized by adding serum albumin which accepts the split-off fatty acids. A less well understood cause of instability is freezing. Some protection against freezing is afforded in some instances by adding glycerol, glucose or sucrose to the medium.

As indicated above, fatty acid molecules are readily exchanged between the lipid-rich plasma lipoproteins and albumin. Other lipids, including cholesterol which is very insoluble in water, are also readily exchanged between one lipoprotein fraction and another or between the plasma lipoproteins and red blood cells. In order for these transfers to occur at measurable rates it appears most likely that lipoprotein molecules can collide and form temporary collision complexes. The exchange of lipid molecules presumably occurs within these collision complexes. On decomposition of the collision complexes the original lipoprotein structures are reconstituted.

Little is known about the structures of the plasma lipoproteins. In view of their solubility in aqueous solution and the difficulty of burying charged groups in a medium of low dielectric constant it seems likely that the protein moieties are exposed to the aqueous environment. The β-lipoproteins in particular are composed of a lipid mixture which by itself does not readily form stable aqueous dispersions. The protein moiety may prevent the extensive aggregation that would otherwise be anticipated and which is indeed seen when the lipoproteins are treated harshly. Again in the case of the β-lipoproteins the protein moiety is too small a proportion of the whole for the entire surface to be composed of it. That fraction of the surface containing lipid (phospholipid?) molecules may present an avenue for the exchange of lipid molecules during the restricted and reversible aggregation process presumed to occur during the exchange.

(b) Lipoproteins of cells

Some of the lipoproteins in cells appear to be present in solution and are isolated as soluble components when the cells are subjected to fractionation. Indeed, immunochemical techniques demonstrate the presence within cells of materials that react strongly with antibodies prepared against plasma lipoproteins.

Little is known of the soluble lipoproteins within cells. In recent years much more attention has been given to the lipids associated with membranous structures. These membranous structures are found in the nuclei, mitochondria and microsomes. The lipoproteins in the mitochondria and microsomes are probably exclusively arranged in membranous structures. Mitochondria are composed of an outer membrane and an inner structure which is highly convoluted. The microsomes as harvested by high-speed centrifugation of a fraction of homogenized cells are composed of debris derived from the endoplasmic reticulum or ergastoplasm. The endoplasmic reticulum is very varied in form and is found in all cells except the mature anucleate red blood cell. Often it extends throughout most of the cytoplasm as tubular or interconnected vesicular structures which may form broad, flat vesicles called cisternae. These cisternae often align themselves like stacks of nearly empty balloons to give a lamellar appearance. The three-dimensional extent of the endoplasmic reticulum is so great that no electron micrograph can reveal more than a part of the structure. There is evidence, however, that it can be continuous with the nuclear membrane and with the outer cell membrane. Varying numbers of small particles are found to be attached to parts of the system either in the cell or in the microsome fraction. These particles consist largely of ribonucleoprotein and are of the order of 150 Å in diameter.

The debris of the endoplasmic reticulum isolated in the microsome fraction is remarkable in that the membranes all appear to be closed in the form of vesicles of various sizes and shapes. Apparently the shearing stress of homogenization causes the structure to divide by pinching off in such a way that the torn edges fuse together sufficiently rapidly that only closed forms are observed.

The microsome fraction is often found to be composed of about one-third lipid, the mitochondrial about one-fifth to one-quarter, and the nuclear somewhat less. The mitochondria and microsomes are very rich in phospholipids and contain small quantities of cholesterol. Triglyceride is mostly found in the supernatant (soluble) fraction. Sometimes the more highly aggregated triglyceride-rich material is classed as a "free fat" fraction. It should be kept in mind that many of the procedures for preparing the cell fractions involve mechanical manipulations that would cause plasma lipoproteins to aggregate and that similar damage may be suffered by the soluble cellular lipoproteins. Some valuable observations on the stability of cellular lipoprotein materials have been reported by Thomas et al.[9].

The membranes of the microsomes have some properties in common with the myelinic forms made by purified phospholipids. The mode of association of lipids with protein may be similar to that illustrated in Fig. 1. The membranes may be disintegrated by the action of deoxycholate. Considering the flexibility of the membranes and their property of flowing together at torn edges it is clear that much of their behavior reflects the tendency of phospholipids to aggregate in ordered layers. It is known that cholesterol affects the rigidity of films of phospholipid and it seems likely that the composition of the mixture of lipids in these structures is of critical importance. What role the protein moieties may play in stabilizing the structures is unknown. It seems very likely that the presence of the protein helps control the spacing between bimolecular layers of lipids, a role which ions such as calcium ion might share. The spontaneous formation of the myelinic bimolecular leaflet structure of phospholipids aggregated in the presence of water and the evidence of spontaneous mending of tears during the formation of the microsomal vesicles suggest that much could be learned by studying the recombination of isolated microsomal lipids with isolated microsomal proteins.

The membranous structure of the interior of the mitochondrion has been correlated hypothetically with the presence of enzyme systems which carry out long sequences of consecutive processes. The mitochondrial membranes may be fragmented by treatment with certain alcohols, detergents, or phospholipases. These agents have made possible the preparation of a variety of particles which retain parts of the many enzyme systems in the intact mitochondrion. The mitochondrion is often thought of as made up of repeating units of enzyme systems set in a lipid-rich matrix. It has been suggested that the lipid matrix makes possible certain steps in the enzymic sequences which could not occur in an aqueous environment where intermediate forms would not survive to perpetuate the chain of reactions. A similar inference might be drawn concerning the enzymic activities of the endoplasmic reticulum.

The studies of enzymic activity and lipid content in the various sub-mitochondrial fragments have shown that the lipids are distributed among these fragments in a characteristic way. The lipid content of the various degraded particles is either higher or lower than the lipid content of the intact mitochondria. Basford and Green[10] reason that the concept of localization of lipid in the form of lipoproteins has to be invoked. Green and collaborators managed to carry the purification of the lipids of one such fragment (the coenzyme Q lipoprotein) to the point where essentially all protein was removed but a stable particle remained. It seems most likely that the mode of association of lipid molecules into such aggregates has an importance comparable to that of the proteins in maintaining the functional alignments within the mitochondrial membranes.

(c) Lamellar lipoprotein systems

Certain specialized tissues have lipoprotein systems quite obviously organized on a macromolecular scale. Examples of these are nerve myelin sheath, chloroplasts and retinal rods.

(d) Proteolipids

Folch and Lees[11] have described a type of lipoprotein which can be extracted from many tissues by homogenizing in a 2:1 mixture of chloroform and methanol. Such chloroform–methanol extracts contain polypeptide material in addition to lipids. Lipoprotein fractions containing both peptide and lipids can be isolated from the chloroform–methanol and are called *proteolipids* because they are insoluble in water. The largest quantities of proteolipids are found in white matter of brain from which 2.0–2.5 % of the wet weight can be recovered. Gray matter of brain, heart muscle, kidney, liver, lung, skeletal muscle, smooth muscle (uterus) and beef heart mitochondria contain less. None is found in blood plasma or peripheral nerve myelin.

White matter has yielded three different proteolipid preparations. One is crystalline and contains 50 % peptide, 20 % cerebrosides, and 30 % phospholipids. All three proteolipid fractions are birefringent, indicating a regular arrangement of lipid and protein moieties. The compositions of the three fractions are distinct with respect both to percentage and type of lipids. All three proteolipid fractions can be denatured by evaporating their solutions in chloroform–methanol mixtures containing water, an effect laid to the formation of two phases during evaporation.

In view of the solubility of the proteolipids in polar non-aqueous solvents, Folch and Lees[11] suggested that the peptide and lipid moieties are combined in such a way that the lipid occupies the external surface. Presumably the charged groups in the lipid molecules come into close contact with the charged groups in the peptide moiety in response to the strong interionic forces that will be active in a medium of low dielectric constant.

REFERENCES

[1] K. J. PALMER, F. O. SCHMITT AND E. CHARGAFF, *J. Cellular Comp. Physiol.*, 18 (1941) 41.

[2] M. A. MACHEBOEUF, in J. L. TULLIS (Ed.), *Blood Cells and Plasma Proteins*, Academic Press, New York, 1953.

[3] E. J. COHN et al., *J. Am. Chem. Soc.*, 68 (1946) 459.

[4] F. R. N. GURD in D. J. HANAHAN (Ed.), *Lipid Chemistry*, John Wiley, New York, 1960, p. 267.

[5] J. L. ONCLEY in F. HOMBURGER AND P. BERNFELD (Eds.), *The Lipoproteins: Methods and Clinical Significance*, Karger, Basle, 1958, p. 14.

[6] N. I. KRINSKY, D. G. CORNWELL AND J. L. ONCLEY, *Arch. Biochem. Biophys.*, 73 (1958) 233.

[7] M. RODBELL AND D. S. FREDRICKSON, *J. Biol. Chem.*, 234 (1959) 562.

[8] J. L. ONCLEY, K. W. WALTON AND D. G. CORNWELL, *J. Am. Chem. Soc.*, 79 (1957) 4666.

[9] L. E. THOMAS, J. T. SMITH AND A. J. FUNCKES, *Exptl. Cell Research*, 13 (1957) 96.

[10] R. E. BASFORD AND D. E. GREEN, *Biochim. Biophys. Acta*, 33 (1959) 185.

[11] J. FOLCH AND M. LEES, *J. Biol. Chem.*, 191 (1951) 807.

Chapter I

Conjugated Proteins

Section b

Glycoproteins and Glycopeptides

ALFRED GOTTSCHALK

*Department of Microbiology, Australian National University,
Canberra (Australia)*

1. Definition, occurrence and general properties of glycoproteins

In animal tissues and fluids most of the proteins are found in conjugation with a prosthetic group, *i.e.* a component distinct from protein or amino acid. Thus, nucleoproteins, heme proteins, lipoproteins and carbohydrate proteins are widely distributed. In an important group of carbohydrate proteins the carbohydrate is a polysaccharide (homo- or heteropolysaccharide) such as chitin, hyaluronic acid, chondroitin sulfate, heparin and others, characterized by a small repeating unit and a high degree of polymerization. The polysaccharide complexes are described in Volume 5, Chapter VII.

In glycoproteins and glycopolypeptides the carbohydrate has a relatively low degree of polymerization and, as far as is known, is lacking a short structure repeating itself. The carbohydrate is invariably linked covalently to the polypeptide chain. The molecular weight of the carbohydrate groups varies considerably; for instance it is 512 in the ovine submaxillary gland glycoprotein and about 3500 in γ-globulin. The individual groups are composed of two or more different sugar residues; most of them contain hexosamine and many possess a terminal sialic acid unit. The term "heterosaccharide" may conveniently cover the wide range of carbohydrate structures present in glycoproteins and glycopolypeptides[1], since these structures are lacking the high degree of polymerization of the common polysaccharides, but sometimes exceed the molecular size of an oligosaccharide (usually defined as a saccharide with 10 units or less). The number of heterosaccharide residues per glycoprotein molecule varies from one, as in ovalbumin and γ-globulin, to about 800 in ovine submaxillary gland glycoprotein. Though difficult to prove, it is commonly believed that within a given glycoprotein the prosthetic groups are of the same composition and structure. The covalency of the bond joining the heterosaccharide to the polypeptide core renders their separation by physical means impossible. In fact the isolation of the undegraded heterosaccharide free from amino acids is very difficult to achieve. In the few cases where it has been done, the yield was far from being quantitative due to the degrading effect on the heterosaccharide of even mild acid or alkali treatment. So far no enzyme has been found to release the prosthetic group from the polypeptide chain of glycoproteins. The overall building plan is that of a polypeptide core with the hetero-saccharides linked covalently to the functional groups of the side chains of amino acid residues[2]. The counterpart of this fundamental structure is present in the cell wall of gram-positive bacteria. Here, small peptide side chains are attached covalently to some of the muramic acid constituents of the glycosaminoglycan backbone[3].

A rich source of glycoproteins is human serum. The classical method of separating the serum proteins is by adding protein precipitating reagents under carefully controlled conditions of concentration and temperature. In this way the albumins were differentiated from the globulins. 25 years ago Tiselius[4] showed the serum proteins could be classified according to their electrophoretic mobility into albumin as the fastest moving fraction followed by the α-, β- and γ-globulin fractions in the order of their decreasing mobility. Further refinements of the method have disclosed the presence in these fractions of a variety of different proteins, altogether more than twenty. Though most electrophoretic components of serum contain carbohydrate, the α-globulins are particularly rich in them.

The submaxillary glands of ruminants provide a source of glycoproteins available in large quantity. The glycoproteins isolated from these glands have simple disaccharides as prosthetic groups. Their physical properties and chemical structure have been studied in great detail. They command a special interest because in addition to their normal function as lubricants they display a high biological activity by preventing influenza virus from agglutinating red blood cells. Some of the hormones are also glycoproteins.

Whereas in the aforementioned compounds the heterosaccharides are attached to a true protein, in the specific blood group substances the carbo-hydrate chains are linked covalently to a peptide or polypeptide. They may, therefore, be described as "glycopeptides".

Concerning the physical properties it may be stated generally that the serum glycoproteins of the α-globulin type and many glycoproteins of the epithelial secretions are acidic, have a low isoelectric point and migrate towards the anode at a relatively high rate in the Tiselius apparatus. These properties are mainly due to the sialic acid (the group name for acylated neuraminic acids[5]) content of the glycoproteins; the sialic acids[6], as α-keto acids, are strongly acidic ($pK_a = 2.60$). Actually it was the low isoelectric point of the glycoproteins which led to their discovery. In 1843 Scherer[7], a disciple of the German chemist Justus von Liebig, observed that the mucus from human bronchial secretions could be precipitated by dilute acetic acid in the cold. We know now that this phenomenon is due to the near coincidence of the pH of dilute acetic acid and the isoelectric point (about pH 3) of the viscous glycoproteins (mucoproteins)of the epithelial secretions. Another physical property common to many, though not all, glycoproteins is their greater solubility in aqueous salt solutions and their greater resistance to heat than that of ordinary proteins. These properties are almost certainly imparted to the glycoproteins by the carbohydrate moiety, *i.e.* by the addition to the protein moiety of a large number of polar groups interacting with the molecules of water. It is in accordance with this view that ovalbumin which has a low carbohydrate content is easily coagulated by heat.

2. Serum glycoproteins

(a) α_1-Acid glycoprotein (orosomucoid)

The multiplicity of the human serum glycoproteins is best demonstrated by zone electrophoresis using, for instance, paper as support for the buffer solution. By elution of the individual fractions and analysis of the eluates the carbohydrate content and the nature of the component sugars may then be readily determined[8]. In this way it was found that the α-globulin fraction contained more than half of the total hexose and of the total hexosamine and about 70 % of the total sialic acid of human serum. The best investigated glycoproteins of human plasma are the low molecular weight proteins characterized by sedimentation constants of approximately 3 S. They are α-globulins. One of them, the α_1-acid glycoprotein, also termed orosomucoid, was obtained crystalline[9,10]. It is the most soluble protein hitherto encountered in human plasma. Over a range of pH values from 1.9 to 9.6 the acid glycoprotein appeared homogeneous in electrophoresis and in the ultracentrifuge. The sedimentation constant at pH 6 and in 0.15 M NaCl was found to be $s_{20,w}^0 = 3.5$ S. Other physico-chemical constants of orosomucoid are: $D_{20,w}^0 = 5.27 \cdot 10^{-7}$ cm^2/sec; $\bar{V} = 0.675$; $[\eta] = 6.9$ ml/g; molecular weight $= 44,100$ and $f/f_0 = 1.78$ (ref. 11).

The isoelectric point of orosomucoid in phosphate buffer at ionic strength 0.1 is at pH 2.7. Its electrophoretic mobility in phosphate buffer (pH 7.6, ionic strength 0.1) is $-6.67 \cdot 10^{-5}$ cm^2/volt·sec. After specific removal of the terminal N-acetylneuraminic acid residues by neuraminidase the isoelectric point was shifted from pH 2.7 to pH 5.0 and the electrophoretic mobility was greatly reduced.

The stability of the orosomucoid molecule is unusually high. It is stable in distilled water at 100°; after such treatment the sedimentation constant of the compound was unchanged. In trichloroacetate buffer solutions the glycoprotein was denatured; however, the denatured compound was very soluble in water and in buffer solutions covering the pH range of the solubility minimum of orosomucoid[10].

The composition of the carbohydrate and protein moieties of orosomucoid is shown in Tables I and II. The protein has a fairly complete complement of amino acids and the percentage of the individual amino acids does not

TABLE I

CARBOHYDRATE COMPOSITION OF OROSOMUCOID[*]

	Grams per 100 g orosomucoid
Galactose residues	5.8
Mannose residues	5.8
Fucose residues	1.3
N-Acetylglucosamine residues	14.0
N-Acetylneuraminic acid residues	10.4
Total carbohydrate	37.3
Protein (by difference)	62.7
Total nitrogen	10.8
Protein nitrogen	14.9

[*] Compiled from refs. 9, 10, 13.

show any characteristic features. An exact evaluation is, however, not possible since only 88 % of the dry weight of the glycoprotein is accounted for (see Table II). A complete recovery of amino acids in the presence of as much as 40 % sugar is at present not feasible. It is noteworthy that no N-terminal amino acid is present; the C-terminal is serine[13].

Native orosomucoid is susceptible to trypsin, but fairly resistant to papain, pepsin, chymotrypsin and carboxypeptidase[12,13]. No information is available about the secondary structure of the protein molecule; it is assumed that the molecule belongs to the compact globular type.

As to the composition of the carbohydrate moiety, each molecule of orosomucoid contains 15 or 16 residues each of N-acetylneuraminic acid, galactose and mannose, twice the number of N-acetylglucosamine residues and 4 fucose residues. N-acetylneuraminic acid and fucose occupy terminal positions in the prosthetic group. The former is completely removable by neuraminidase and is linked to C-4 of galactose[14]. Galactose, in turn, is linked to C-4 of

TABLE II

AMINO ACID COMPOSITION OF OROSOMUCOID[9]

	Grams of amino acid* per 100 gram of orosomucoid	Grams of amino acid residue per 100 gram of orosomucoid
Arginine	3.65	3.27
Aspartic acid	7.44	6.43
Cystine	0.60	0.51
Glutamic acid	10.73	9.42
Glycine	0.82	0.62
Histidine	1.31	1.16
Isoleucine	3.15	2.72
Leucine	5.21	4.50
Lysine	5.03	4.41
Methionine	0.65	0.57
Phenylalanine	3.91	3.48
Proline	2.37	2.00
Serine	2.51	2.08
Threonine	4.80	4.07
Tryptophan	1.25	1.14
Tyrosine	1.99	1.79
Valine	2.82	2.39
Total of amino acid residues		50.56
Total of carbohydrate residues		37.30
Deficit		12.14
		100.00

* Grams of amino acid recovered from the hydrolysate of 100 g dry and ash-free orosomucoid.

N-acetylglucosamine. Two such trisaccharides, some of them with L-fucose instead of N-acetylneuraminic acid, are linked to the mannose residues of the core mannose–N-acetylglucosamine–mannose–N-acetylglucosamine. About eight prosthetic groups of molecular weight approximately 2000 are linked to side chains of the polypeptide[15,16].

(b) α₂-Glycoproteins

Another group of low molecular weight acidic α-glycoproteins are the α₂-glycoproteins. Their isoelectric points in acetate buffer (0.1 ionic strength) are at pH values 3.7–4.4. Like the acid α₁-globulin they are negatively charged at pH 4.5 in contrast to the other serum proteins. The α₂-glyco-proteins can be resolved into two subfractions, one consisting of two glyco-proteins which are rendered insoluble specifically with Ba ions (Ba-α₂-glycoproteins) and the other containing as major component a third glyco-protein precipitable with Zn ions (Zn-α₂-glycoprotein). The physico-chemical characteristics and chemical composition of Zn-α₂-glycoprotein are shown in Tables III and IV. Noteworthy is the high content of tyrosine and tryptophan. The NH_2-terminal amino acid does not possess a free amino group. Similar to orosomucoid, the backbone of the Zn-α_2-glycoprotein appears to consist of a single polypeptide chain to which several hetero-saccharides are attached. These heterosaccharides terminate in a sialic acid residue removable by neuraminidase. Proteolytic enzymes (pepsin at pH 3.0; papain, trypsin, chymotrypsin and streptomyces proteases at pH 7.5) digested the glycoprotein[17].

TABLE III

PHYSICO-CHEMICAL CHARACTERISTICS OF Zn-α_2-GLYCOPROTEIN[17]

Sedimentation constant, $s^0_{20,w}$	3.2 S
Intrinsic viscosity, $[\eta]$, in 0.1 M NaCl	0.053 dl/g
Calculated partial specific volume, V	0.706 ml/g
Molecular weight, M (s, η, V)	41,000
Electrophoretic mobility at pH 8.6, barbiturate–NaCl, ionic strength 0.1	$-4.2 \cdot 10^{-5}$ cm^2/volt·sec
Isoelectric point at pH	3.8–3.9
Isoionic point (resin deionized) at pH	4.4

TABLE IV

CHEMICAL COMPOSITION OF Zn-α_2-GLYCOPROTEIN[17]

	Grams/100 g glycoprotein*	Moles/41,000
Galactose	2.8	6
Mannose	4.2	10
Fucose	0.2	1
Glucosamine	4.0	10
Sialic acid	7.0	10
Alanine	3.65	17
Arginine	4.53	11
Aspartic acid	8.65	27
½ Cystine	0.96	3
Glutamic acid	13.09	36
Glycine	2.70	15
Histidine	2.48	7
Isoleucine	2.62	8
Leucine	5.90	18
Lysine	7.02	20
Methionine	1.04	3
Phenylalanine	3.30	8
Proline	4.60	16
Serine	3.68	14
Threonine	2.86	10
Tryptophan		10
Tyrosine	6.88	15
Valine	5.51	19

* Figures are not corrected for water taken up during hydrolysis.

The Ba-α_2-glycoproteins were resolved by starch-gel electrophoresis at pH 8.9. Their average molecular weight is 49,000, their isoelectric points are at pH 4.1 and 4.3 respectively and their electrophoretic mobility at pH 8.6 (in diethylbarbiturate, ionic strength 0.1) is $-4.2 \cdot 10^{-5}$ cm^2/volt·sec. They contain 80 % protein, 6 % hexose (galactose and mannose), 5 % hexosamine (essentially glucosamine), 5 % sialic acid and 0.3 % fucose. Treatment with neuraminidase released free sialic acid. There is evidence that the terminal sialic acid is linked α-ketosidically to carbon atom 3 of galactose and that several heterosaccharide residues are attached to the individual protein. Pepsin at pH 3.0 liberated peptides from the Ba-α_2-glycoproteins, and papain, chymotrypsin and streptomyces protease hydrolyzed effectively the proteins, but at different sites and rates[18,19].

(c) Fetuin

Fetuin[20], the predominant protein of fetal calf serum, representing more than 40 % of the total fetal serum protein, is an α-globulin. Its physical properties and chemical composition[21,22] are shown in Tables V and VI.

TABLE V

PHYSICO-CHEMICAL PROPERTIES OF FETUIN[21]

Sedimentation constant, $s^0_{20,w}$	3.47 S
Diffusion constant, $D^0_{20,w}$	$5.73 \cdot 10^{-7}$ cm^2/sec
Partial specific volume, $\bar{V}$, at pH 6.5	0.696 ml/g
Molecular weight, M (s, D, $\bar{V}$)	48,400
Frictional ratio, f/f_0	1.58
Intrinsic viscosity, $[\eta]$, at pH 6.5	0.078 dl/g
Electrophoretic mobility at pH 8.6, barbiturate–citrate buffer, ionic strength 0.1	$-5.6 \cdot 10^{-5}$ cm^2/volt·sec
Isoelectric point at pH	3.3
Isoionic point at pH	4.0

There are probably three heterosaccharides of an approximate molecular weight of 3500 present in the molecule[23]. The heterosaccharides must have a branched structure since all sialic acid residues occupy a terminal position (readily removable by neuraminidase). The sialic acid residues are linked through an α-ketosidic linkage to galactose which in turn is bonded to C-3 of N-acetylglucosamine[24]. The sialic acid of fetuin consists of 93 % N-acetyl-neuraminic acid and 7 % N-glycolylneuraminic acid. These acids are mainly responsible for the acidic nature of fetuin, as evidenced by a rise in the iso-

References p. 36

TABLE VI

CHEMICAL COMPOSITION OF FETUIN[21, 22]

	Grams/100 g glycoprotein*	Moles/48,400
Galactose	4.6	12.4
Mannose	3.0	8.1
Glucosamine	4.9	13.2
Galactosamine	0.6	1.6
Sialic acid	8.7	13.6
Alanine	5.15	28
Arginine	5.76	16
Aspartic acid	7.42	27
½ Cystine	3.48	14
Glutamic acid	9.42	31
Glycine	2.79	18
Histidine	3.53	11
Hydroxyproline	1.08	4
Isoleucine	3.25	12
Leucine	7.59	28
Lysine	4.83	16
Phenylalanine	3.07	9
Proline	8.33	35
Serine	4.56	21
Threonine	3.94	16
Tryptophan	0.84	2
Tyrosine	2.62	7
Valine	7.99	33

* Figures not corrected for water taken up during hydrolysis.

electric point from pH 3.3 to pH 5.2 upon sialic acid removal. Fetuin is susceptible to trypsin, chymotrypsin, pepsin, papain and a *B. subtilis* protease.

3. Salivary glycoproteins

Glycoproteins with spectacular physiological properties and biological activity have been prepared from the submaxillary glands of ruminants. These glycoproteins form highly viscous aqueous solutions suited to cover the foodstuffs with a lubricant layer of mucus thus assisting swallowing and protecting teeth and the lining cells of the mucosa against injury. Furthermore, they inhibit in high dilution ($1:10^7$) haemagglutination by viruses of the influenza group. They are easily soluble in water when adjusted to neutrality and even in high concentration of methanol. They are acidic, have low isoelectric points (pH 3.3–3.8) and move at neutral pH towards the anode in electrophoresis[6].

Ovine (sheep) submaxillary gland glycoprotein has been obtained homogeneously on both electrophoretical and ultracentrifugal standards. Its molecular weight[25] is $(1.0 \pm 0.2) \cdot 10^6$. It consists of 42 % carbohydrate and 58 % protein. The amino acid analysis[26] of the protein is shown in Table VII. The content of aromatic and sulphur containing amino acids is low and that of proline, glycine and α-amino-β-hydroxy amino acids is high. The prosthetic group has been isolated free from amino acids and identified as the disaccharide α-D-N-acetylneuraminyl-$(2 \rightarrow 6)$-N-acetylgalactosamine[27]. About 800 prosthetic groups are distributed along the polypeptide chain.

TABLE VII

AMINO ACID ANALYSIS OF
OVINE SUBMAXILLARY GLAND GLYCOPROTEIN (OSM)[26]

	Grams of amino acid* per 100 gram of OSM	Grams of amino acid residue
Alanine	5.08	4.05
Arginine	3.31	2.97
Aspartic acid	4.10	3.55
Cystine	0.63	0.54
Glutamic acid	6.17	5.42
Glycine	5.97	4.54
Histidine	0.30	0.27
Isoleucine	1.90	1.64
Leucine	2.92	2.52
Lysine	1.50	1.32
Methionine	0.40	0.35
Phenylalanine	1.96	1.75
Proline	5.60	4.72
Serine	7.57	6.27
Threonine	7.00	5.94
Tryptophan	0 or trace	
Tyrosine	0.68	0.61
Valine	4.20	3.55
Total of amino acid residues		50.01
Total of carbohydrate residues		40.52
Deficit		9.47
		100.00

* Figures not corrected for water taken up during hydrolysis.

As to the linkage of the disaccharide residues to the protein core it was shown that about 82 % of them are joined through their potential reducing ends to the free carboxyl groups of aspartyl and glutamyl residues by an

$$2\ RCO \cdot O \cdot R' + LiBH_4 \rightarrow Li^+[(RCH_2O)_2B(O \cdot R')_2]^- \tag{1}$$

alkali-labile glycosidic-ester type of linkage[28]. This was demonstrated by the reductive cleavage of this linkage on treatment of OSM with lithium borohydride in tetrahydrofuran. When at the end of the reducing process

References p. 36

the boron-intermediate complex, formed according to the general equation (1) was decomposed, the disaccharide was recovered with its reducing group intact. This indicated that the potential reducing group of the disaccharide was shielded against the reducing agent by engagement in the ester linkage. The residual 18 % of the prosthetic groups are probably joined through an O-glycosidic linkage to the hydroxyl group of serine[1,29] (see Fig. 1).

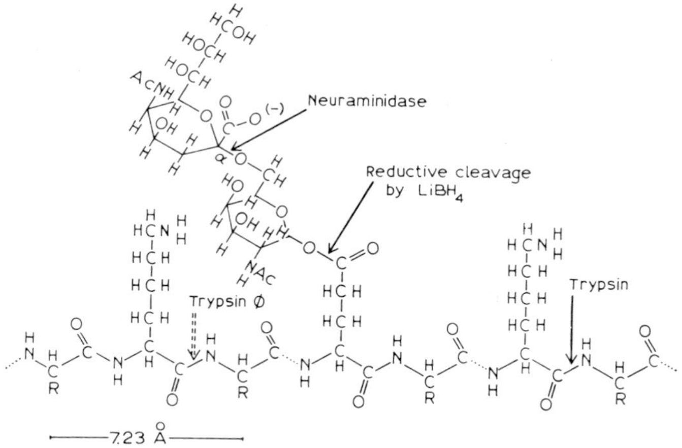

Fig. 1. Diagrammatic segment of ovine submaxillary gland glycoprotein showing (1) the structure of the prosthetic group; (2) the lithium borohydride susceptible glycosidic-ester linkage between the prosthetic group and the γ-carboxyl of a glutamyl residue; (3) the neuraminidase susceptible α-ketosidic linkage and (4) the steric hindrance to trypsin action by the negatively charged prosthetic group.

It may be mentioned that in bovine submaxillary gland glycoprotein, 84 % of the prosthetic groups (α-D-sialyl-(2 → 6)-N-acetylgalactosamine) are linked through their reducing group to the β- and γ-carboxyl groups respectively of aspartyl and glutamyl residues, as evidenced by the isolation of homoserine and α-amino-δ-hydroxy-n-valeric acid from the LiBH$_4$-treated glycoprotein[30,31].

The susceptibility of OSM to trypsin is sterically hindered by the bulky and negatively charged prosthetic groups. One out of 6.4 amino acid residues carries a prosthetic group and one out of 16 amino acid residues is a lysyl or arginyl residue, i.e. the ratio prosthetic group/potentially trypsin susceptible bond is 2.5. Removal by neuraminidase of the terminal N-acetylneuraminic acid units increased by 45 % the number of peptide bonds split by trypsin[32]. It is suggestive that the main factor for the increased susceptibility to trypsin after removal of sialic acid is the loss of its negative charge. This charge may have a screening effect on the positive charge of the side chains of the basic amino acids lysine and arginine required for trypsin action.

Sedimentation velocity measurements at various concentrations revealed $s^{\circ}_{20,w} = 8.5 \pm 0.8$ S; the intrinsic viscosity $[\eta]$ was found to be 3.4 ± 0.1 dl/g at $25°$ and pH 7.6 (0.1 M phosphate) and the partial specific volume $\overline{V} = 0.69 \pm 0.01$. The glycoprotein is polydisperse with regard to particle size, but homogeneous in chemical composition. That the purified OSM is closely similar to the glycoprotein as secreted by the submaxillary glands was seen from the sedimentation pattern of the first crude aqueous extract of the minced glands; this pattern contained a hypersharp peak very similar to that given by purified OSM. When the sedimentation and viscosity data were interpreted in terms of a spheroidal model of the particle, the results (J, the ellipticity, $= 8.7$ and V', the hydrodynamic volume, $= 30$ ml/g) indicated that OSM is only slightly elongated and transports an appreciable amount of solvent with it. This suggests that the particle in solution resembles a random chain polymer with some rigidity. The absence of a well defined wide-angle X-ray pattern for OSM would be consistent with a random coil conformation[25].

It is of interest that OSM and hyaluronic acid owe their physical property of a high degree of viscosity, so essential for their physiological function as lubricants, to similar structural features. They are both macromolecules of high molecular weight and of random coil conformation. In both molecules mutual repulsion between negatively charged groups (carboxyl groups of glucuronic and sialic acid residues respectively) will result in an expansion and stiffening of the coil. This was demonstrated for hyaluronic acid and OSM by a sharp increase in viscosity when the ionic strength was reduced below 0.1 (refs. 25, 33). Conversely, an appreciable decrease in the viscosity of OSM was observed when the dissociation of the sialic acid residues (pK_a of sialic acid $= 2.6$) was depressed by shifting the pH to 1.7 (ionic strength 0.5). On readjustment of the pH to 6.1 the viscosity was restored[34].

The biological activity of OSM as an inhibitor of influenza virus haemagglutination was reduced from an inhibitory titre of $1.4 \cdot 10^7$ to $7 \cdot 10^3$/mg OSM on removal of 80 % of the terminal sialic acid residues by neuraminidase known[6] to act specifically on the α-ketosidic linkage joining a terminal sialic acid unit to an adjacent galactosamine or galactose residue. It would, therefore, appear that the presence of accessible sialic acid residues is required for attachment of the inhibitor to the virus surface. Moreover, a negative charge at the carboxyl group of the terminal sialic acid seems to be essential for virus surface–inhibitor association since the methyl ester of OSM is not an inhibitor of virus haemagglutination. OSM methyl ester is also only slowly acted upon by *Vibrio cholerae* neuraminidase indicating the importance of the negative charge at the carboxyl group of sialic acid for the formation of the enzyme–substrate intermediate complex[35].

4. Other glycoproteins inhibiting influenza virus haemagglutinins

In addition to the submaxillary gland glycoproteins of ruminants a number of other glycoproteins present in epithelial secretions and inhibiting strongly influenza virus haemagglutination has been isolated. From male human urine an inhibitory glycoprotein with the following physical properties was prepared[36,37] in a homogeneous state: $s^0_{20,w} = 29.2$ S; $D_{20,w} = 3.25 \cdot 10^{-8}$ cm^2/sec; $[\eta]_{20} = 3.70$ dl/g at pH 6.8; $f/f_0 = 5.32$ and molecular weight $= 7 \cdot 10^6$. Its carbohydrate composition[38,39] is shown in Table VIII. By mild alkali treatment the heterosaccharides could be detached and revealed, on acid hydrolysis, the same sugar components in about the same ratio as found in the acid hydrolysate of the intact glycoprotein. Approximately 200 individual prosthetic groups are attached to the protein core, though this figure represents only a rough estimate[2,40].

Epithelial secretions of the respiratory and digestive tracts are further sources of potent influenza virus haemagglutinin inhibitory glycoproteins. An electrophoretically homogeneous inhibitory glycoprotein from bronchial secretions of patients with chronic bronchitis was described by Marmion et al.[41], and Werner[42] analyzed the gently purified mucus from a bronchitis case for its carbohydrate components (see Table VIII). Meconium from new-born infants also contains an inhibitory glycoprotein which has been purified and analyzed[43] (see Table VIII).

TABLE VIII

CARBOHYDRATE ANALYSIS OF SOME INFLUENZA VIRUS HAEMAGGLUTININ INHIBITORY GLYCOPROTEINS*

Source	Galactose	Mannose	Fucose	Glucos-amine**	Galactos-amine**	Sialic acid+
Submaxillary glands++ (ovine)	0.3	0.1	0.4	trace	15.0	25.4
Submaxillary glands++ (bovine)	0.7	0.2	0.7	2.1	12.7	22.4
Male urine (human)	5.4	2.7	1.1	5.7	1.9	9.1
Bronchial secretion (human)	3.6	trace	3.0	7.0	1.3	3.8
Meconium (human)	7.9	trace	4.9	11.8 (total hexosamine)		5.0

* Values for the individual components refer to the recovery (in g) from the acid hydrolysate of 100 g dry glycoprotein.

** Free base.

+ Expressed as N-acetylneuraminic acid.

++ The small amounts of galactose, mannose, fucose and glucosamine are regarded as components of a contaminating glycoprotein present in very small amounts.

From human erythrocytes a fairly homogeneous glycoprotein inhibiting in high dilution influenza virus haemagglutination has been prepared recently[44]. Its physical constants are: $s^0_{20,w} = 2.16$ S; $D_{20,w} = 0.575 \cdot 10^{-6}$ cm^2/sec and molecular weight 31,400. It is composed of about 55 % protein and 45 % carbohydrate, the latter consisting of about 22 residues each of N-acetylneuraminic acid, galactosamine and galactose. As the sialic acid is almost completely removed by mild acid hydrolysis without release of any other sugar, this acid is supposed to occupy the terminal position in an oligosaccharide extending from the polypeptide chain. On treatment with neuraminidase the inhibitory property of the compound was lost. There is reason to believe that this inhibitor is the red cell receptor for the influenza virus.

All sialo-glycoproteins have some features in common. Invariably their sialic acid residues occupy a terminal position and are linked through a neuraminidase susceptible α-ketosidic linkage to another sugar residue, never directly to the polypeptide chain. At neutral pH the sialo-glycoproteins are negatively charged and move in electrophoresis towards the anode. After enzymic removal of most of the terminal sialic acid residues the electrophoretic mobility towards the anode is greatly reduced, for instance from $-5.4 \cdot 10^{-5}$ to $-2.9 \cdot 10^{-5}$ cm^2/volt·sec with bovine submaxillary gland glycoprotein (phosphate buffer, pH 6.9, ionic strength 0.2)[45]. All sialo-glycoproteins tested combine with the influenza virus surface; however, only those with an affinity for the viral surface comparable to that of the red cell receptors combine firmly enough to inhibit in high dilution influenza virus haemagglutination. The mere removal of sialic acid inactivates the inhibitors[35].

5. Glycoproteins with hormone activity

Other biologically active glycoproteins are the gonadotropic hormones and erythropoietin. It has long been recognized that the follicle stimulating hormone (FSH) and the interstitial-cell stimulating hormone, both gonadotropins derived from the pituitary glands, and the chorionic gonadotropins present in pregnant mare's serum and in urine of pregnant women, contain carbohydrate and have a low isoelectric point[46]. However, the earlier carbohydrate analyses were inadequate and the purity of the preparations was not always of a high standard. Recent investigations have demonstrated conclusively that sialic acid is an essential component of the gonadotropins and that its enzymic removal inactivates the hormone. Thus, FSH from sheep pituitary glands was shown to contain 5 % sialic acid. The sialic acid residues occupy a terminal position, are linked α-ketosidically to their partners and are completely removable by neuraminidase. The release

References p. 36

resulted in a reduction of the hormonal activity by 97% or more[47]. For human menopausal gonadotropin (derived from pituitary tissue) it was reported[48] that it contained 7.8 % sialic acid and that removal of 60 % of the sialic acid residues decreased its biological activity by 80 %. An electrophoretically and ultracentrifugally homogeneous chorionic gonadotropin (human origin) of molecular weight 30,000 was analyzed for its carbohydrate composition by Got, Bourrillon and Michon[49]. It contained 9 residues each of galactose and mannose, 12 residues of glucosamine and 3 of galactosamine, 2 fucose and 8 sialic acid residues (N-acetyl and N-glycolylneuraminic acids). Inactivation of chorionic gonadotropin by neuraminidase has been found by several authors (for literature see ref. 49).

An electrophoretically homogeneous glycoprotein with erythropoietic activity was obtained from plasma of rabbits made anemic with phenylhydrazine. Its isoelectric point was at pH 2.8 and its electrophoretic mobility at pH 8.75 (barbiturate buffer, ionic strength 0.1) was $-5.40 \cdot 10^{-5}$ cm^2/volt sec. It contained 9.4 % hexose, 9.0 % hexosamine, 0.8 % methylpentose and 14% sialic acid. On treatment with neuraminidase all the sialic acid was split off, resulting in loss of biological activity[50]. The erythropoiesis stimulating factor in the urine of children with thalassemia major is also greatly reduced in its specific activity by neuraminidase[51]. A highly purified glycoprotein with erythropoietic activity was isolated from the plasma of anemic sheep (treated with phenylhydrazine). It contained 4.1 % galactose, 4.1 % mannose, 7.1 % hexosamine and 6.9 % sialic acid; molecular weight = 40,000. Since, however, a biologically inert counterpart, identical in all chemical and physical properties tested, was isolated by the same procedure from normal sheep plasma, this constituent is regarded as a carrier of the true hormone or alternatively as a precursor converted to active erythropoietin by the anemic process[52].

6. Ovalbumin

Ovalbumin is a representative of the type of glycoproteins with a low proportion of carbohydrate. Available data[53] indicate that ovalbumin has a molecular weight of 45,000 and contains per molecule a single prosthetic group consisting of 5 mannose residues, 3 glucosamine residues and 3 acetyl groups (molecular weight of prosthetic group about 1440, *i.e.* 3.2 g carbohydrate/100 g ovalbumin). Johansen, Marshall and Neuberger[54] have fragmented ovalbumin by successive digestion with pepsin, trypsin, chymotrypsin and a mold protease and isolated a glycopeptide by chromatographic and electrophoretic procedures. The amino acid sequence in this peptide was Tyr·Asp(carbohydrate)·(Leu,Ser,Thr)·Val. The carbohydrate seems to be linked to one of the carboxyl groups, probably the β-carboxyl, of aspartic acid. In view of the facile evolution, on acid hydrolysis of the glycopeptide, of 1 residue of ammonia, the authors proposed tentatively a β-aspartylglycosylamine structure, *i.e.* an *N*-glycosidic linkage involving the amide group of asparagine and the reducing group of the oligosaccharide, in analogy to glycinamide ribotide[55], an intermediate in purine biosynthesis. Nuenke and Cunningham[56] have arrived at the same results and conclusions. Other glycoproteins with low carbohydrate content are prothrombin, thrombin, fibrinogen, fibrin and casein.

7. Glycopeptides

(a) *Human blood group specific substances*

In 1900 Landsteiner observed that addition of serum from one person to the red blood cells of another person frequently, though not always, resulted in agglutination of the cells. The extension of these findings led to the classification of human red cells into the four groups A, B, AB and O, depending on whether the red cells contained factor A, factor B or both or neither factor. The complementary structures in serum, anti-A or anti-B agglutinin (isoagglutinins), occur naturally and are responsible for the agglutination of erythrocytes containing at their surface the A and B factor respectively. Fundamentally the interaction between the red cells and their specific isoagglutinins is an antigen–antibody reaction. Antibodies agglutinating O cells specifically are not normally present in man. Blood group characters are genetically determined and do not change during life. The specific group substances A, B and O are found not only at the surface of human red cells but also in water-soluble form in saliva, gastric juice, ovarian cyst fluids, urine, meconium etc. of about 75 % of all persons. Individuals of group O secrete a substance neutralizing a number of products of human, animal and plant origin which agglutinate group O cells. Since the same substance is secreted by A, B and AB persons, the latter category being devoid of an O gene, Morgan and Watkins designated as H substance the serologically specific component present in the secretions of group O persons and of persons of other groups. There is evidence to suggest that the H active factor is a precursor substance which under the impact of the A and B genes is converted to A and B specific material. The 25 % of persons not secreting A, B or H substances in soluble form produce the so called Lewis or Le^a substance, controlled by a separate gene Le^a. Since the group specific substances on the red cell surface are difficult to isolate in amounts required for comprehensive analysis, most of the work has been carried out with the specific substances in the secretions which are available in good supply[57, 58].

It has been established that the water-soluble blood group substances, isolated from secretions in highly purified form, are glycopeptides of the same qualitative composition irrespective of their specific character within the ABO and Le^a blood group systems. They all contain D-galactose, L-fucose, N-acetylglucosamine and N-acetylgalactosamine though in ratios varying with the serological specificity (Table IX). Sialic acid is present in most preparations at very low concentration only, but in view of the ease of its liberation from glycoproteins some figures of the literature may be an

TABLE IX[57,60]

ANALYSES OF HUMAN BLOOD GROUP SUBSTANCES

	Nitrogen %	Fucose %	Acetyl %	Hexosamine %	Reducing sugar %	[α]$_D$
A substance	5.2	18	9.0	30	52	+10°
H substance	6.0	18	8.6	25	45	—30°
Le^a substance	4.9	12	9.9	30	56	—48°
B substance	5.6	16	7.0	24	52	—
AB substance	5.4	18	—	29	53	+ 1°

underestimate. The sugar residues constitute about 80 % of the molecule; a polypeptide or peptides account for the balance. The amino acids found in these peptides are threonine, serine, proline, aspartic and glutamic acids, lysine and arginine, glycine, alanine, valine, leucine (isoleucine), the first three amino acids making up about half of the total amino acids present. Aromatic and sulphur containing amino acids are either missing or present in very small amounts. The molecular weights range from $2.5 \cdot 10^5$ to $1 \cdot 10^6$. Little is known about the shape of the macromolecules.

The serological characters of human blood group specific substances are determined by the nature, sequence and stereochemical arrangement of a few sugar residues only of the carbohydrate chains. Thus, group A specificity is probably due to the disaccharide residue O-α-N-acetylgalactosaminyl-(1 → 3)-O-β-galactosyl-(1 - - →, since this disaccharide and two trisaccharides in which the disaccharide residue is linked to C-3 and C-4 respectively of N-acetylglucosamine, all isolated from group A substance by partial hydrolysis, inhibit in high dilution the agglutination of A cells by human iso-agglutinins[59]. Group B specificity seems to be associated with an O-α-D-galactosyl-(1 → 3) end unit, and for the H specific structure the presence of an O-α-L-fucosyl residue is essential. The Le^a specificity most probably is determined by a branched trisaccharide residue composed of the two non-reducing end units O-β-D-galactosyl and O-α-L-fucosyl joined by (1 → 3) and (1 → 4) glycosidic linkages respectively to N-acetylglucosamine. These, apparently, are the structures of the group specific antigens primarily involved in the binding of the iso-agglutinins (antibodies)[60].

It is an interesting observation that cleavage by crystalline ficin and papain respectively of blood group substance A into no more than 2 or 3 fragments inactivates the inhibitory capacity though the heterosaccharides and their linkages to the peptide chain(s) are not affected by the enzymic treatment; however, the largest fragment still precipitates 80% of the amount of antibody nitrogen precipitable by the intact blood group substance[60]. Obviously, in the inhibition test which essentially is a competition between the group specific substance at the surface of the red cell and the water soluble chemical analogue for the iso-agglutinin, a high degree of integrity of the fine structure of the analogue is essential for successful competition. In the precipitin test a fragment of the glycopeptide macromolecule still containing the binding site(s) combines with the specific iso-agglutinin with less affinity than the intact glycopeptide but firmly enough to effect precipitation. In this case the somewhat less tight fit of the complementary structures is not challenged by a tightly fitting competitor.

It seems to be of relevance that the influenza virus haemaglutinin inhibitors and the water-soluble blood group substances share a number of characteristic properties: Both types of compounds are chemical analogues to specific haemagglutinin receptors at the red cell surface, are found in the same epithelial secretions (saliva, ovarian cyst fluid, gastric juice, urine, meconium, etc.) and inhibit in high dilution competitively haemagglutination by influenza virus haemagglutinin and the specific iso-agglutinin respectively. With both the viral haemagglutinin inhibitors and the soluble blood group specific substances the biological activity resides in the carbohydrate moiety and in each case one particular grouping was found to be essential for specific combination. Controlled cleavage by proteolytic enzymes of the macromolecule into a few fragments results in both cases in loss of the inhibitory capacity although the carbohydrate structure of the fragments remains intact; however, in both cases the fragments can still combine with the agglutinin, if not challenged by the red cell agglutinogen.

That the specific structures responsible for blood group activity and for influenza virus anti-haemagglutinin activity can be produced within the same mammalian cell is shown by the isolation of a homogeneous macromolecular glycopeptide from ovarian cyst fluid of a person of blood phenotype A Le(a+). This rather unique compound had the composition shown in Table X[61].

The material was polydisperse in size. Its physical characteristics were: $s_{20,w}^0 = 7.7$ S; $[\eta] = 0.605$ dl/g; $\overline{V} = 0.63$; molecular weight about 350,000 (the values for $s_{20,w}^0$ and mol. weight were calculated from the experimental

TABLE X

ANALYSIS OF A GLYCOPEPTIDE ACTIVE AS BLOOD GROUP SUBSTANCE
WITH Le^a SPECIFICITY AND AS
INHIBITOR OF INFLUENZA VIRUS HAEMAGGLUTININ[61]

	Grams/100 g glycopeptide*
Fucose	8.4
Galactose	28.8
Glucosamine	20.0
Galactosamine	6.0
N-Acetylneuraminic acid	18.0
Alanine	1.36
Arginine	0.32
Aspartic acid	0.49
Cysteine	0.15
Glutamic acid	0.87
Glycine	0.64
Histidine	0.37
Isoleucine	0.38
Leucine	0.87
Lysine	0.28
Methionine	0.09
Phenylalanine	0.31
Proline	2.04
Serine	1.91
Threonine	4.48
Tyrosine	0.17
Valine	0.89

* Figures are not corrected for water taken up during hydrolysis; the values for the amino acids have been calculated from the data in ref. 61.

data presented by Pusztai and Morgan[61]); electrophoretic mobility (phosphate buffer, pH 8, ionic strength 0.2) $= -7.6 \cdot 10^{-5}$ cm^2/volt·sec. It was an active Le^a specific substance and a potent inhibitor of influenza virus haemagglutination. The removal by neuraminidase of the terminal N-acetylneuraminic acid residues inactivated the property of the compound to inhibit virus haemagglutinins but did not affect its capacity to inhibit Le^a specific iso-agglutination. On the other hand, destruction of the Le^a specificity by a Le^a destroying enzyme from Trichomonas foetus did not impair the virus haemagglutinin inhibitory quality of the compound. This glycopeptide, then, is a naturally occurring macromolecule possessing two biological activities, each of which is associated with a distinct chemical structure and each of which can be destroyed specifically and separately.

(b) Bacterial glycopeptides

The cell walls of bacteria may be visualized as rigid porous envelopes protecting the delicate cytoplasmic membrane within against injury. There is good reason to believe that the insoluble rigid structure consists of amino sugar containing heteropolysaccharide chains (backbone) cross-linked by small peptides (for review see Salton[62] and Work[63]). Subunits of the assumed structure have been obtained by the action of lysozyme and bacteriolytic enzymes on the cell wall. Thus, Ghuysen[64] has reported the isolation of a small molecular weight glycopeptide from the dialyzable fraction of lysozyme digested walls of *Micrococcus lysodeikticus*. Its structure is shown in Fig. 2.

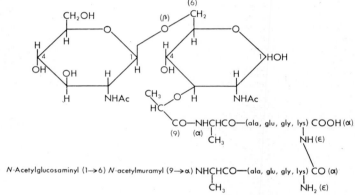

Fig. 2. Structure of dimer of the disaccharide–peptide complex obtained by the action of *N*-acetylglycosaminidases on the cell wall of *Micrococcus lysodeikticus*.

   The main glycopeptide released by lytic enzymes from the coat of germinating spores of *Bacillus* species was found[65] to consist of D-glutamic acid, alanine (D- and L-isomers), meso-diaminopimelic acid and a mixture of *N*-acetylglucosamine and *N*-acetylmuramic acid in the molar ratios 1:3:1:8. Its molecular weight was about 15,000. According to Work[63] a glycopeptide with the sequence *N*-acetylmuramyl-L-alanine-D-glutamic acid-(diaminopimelic acid or lysine)-D-alanine-D-alanine may be the "basal unit" of the various heteropolymers of the walls of both gram-positive and gram-negative bacteria.

REFERENCES

[1] A. GOTTSCHALK, W. H. MURPHY AND E. R. B. GRAHAM, *Nature*, 194 (1962) 1051.
[2] A. GOTTSCHALK, *Nature*, 170 (1952) 662.
[3] M. R. J. SALTON, *Bacteriol. Rev.*, 25 (1961) 77.
[4] A. TISELIUS, *Trans. Faraday Soc.*, 33 (1937) 524.
[5] G. BLIX, A. GOTTSCHALK AND E. KLENK, *Nature*, 179 (1957) 1088.
[6] A. GOTTSCHALK, *The Chemistry and Biology of Sialic Acids and Related Substances*, Cambridge University Press, 1960.
[7] J. J. SCHERER, *Chemische und Mikroskopische Untersuchungen*, C. F. Winter, Heidelberg, 1843, p. 93.
[8] R. J. WINZLER, *Glycoproteins of Plasma*, In *Ciba Symposium on Chemistry and Biology of Mucopolysaccharides*, J. and A. Churchill, London, 1958, p. 245.
[9] H. E. WEIMER, J. W. MEHL AND R. J. WINZLER, *J. Biol. Chem.*, 185 (1950) 561.
[10] K. SCHMID, *J. Am. Chem. Soc.*, 75 (1953) 60.
[11] E. L. SMITH, D. M. BROWN, H. E. WEIMER AND R. J. WINZLER, *J. Biol. Chem.*, 185 (1950) 569.
[12] R. BOURRILLON AND J. MICHON, *Biochim. Biophys. Acta*, 44 (1960) 608.
[13] K. SCHMID, W. L. BENCZE, T. NUSSBAUMER AND J. O. WEHRMÜLLER, *J. Biol. Chem.*, 234 (1959) 529.
[14] E. H. EYLAR AND R. W. JEANLOZ, *J. Biol. Chem.*, 237 (1962) 1021.
[15] E. H. EYLAR AND R. W. JEANLOZ, *J. Biol. Chem.*, 237 (1962) 622.
[16] S. A. BARKER, G. I. PARDOE, M. STACEY AND J. W. HOPTON, *Nature*, 197 (1963) 231.
[17] W. BÜRGI AND K. SCHMID, *J. Biol. Chem.*, 236 (1961) 1066.
[18] K. SCHMID AND W. BÜRGI, *Biochim. Biophys. Acta*, 47 (1961) 440.
[19] S. KAMIYAMA AND K. SCHMID, *Biochim. Biophys. Acta*, 49 (1961) 250.
[20] H. F. DEUTSCH, *J. Biol. Chem.*, 208 (1954) 669.
[21] R. G. SPIRO, *J. Biol. Chem.*, 235 (1960) 2860.
[22] H. W. FISHER, D. O'BRIEN AND T. T. PUCK, *Fed. Proc.*, 20 (1961) 150.
[23] R. G. SPIRO, *J. Biol. Chem.*, 237 (1962) 382.
[24] E. R. B. GRAHAM, *Australian J. Science*, 24 (1962) 140.
[25] A. GOTTSCHALK AND H. A. MCKENZIE, *Biochim. Biophys. Acta*, 54 (1961) 226.
[26] A. GOTTSCHALK AND D. H. SIMMONDS, *Biochim. Biophys. Acta*, 42 (1960) 141.
[27] E. R. B. GRAHAM AND A. GOTTSCHALK, *Biochim. Biophys. Acta*, 38 (1960) 513.
[28] A. GOTTSCHALK AND W. H. MURPHY, *Biochim. Biophys. Acta*, 46 (1961) 81.
[29] G. BLIX, *Conference on Mucous Secretions, The New York Academy of Sciences, May 2–5, 1962*.
[30] W. H. MURPHY AND A. GOTTSCHALK, *Biochim. Biophys. Acta*, 52 (1961) 349.
[31] A. GOTTSCHALK AND E. R. B. GRAHAM, *Biochim. Biophys. Acta*, 34 (1959) 380.
[32] A. GOTTSCHALK AND S. FAZEKAS DE ST. GROTH, *Biochim. Biophys. Acta*, 43 (1960) 513.
[33] B. S. BLUMBERG AND A. G. OGSTON, *Physicochemical Studies on Hyaluronic Acids*, In *Ciba Symposium on Chemistry and Biology of Mucopolysaccharides*, J. and A. Churchill, London, 1958, p. 22.
[34] A. GOTTSCHALK AND M. A. W. THOMAS, *Biochim. Biophys. Acta*, 46 (1961) 91.
[35] A. GOTTSCHALK, *Perspectives in Biology and Medicine*, 5 (1962) 327.
[36] I. TAMM AND F. L. HORSFALL, *J. Exptl. Med.*, 95 (1952) 71.
[37] I. TAMM, J. C. BUGHER AND F. L. HORSFALL, *J. Biol. Chem.*, 212 (1955) 125.
[38] A. GOTTSCHALK, *Nature*, 170 (1952) 662.
[39] L. ODIN, *Nature*, 170 (1952) 663.
[40] A. GOTTSCHALK, *The Prosthetic Group of Some Mucoproteins and its Relationship to Influenza Virus*, In *Ciba Symposium on Chemistry and Biology of Mucopolysaccharides*, J. and A. Churchill, London, 1958, p. 287.
[41] B. P. MARMION, C. C. CURTAIN AND J. PYE, *Australian J. Exptl. Biol. Med.*, 31 (1953) 505.
[42] I. WERNER, *Acta Soc. Med. Upsaliensis*, 58 (1953) 1.
[43] L. ODIN, *Acta Chem. Scand.*, 9 (1955) 862.
[44] R. H. KATHAN, R. J. WINZLER AND C. A. JOHNSON, *J. Exptl. Med.*, 113 (1961) 37.
[45] C. C. CURTAIN AND J. PYE, *Australian J. Exptl. Biol. Med.*, 33 (1955) 315.

[46] For review C. H. Li, *Vitamins and Hormones*, 7 (1949) 223.
[47] A. Gottschalk, W. K. Whitten and E. R. B. Graham, *Biochim. Biophys. Acta*, 38 (1960) 183.
[48] R. Got and R. Bourrillon, *Nature*, 189 (1961) 234.
[49] R. Got, R. Bourrillon and J. Michon, *Bull. soc. chim. biol.*, 42 (1960) 41.
[50] P. H. Lowy, G. Keighley and H. Borsook, *Nature*, 185 (1960) 102.
[51] J. W. Winkert and A. S. Gordon, *Biochim. Biophys. Acta*, 42 (1960) 170.
[52] B. J. Campbell, R. J. Schlueter, G. F. Weber and W. F. White, *Biochim. Biophys. Acta*, 46 (1961) 279.
[53] P. G. Johansen, R. D. Marshall and A. Neuberger, *Biochem. J.*, 77 (1960) 239.
[54] P. G. Johansen, R. D. Marshall and A. Neuberger, *Biochem. J.*, 78 (1961) 518.
[55] R. A. Peabody, D. A. Goldthwait and G. R. Greenberg, *J. Biol. Chem.*, 221 (1956) 1071.
[56] R. H. Nuenke and L. W. Cunningham, *J. Biol. Chem.*, 236 (1961) 2452.
[57] W. T. J. Morgan, *The Croonian Lecture, Proc. Royal Soc. (London), B*, 151 (1960) 308.
[58] E. A. Kabat, *Blood Group Substances: Their Chemistry and Immunochemistry*, Academic Press, New York, 1956.
[59] L. Cheese and W. T. J. Morgan, *Nature*, 191 (1961) 149.
[60] W. T. J. Morgan, *Bull. soc. chim. biol.*, 42 (1960) 1591.
[61] A. Pusztai and W. T. J. Morgan, *Biochem. J.*, 78 (1961) 135.
[62] M. R. J. Salton, *Microbial Cell Walls*, John Wiley and Sons, New York, 1960.
[63] E. Work, *J. Gen. Microbiol.*, 25 (1961) 167.
[64] J. M. Ghuysen, *Biochim. Biophys. Acta*, 47 (1961) 561.
[65] R. E. Strange, *Bacteriol. Rev.*, 23 (1959) 1.

Chapter I

Conjugated Proteins

Section c

Non-Porphyrin Metalloproteins

ENZO BOERI*

Institute of Human Physiology, University of Ferrara (Italy)

This chapter deals with those metalloproteins which do not contain porphyrins, and in which an enzymic activity is either absent or but accessory. The material is divided into three sections: (*1*) iron proteins; (*2*) copper proteins; (*3*) other metalloproteins.

1. Iron proteins

(*a*) Ferritin

(*i*) Occurrence

Crystals of ferritin were obtained first by Laufberger[1] from the spleen and liver of horses. Laufberger's method, with cadmium sulfate**, is still widely used. Ferritin is very common in mammals: spleen and liver are the richest sources of it, but intestinal mucosa, bone marrow and placenta are also good sources. The content of ferritin of the normal adult man has been estimated as 2–4 g. Ferritin is an intracellular substance: a part of it is in the cytoplasm, another part is in the microsomes[2].

(*ii*) Structure

Ferritin contains up to 23 % iron. Iron is present as micelles of average composition $[(FeOOH)_8FeOPO_3H_2]n$. Magnetic susceptibility studies[3] show

---

* Deceased on October 28th, 1960.
** Controversial spelling is decided according to etymology. Sulfate and not sulphate, as it derives from latin *sulfur*. Haemocyanin and not hemocyanin as it derives from αἷμα, blood.

that ferritin is an intermediate between ferric high-spin and ferric low-spin compounds: 3.78 Bohr magnetons per mole. The iron is easily removed by dialysis in the presence of a reducing (ascorbate, reduced glutathione, dithionite) and a complexing (α,α'-dipyridyl, o-phenanthroline) agent. The iron-free protein is called *apoferritin*. Analysis of the apoferritin of horse spleen gives the following distribution of amino acids (g/100 g): glutamic 17.2, aspartic 6.8, lysine 7.8, arginine 9.1, histidine 4.8, cysteine + cystine 1.7, methionine 1.9, tyrosine 5.0, phenylalanine 6.1, leucine 19.1, isoleucine 1.4, glycine 3.4, valine 4.3, alanine 1.9, threonine 4.3, proline 1.5, tryptophan 1.2 (Mazur *et al.*[4]). Also serine was found to be present[5]. The protein constitutes 60% by weight and the iron micelles 40% of the molecule. There are intermediates between apoferritin and ferritin: they have an incomplete saturation of the iron sites. As the iron micelles confer a high specific gravity, a mixture of molecules of different iron saturation can be separated in the ultracentrifuge (Rothen[6]).

It is surprising that ferritin and apoferritin have similar intrinsic viscosity[4], crystallize with the same shape of crystals[7], give crossed immunological reactions[8], and have similar electrophoretic properties[4]. The explanation is given by electron microscopy, which shows ferritin and apoferritin to be particles of comparable dimensions (diameter 55 Å), the former containing a core of iron micelles (diameter 27 Å) arranged in typical tetraplets, the latter instead having this iron place filled with the solvent[9]. X-ray crystallography confirms this finding[10]. The isoelectric point of human liver ferritin[4] is 5.4.

(iii) Functions

The principal function of ferritin is storage of iron; this function is shared with haemosiderin. Apoferritin binds iron derived either from the inorganic form (this occurs in the intestinal mucosa) or from iron-saturated transferrin (this occurs mainly in liver, spleen and bone marrow). Ferritin in its turn transfers iron to iron-depleted transferrin or directly to intracellular porphyrins for the synthesis of haem groups. The transfer of iron from ferritin to iron-free transferrin has been performed *in vitro* by Bielig and Bayer[11]: 5 ml 0.5% ferritin and 0.34% ascorbic acid (to reduce the iron) were placed in a cellophane bag, which was then placed inside a second cellophane bag containing 100 mg iron-free transferrin in 10 ml 0.19% $NaHCO_3$. The outer solution was concentrated $NaHCO_3$; after 12 h the transferrin had incorporated 0.13% Fe. The same authors were able to incorporate *in vitro* iron into apoferritin, from ferrous ammonium sulfate, aerobically[12]. These transfers occur jointly with changes of the iron valence, as only ferrous iron moves, and only ferric iron is firmly bound. The physiological reducing agent necessary for the transfer of iron appears to be ascorbate[13], and the oxidizing agent necessary for its fixation appears to be molecular oxygen. Other reducing agents could also act, like uric acid, produced in the liver by the reaction catalysed by xanthine oxidase[14]. Thus, oxygen acts to keep iron fixed to the storage protein, whereas a reducing milieu favours its mobilization. The fate of iron in ferritin-containing organs is hence a function of the oxygen pressure, aerobic conditions meaning storage, anaerobic escape; this is obviously of physiological importance. Besides, in a well oxygenated organ ferritin is in a state where most sulfhydryl groups have been oxidized to disulfides, whereas at a low oxygen pressure most of them are in the reduced form (so-called *ferritin-SH*; the difference between ferritin and ferritin-SH is 26 sulfhydryl groups per molecule[15]). Finally, anaerobic conditions do not only facilitate the escape of iron from the ferritin molecule, but also that of the ferritin molecule itself, which enters the general circulation[15]. Thus, haemorrhagic shock, shock in general, and other conditions of sluggish transhepatic circulation, as well as anoxia from other causes, liberate ferritin into the blood, mainly in the ferritin-SH form. Mazur and Shorr were able to show that ferritin-SH and apoferritin-SH (but not their oxidized forms) prevent the vasomotor effect of epinephrine on metarterioles[16]. This action gives ferritin an important position as a factor in shock. As a matter of fact, the identity of ferritin-SH and VDM (the *vasomotor depressor material*, discovered by Chambers *et al.*[17]) is well established. Finally, ferritin-SH and apoferritin-SH also exert an antidiuretic effect, which is due to a neurohormonal mechanism, with liberation of the antidiuretic hormone[16].

(iv) Biosynthesis

The daily amount of apoferritin and ferritin which is synthesized in the body is very variable. Granick[18] showed that feeding of iron induces a large formation of ferritin. Most of this ferritin is not formed by coupling iron to preexisting apoferritin, but both apoferritin and ferritin are formed *de novo* as a consequence of the administration of iron. Ferritin is not formed d'emblée, but apoferritin is formed first as an intermediate compound[19]; this was shown clearly by the use of isotopes and of Rothen's technique for separating ferritins of different iron content. There is a basal biosynthesis of ferritin, independent of iron administration but probably dependent on the iron which is released in the catabolism of the haemoproteins; in the adult guinea pig, labelled ferritin disappears from the liver with a $t^{\frac{1}{2}}$ of two weeks[20]. The iron-induced synthesis of ferritin is very rapid, as 6 min were estimated as sufficient to synthesize the whole molecule[21].

As to the further destiny of ferritin, part is changed to haemosiderin, and part is demolished. Proteolytic digestion is easier with apoferritin than with ferritin[22].

function. However, experiments of Gitlin and Janeway[94] on mice, also with ^{64}Cu, show that very little of the copper absorbed by the intestine is taken up by caeruloplasmin. The oxidase activity possibly has a physiological significance; ascorbate, adrenaline, noradrenaline and 5-hydroxytryptamine are possible substrates.

(d) Erythrocuprein

Erythrocuprein is a copper protein present in the red cells of mammals. It was discovered and crystallized from the red cells of ox, horse and sheep by Mann and Keilin[95]. They called it haemocuprein, but this substance is better called erythrocuprein, as suggested by Markowitz et al.[96], to indicate its presence in the red cells, keeping the name haemocuprein for the analogous substance found in plasma. Markowitz et al.[96] and Kimmel et al.[97] have purified the protein from the red cells of man, which contain it in a concentration of 30 mg/100 ml.

Bovine erythrocuprein, prepared by Mann and Keilin, is a blue protein, containing 0.34% Cu, 14.35% N and 1.12% S. The molecular weight in the ultracentrifuge is 35,000 indicating 2 copper atoms per molecule. The substance obtained from horse cells had 0.31 and that from sheep cells 0.22% Cu. The substance is devoid of oxidase activity.

Erythrocuprein prepared from man has 0.36% Cu, 16.53% N and 1.05% S. One molecule contains two copper atoms, 41 aspartic, 18 threonine, 20 serine, 28 glutamic, 11 proline, 46 glycine, 21 alanine, 23 valine, 11 isoleucine, 18 leucine, 2 tyrosine, 10 phenylalanine, 20 lysine, 14.5 histidine, 9 arginine, 11 cyst(e)ine, 0.6 tryptophan residues. It also contains 3.4 hexosamine, 1.8 hexose, 1.6 sialic residues for each two copper atoms. The isoelectric point is 5.02. s_{20} is $3.02 \cdot 10^{-13}$ sec and D_{20} $9.3 \cdot 10^{-7}$ cm^2/sec. Copper is firmly held between pH 4.5 and 8.6. At pH 8 cyanide removes the copper. Human erythrocuprein is colourless but shows absorption lines at 655 and 265 mμ.

(e) Haemocuprein

The name *haemocuprein* is given to the copper protein isolated by Mann and Keilin[95] from horse serum in a crystalline state. Horse haemocuprein has 0.25% copper and is blue. It differs from caeruloplasmin because its reduction with dithionite is irreversible.

(f) Hepatocuprein

Hepatocuprein is a copper-protein present in the liver of mammals. It was discovered by Gruzewska and Roussel[98], and purified by Mann and Keilin[95], who prepared it from ox liver. It contained 0.34 % copper, and was colourless. Later, Mohamed and Greenberg[99] crystallized from liver a hepatocuprein containing from 0.31 to 0.41 % copper. The molecular weight in the ultracentrifuge was between 30 and 40,000. The copper could be partly removed by dialysis against cyanide, and the copper protein could then again be reconstituted, by dialysis against copper acetate. The protein had no oxidase activity.

(g) Cerebrocuprein

Cerebrocuprein is a copper protein isolated from the brain of man and animals. The bovine protein was prepared by Porter and Folch[100] and found to contain 0.25–0.3 % copper. Its molecular weight is between 30 and 40,000; it therefore contains two copper atoms per molecule. Copper is released at pH under 3.9. The human cerebrocuprein was prepared by Porter and Ainsworth[101]. It contains 15.7 % N and 0.29 % Cu. The molecular weight is also between 30 and 40,000. The absorption spectrum reveals peaks at 270 and 655 mμ.

(h) Milk copper protein

Dills and Nelson[102] have isolated from milk a copper protein containing 0.19 % copper and 15 % nitrogen. Dialysis at pH 3.5 removes the copper.

3. Other metalloproteins

(i) Zinc protein of leucocytes

A zinc protein has been purified from human leucocytes by Vallee et al.[103]. Its isoelectric point is 6.5. Its zinc content is 0.3 %.

(ii) Cadmium protein of kidney

Margoshes and Vallee[104] have isolated a cadmium protein from equine kidney cortex. It contains 14 % nitrogen, 2–2.5 % cadmium and 1 % hexosamine. The substance has no peculiar spectral properties. s_{20} is from 0.94 to $1.22 \cdot 10^{-13}$ sec, indicating a low-molecular weight protein.

(iii) Pinnaglobin

Pinnaglobin is the name given by Griffiths[105] to a brown protein he claimed to have discovered in the body fluid of the mussel Pinna squamosa. Winterstein[106] has been unable to extract more oxygen from the blood of Pinna saturated with air than from sea water. Later on Henze[107] showed that the brown substance discovered by Griffiths in Pinna is not a protein, and that it is not in the blood, but in the pericardial fluid.

(iv) Haemosycotypin

Haemosycotypin is a zinc protein discovered in *Busycon* (then called *Sycotypus*) *canaliculatum* and in *Busycon* (then called *Fulgur*) *carica* by Bradley[108] and described as an oxygen carrier by Mendel and Bradley[109]. However, all subsequent research on *Busycon* found haemocyanin as the only oxygen carrier. Haemosycotypin should be considered as non-existent.

(v) Haemovanadium

Haemovanadium is the name given by Califano and Caselli[110] to the vanadium compound present in blood cells of tunicates, and particularly in *Phallusia mamillata*. This compound was discovered by Henze[111]. Bielig and Bayer[112] consider it a protein of molecular weight 24,000 containing 24 vanadium atoms and 48 SO_4 groups. Vanadium is in the trivalent state as shown by Lybing[113] spectrophotometrically, by Bielig *et al.*[114] by analogy with the properties of models and by magnetic measurements, and by Boeri and Ehrenberg[115] by magnetic, spectrophotometric and reductiometric methods. However, Lybing, Boeri and Ehrenberg, and Webb[116] were unable to convince themselves that the vanadium was bound to a protein: if it is so, it must be very weakly bound.

REFERENCES

[1] V. LAUFBERGER, *Bull. soc. chim. biol.*, 19 (1937) 1574.
[2] R. B. LOFTFIELD AND R. BONNICHSEN, *Acta Chem. Scand.*, 10 (1956) 1547.
[3] L. MICHAELIS, C. D. CORYELL AND S. GRANICK, *J. Biol. Chem.*, 148 (1943) 463.
[4] A. MAZUR, I. LITT AND E. SHORR, *J. Biol. Chem.*, 187 (1950) 473; 485; 497.
[5] B. W. GABRIO AND G. H. TISHKOFF, *Science*, 112 (1950) 358.
[6] A. ROTHEN, *J. Biol. Chem.*, 152 (1944) 679.
[7] I. FANKUCHEN, *J. Biol. Chem.*, 150 (1943) 57.
[8] S. GRANICK, *J. Biol. Chem.*, 149 (1943) 157.
[9] J. L. FARRANT, *Biochim. Biophys. Acta*, 13 (1954) 569.
[10] P. M. HARRISON, *J. Molecular Biol.*, 1 (1959) 69.
[11] H. J. BIELIG AND E. BAYER, *Naturwiss.*, 42 (1955) 466.
[12] H. J. BIELIG AND E. BAYER, *Naturwiss.*, 42 (1955) 125.
[13] M. W. LOEWUS AND R. A. FINEBERG, *Biochim. Biophys. Acta*, 26 (1957) 441.
[14] S. GREEN AND A. MAZUR, *J. Biol. Chem.*, 227 (1957) 653.
[15] E. SHORR, B. W. ZWEIFACH AND R. F. FURCHGOTT, *Science*, 102 (1945) 489.
[16] E. SHORR, *Harvey Lectures*, Series L, Academic Press, New York, 1956, p. 112.
[17] R. CHAMBERS, B. W. ZWEIFACH AND B. E. LOWENSTEIN, *Am. J. Physiol.*, 139 (1943) 123.
[18] S. GRANICK, *J. Biol. Chem.*, 164 (1946) 737.
[19] R. A. FINEBERG AND D. M. GREENBERG, *J. Biol. Chem.*, 214 (1955) 107.
[20] H. L. HELWIG AND D. M. GREENBERG, *J. Biol. Chem.*, 198 (1952) 703.
[21] R. B. LOFTFIELD AND E. A. EIGNER, *J. Biol. Chem.*, 231 (1958) 925.
[22] E. TRIA AND A. TORBOLI, *Boll. soc. ital. biol. sper.*, 20 (1945) 38.
[23] M. BEHRENS AND T. ASHER, *Z. physiol. Chem.*, *Hoppe-Seyler's*, 220 (1933) 97.
[24] M. BESSIS AND J. BRETON-GORIUS, *Compt. rend.*, 245 (1957) 1271.
[25] G. W. RICHTER, *J. Biophys. Biochem. Cytol.*, 4 (1958) 55.
[26] A. SHODEN, B. W. GABRIO AND C. A. FINCH, *J. Biol. Chem.*, 204 (1953) 823.
[27] B. A. KOECHLIN, *J. Am. Chem. Soc.*, 74 (1952) 2649.
[28] C. B. LAURELL, *Acta Chem. Scand.*, 7 (1953) 1407.
[29] D. SURGENOR, B. KOECHLIN AND L. STRONG, *J. Clin. Invest.*, 28 (1949) 73.
[30] A. EHRENBERG AND C. B. LAURELL, *Acta Chem. Scand.*, 9 (1955) 68.
[31] H. HARRIS, E. B. ROBSON AND M. SINISCALCO, *Ciba Foundation Symposium on Biochemistry of Human Genetics*, J. & A. Churchill, London, 1959, p. 151.
[32] O. SMITHIES AND G. E. CONNELL, *Ciba Foundation Symposium on Biochemistry of Human Genetics*, J. & A. Churchill, London, 1959, p. 178.
[33] A. MAZUR, S. GREEN AND A. CARLETON, *J. Biol. Chem.*, 235 (1960) 595.
[34] T. B. OSBORNE, *J. Am. Chem. Soc.*, 21 (1899) 477.
[35] R. C. WARNER AND I. WEBER, *Federation Proc.*, 9 (1950) 243.
[36] J. A. BAIN AND H. F. DEUTSCH, *J. Biol. Chem.*, 172 (1948) 547.
[37] J. C. LEWIS, N. S. SNELL, D. J. HIRSCHMAN AND H. FRAENKEL-CONRAT, *J. Biol. Chem.*, 186 (1950) 23.
[38] F. SANGER (1955), quoted from J. T. EDSALL AND J. WYMAN, *Biophysical Chemistry*, Vol. I, Academic Press, New York, 1958, p. 84.
[39] R. C. WARNER, *Trans. N.Y. Acad. Sci.*, 2nd Series, 16 (1953–54) 182.
[40] H. FRAENKEL-CONRAT, *Advances in Protein Chem.*, 6 (1951) 187.
[41] R. C. WARNER AND I. WEBER, *J. Am. Chem. Soc.*, 75 (1953) 5094.
[42] S. DELLE CHIAIE, *Memorie sulla Storia e Notomia degli Animali del Regno di Napoli*, Fernandes, Naples, 1823.
[43] C. F. W. KRUKENBERG, *Vergleichende Physiologische Studie*, Abt. III, Winter, Heidelberg, 1880, p. 82.
[44] G. F. MARRIAN, *J. Exptl. Biol.*, 4 (1927) 357.
[45] M. FLORKIN, *Arch. intern. physiol.*, 36 (1933) 247.
[46] C. MANWELL, *Science*, 127 (1958) 592.
[47] C. MANWELL, *Science*, 132 (1960) 550.
[48] J. ROCHE, *Bull. soc. chim. biol.*, 15 (1933) 1415.
[49] J. ROCHE, *Skand. Arch. Physiol.*, 69 (1934) 87.

[50] A. ROCHE AND J. ROCHE, *Bull. soc. chim. biol.*, 17 (1935) 1494.
[51] W. E. LOVE, *Biochim. Biophys. Acta*, 23 (1957) 465.
[52] R. A. RESNIK AND I. M. KLOTZ, *Biol. Bull.*, 101 (1951) 227.
[53] A. S. BRILL AND J. M. OLSON, *Biol. Bull.*, 105 (1953) 371.
[54] I. M. KLOTZ, T. A. KLOTZ AND H. A. FIESS, *Arch. Biochem. Biophys.*, 68 (1957) 284.
[55] E. BOERI AND A. GHIRETTI-MAGALDI, *Biochim. Biophys. Acta*, 23 (1957) 493.
[56] I. M. KLOTZ, S. RAPAPORT AND E. V. H. ROSENBERG, *Biol. Bull.*, 105 (1953) 377.
[57] I. M. KLOTZ AND T. A. KLOTZ, *Science*, 121 (1955) 477.
[58] M. KUBO, *Bull. Chem. Soc. Japan*, 26 (1953) 244.
[59] E. HARLESS, *Müller's Arch. f. Anat. Physiol. u. Wiss. Med.*, 1847, p. 148.
[60] L. FREDERICQ, *Arch. zool. exptl. gén.*, 7 (1878) 535.
[61] A. C. REDFIELD, T. COOLIDGE AND M. A. SHOTTS, *J. Biol. Chem.*, 76 (1928) 185.
[62] M. HENZE, *Z. physiol. Chem., Hoppe-Seyler's*, 43 (1904) 290.
[63] F. KUBOWITZ, *Biochem. Z.*, 299 (1938) 32.
[64] A. TISELIUS, S. HJERTEN AND O. LEVIN, *Arch. Biochem. Biophys.*, 65 (1956) 132.
[65] G. QUAGLIARIELLO in H. WINTERSTEIN (Ed.), *Handbuch der Vergleichenden Physiologie*, Vol. I, Fischer, Jena, 1925, p. 597.
[66] G. FELSENFELD, *Arch. Biochem. Biophys.*, 87 (1960) 247.
[67] J. ROCHE, *Arch. phys. biol.*, 7 (1930) 207.
[68] T. SVEDBERG AND K. O. PEDERSEN, *The Ultracentrifuge*, Clarendon Press, Oxford, 1940.
[69] A. TISELIUS AND F. L. HORSFALL JR., *J. Exptl. Med.*, 69 (1939) 83.
[70] J. BROSTEAUX, *Naturwiss.*, 25 (1937) 249.
[71] T. SVEDBERG AND S. BROHULT, *Nature*, 142 (1938) 830.
[72] N. F. BURK, *J. Biol. Chem.*, 133 (1940) 511.
[73] S. BROHULT, *Intern. Congr. Biochem., 1st Congr., Cambridge, Engl., 1949. Abstr. Communs.*
[74] W. M. STANLEY AND I. F. ANDERSON, *J. Biol. Chem.*, 146 (1947) 25.
[75] M. A. LAUFFER AND L. SWABY, *Biol. Bull.*, 108 (1955) 290.
[76] A. POLSON AND R. W. G. WYCKOFF, *Nature*, 160 (1947) 153.
[77] G. A. MILLIKAN, *J. Physiol. (London)*, 79 (1933) 158.
[78] E. STEDMAN AND E. STEDMAN, *Biochem. J.*, 20 (1926) 949.
[79] I. M. KLOTZ AND R. E. HEINEY, *Proc. Natl. Acad. Sci. U.S.*, 43 (1957) 717.
[80] W. A. RAWLINSON, *Australian J. Exptl. Biol. Med. Sci.*, 18 (1940) 131.
[81] W. A. RAWLINSON, *Australian J. Exptl. Biol. Med. Sci.*, 19 (1941) 137.
[82] F. GHIRETTI, *Arch. Biochem. Biophys.*, 63 (1956) 165.
[83] K. BHAGVAT AND D. RICHTER, *Biochem. J.*, 32 (1938) 1397.
[84] A. E. NEEDHAM, *Nature*, 181 (1960) 194.
[85] J. A. LUETSCHER, *J. Clin. Invest.*, 19 (1940) 313.
[86] C. G. HOLMBERG AND C. B. LAURELL, *Acta Chem. Scand.*, 5 (1951) 476.
[87] A. G. MORELL AND S. SCHEINBERG, *Science*, 127 (1958) 588.
[88] I. H. SCHEINBERG AND A. G. MORELL, *J. Clin. Invest.*, 36 (1957) 1193.
[89] B. E. SANDERS, O. P. MILLER AND M. N. RICHARD, *Arch. Biochem. Biophys.*, 84 (1959) 60.
[90] J. DE GROUCHY, *Rev. franç. études clin. et biol.*, 3 (1958) 621.
[91] G. CURZON AND S. O'REILLY, *Biochem. Biophys. Research Communs.*, 2 (1960) 284.
[92] I. H. SCHEINBERG AND D. GITLIN, *Science*, 116 (1952) 484.
[93] A. G. BEARN AND H. G. KUNKEL, *J. Lab. Clin. Med.*, 45 (1955) 623.
[94] D. GITLIN AND C. A. JANEWAY, *Nature*, 185 (1960) 693.
[95] T. MANN AND D. KEILIN, *Proc. Roy. Soc. (London), B*, 126 (1939) 303.
[96] H. MARKOWITZ, G. E. CARTWRIGHT AND M. M. WINTROBE, *J. Biol. Chem.*, 234 (1959) 40.
[97] J. R. KIMMEL, H. MARKOWITZ AND D. M. BROWN, *J. Biol. Chem.*, 234 (1959) 46.
[98] Z. GRUZEWSKA AND G. ROUSSEL, *Compt. rend. soc. biol.*, 125 (1931) 957.
[99] M. S. MOHAMED AND D. M. GREENBERG, *J. Gen. Physiol.*, 37 (1954) 179.
[100] H. PORTER AND J. FOLCH, *J. Neurochem.*, 1 (1957) 260.
[101] H. PORTER AND S. AINSWORTH, *J. Neurochem.*, 5 (1959) 91.
[102] W. L. DILLS AND J. M. NELSON, *J. Am. Chem. Soc.*, 64 (1942) 1616.

[103] B. L. VALLEE, F. L. HOCH AND W. L. HUGHES JR., *Arch. Biochem. Biophys.*, 48 (1954) 347.

[104] S. MARGOSHES AND B. L. VALLEE, *J. Am. Chem. Soc.*, 79 (1957) 4813.

[105] A. B. GRIFFITHS, *Compt. rend.*, 114 (1892) 840.

[106] H. WINTERSTEIN, *Biochem. Z.*, 19 (1909) 384.

[107] M. HENZE, *Z. physiol. Chem., Hoppe-Seyler's*, 162 (1927) 136.

[108] H. C. BRADLEY, *Science*, 19 (1904) 196.

[119] L. B. MENDEL AND H. C. BRADLEY, *Am. J. Physiol.*, 17 (1906) 167.

[110] L. CALIFANO AND P. CASELLI, *Pubbl. staz. zool. Napoli*, 21 (1948) 235.

[111] M. HENZE, *Z. physiol. Chem., Hoppe-Seyler's*, 72 (1911) 494.

[112] H. J. BIELIG AND E. BAYER, *Experientia*, 10 (1954) 300.

[113] S. LYBING, *Arkiv Kemi*, 6 (1953) No. 21.

[114] H. J. BIELIG, E. BAYER, L. CALIFANO AND L. WIRTH, *Pubbl. staz. zool. Napoli*, 25 (1953) 26.

[115] E. BOERI AND A. EHRENBERG, *Arch. Biochem. Biophys.*, 50 (1954) 404.

[116] D. A. WEBB, *J. Exptl. Biol.*, 16 (1939) 459.

Elsevier's Scientific Publications

or information about new books in the following fields, please
heck square(s) and complete reverse of this card.

- ☐ PHYSICAL AND THEORETICAL CHEMISTRY
- ☐ ORGANIC CHEMISTRY
- ☐ INORGANIC CHEMISTRY
- ☐ ANALYTICAL CHEMISTRY
- ☐ BIOLOGY
- ☐ SUGAR PUBLICATIONS
- ☐ BIOCHEMISTRY
- ☐ BIOPHYSICS
- ☐ CLINICAL CHEMISTRY
- ☐ PHARMACOLOGY
- ☐ TOXICOLOGY
- ☐ PSYCHIATRY
- ☐ NEUROLOGY
- ☐ ATHEROSCLEROSIS

lease print or type)

ame: ....

ddress: ....

....

....

....

Elsevier's Scientific Publications

You received this card in one of our publications. It would greatly assist us in serving you further if, when returning it for more information, you would indicate below how you heard of the book or books now in your possession. We thank you for your co-operation.

- ☐ Bookseller's recommendation
- ☐ Books sent on approval by bookseller
- ☐ Displays in bookshops
- ☐ Reviews
- ☐ Advertisements
- ☐ Personal recommendation
- ☐ References in books and journals
- ☐ Publisher's catalogue
- ☐ Circular received from publisher
- ☐ Circular received from bookseller
- ☐ Listing in a subject catalogue of
  bookseller

POSTCARD

ELSEVIER PUBLISHING COMPANY

P.O. BOX 211

AMSTERDAM

Conjugated Proteins

Section d

Haemoglobin and Myoglobin

H. LEHMANN

Department of Pathology, St. Bartholomew's Hospital, London (Great Britain)

AND

R. G. HUNTSMAN

*Department of Pathology, Memorial Hospital,
Peterborough, Northants (Great Britain)*

Haemoglobin has been described as the second most interesting substance in the world—the first presumably being chlorophyll[1]. The replacement of Mg in chlorophyll by Fe in haem was the key that opened the door to the whole of aerobic life[2].

1. Distribution of haemoglobin

Circulating haemoglobin in the red cell can raise the oxygen combining capacity of plasma from 0.5 ml O_2 per 100 ml to about 25 ml O_2 per 100 ml of mammalian blood. This enables an animal to transfer oxygen rapidly and efficiently to an active tissue far removed from the respiratory surface. For example the red cell supplying the tail of the blue whale completes a round trip of approximately 120 feet in the process.

However, in contrast, if the organism is less than 1 mm in diameter or flat like a tapeworm or eel larva, then simple diffusion is adequate and a respiratory pigment would be valueless. Alternatively, if the basal metabolism is at a low level, which is possible in cold-blooded animals, then again survival without a respiratory pigment would be possible.

Haemoglobin appears in evolution not as a sudden response to increasing size or complexity of the animal, but in a peculiarly haphazard manner.

The occurrence of haemoglobin in such unicellular organisms as yeast and paramecium[3], where diffusion of oxygen is adequate, is at first strange. However, Barcroft[4] realised that although haemoglobin is widespread in nature it occupies only a corner of the field which cytochrome covers. Cytochrome occurs in both plant and animal kingdoms and like haemoglobin it is a protein molecule with haem prosthetic groups. It is absent in absolutely anaerobic organisms such as the anaerobic bacteria. The function of cytochrome is to link cellular metabolites donating hydrogen with molecular oxygen. It appears then probable that haemoglobin might be produced as a byproduct of cytochrome formation and requires no new enzyme system in the cell for its manufacture.

In the higher invertebrates the function of a respiratory pigment is not always clear. There is a tendency for the pigment to occur in mud dwelling animals where there is a potentially anaerobic environment and also in some species in response to comparative oxygen lack. The possession of a respiratory pigment has a survival value only in times of stress due to periods of relative or absolute lack of oxygen.

In the vertebrates, Redfield[5] considers that haemoglobin appeared *de novo* and the absence of haemoglobin in present-day primitive chordates suggests that this may be so. Fishes and amphibians are able to survive in some cases without any respiratory pigment. Ice fish living in the Antarctic lack haemoglobin and yet attain a weight[6] of over 1 kg. With warm-blooded animals, however, the presence of a respiratory pigment is obligatory.

2. Distribution of myoglobin

Myoglobin is equivalent in man to about a quarter of the body's total haemoglobin. In invertebrates it occurs like haemoglobin sporadically. Although the muscle and heart of most invertebrates contain cytochrome they usually possess no myoglobin. It is however found in active muscle such as in the pharynx of some molluscs. In invertebrates haemoglobin and myoglobin are not confined to muscle and in the water flea, *Daphnia*, it has also been found in fat, eggs and nerve[7].

In vertebrates the amount of myoglobin in a muscle depends on the type as well as the amount of work that the muscle has to perform. The very need for myoglobin depends on the paradoxical situation that a muscle when in a firm contraction can receive little blood at the very time that the oxygen need is greatest. High-frequency contracting muscles such as insect wing muscles or bird hearts may contain much cytochrome, but would need and indeed possess little myoglobin. The influence of the quantity of work on the total store of myoglobin is illustrated by the marked drop in myoglobin that occurs on denervation of a muscle and the greater quantity found in trained as compared with untrained horses. One also finds that birds that mainly run on the ground have dark leg muscles and pale breast muscle whilst exactly the oppositive holds in birds capable of flying great distances.

The quantity of myoglobin present in a muscle is variable and in man the myoglobin content given as percentage of dry weight is 2.5 for striated muscle, 1.4 for heart muscle and 0.3 for smooth muscle[8] (uterus). Aquatic mammals have a greater quantity of myoglobin present in their muscles, several times the amount of land mammals. This appears sufficient to supply oxygen not only during a single period of contraction but also to act as a long-term oxygen store to help to permit periods of prolonged apnoea.

3. The oxygen dissociation curve

To be of value to the host, a respiratory pigment must not only be capable of acquiring oxygen, but must also be able to give it up at tensions suitable for the functioning of the tissues of that particular species. Thus, the ability to carry oxygen is not confined to haemoglobin and is shared by other respiratory pigments including the naturally occurring copper containing haemocyanin and also certain compounds of cobalt[9]. The uniqueness of haemoglobin lies in the capacity of the globin portion of the molecule to alter the avidity of haem for oxygen. Indeed if man had the haemoglobin of *Arenicola*, the lug worm, he would die of asphyxia due to the great affinity of the invertebrate pigment for oxygen.

The haemoglobin of the lamprey, like the myoglobin of the mammalian muscle, contains only one haem group per molecule and has a dissociation curve of a hyperbolic shape. The haemoglobin pattern changes during metamorphosis[10]. With increasing age the haemoglobin molecule also matures by conjugating into units of larger size. It will be apparent (Fig. 1) that a sigmoid-shaped curve will deliver more oxygen to the tissues and would therefore be an advance. To obtain this sigmoid-shaped curve requires an interaction of the haem groups in the molecule and therefore one haem group must have some influence over its neighbours in the same molecule.

In mammalian haemoglobin with four haem groups per molecule, these are probably too far apart for the oxygenation of any one of them to influence the oxygen affinity of its neighbours directly. Any interaction must work in an indirect manner. The combination of reduced myoglobin with oxygen results in no change detectable by X-ray analysis but in contrast, the oxygenated and reduced form of haemoglobin in man and horse are crystallographically different. In haemoglobin, there is some alteration of the position of the haems in relation to each other when oxygen is added or removed from the iron atom. In addition, the blocking of the sulphydryl groups of cysteine (horse haemoglobin contains four cysteine residues in each haemo-globin molecule) with p-chloromercuribenzoate abolishes this haem–haem interaction and therefore SH groups appear to play some part in this phenomenon.

The attachment of oxygen is not a random process, for the affinity of a haem group depends on the degree of oxygenation of its neighbours on the same molecule. As a result of this interdependence a haemoglobin solution which is 75 % saturated with oxygen will have *all* its molecules only three quarters saturated, and there will not be a mixture of fully, half, quarter and non-saturated molecules. The sigmoid-shaped dissociation curve is the outcome of this differing affinity for oxygen of the iron atoms.

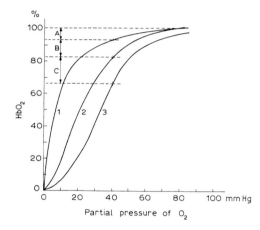

Fig. 1. A diagrammatic representation to illustrate the advantage of a sigmoid-shaped curve and the further advantage gained following the acquisition of the Bohr effect. Curve 1, hyperbolic curve; Curve 2, sigmoid curve; Curve 3, sigmoid curve showing Bohr effect. A = oxygen released by haemoglobin with hyperbolic curve at 40 mm oxygen pressure. B = advance in efficiency achieved by sigmoid curve. C = further advance attained by acquisition of Bohr effect.

Additional efficiency is the result of the Bohr effect, *i.e.* a reduction in the affinity of haemoglobin for oxygen with rising hydrogen ion concentra-tion. When haemoglobin comes under the influence of the acid tissue metabolites, it is therefore able to liberate more oxygen. This advantage is absent in the primitive haemoglobin such as that occurring in the coelomic cavity of some invertebrates[11]. It is of interest that the Bohr effect is shown by the haemoglobin of the mature frog but is lacking in the tadpole. The magnitude of the Bohr effect in mammalian haemoglobins appeared proportional to the number of sulphydryl groups titratable by mercuric ions. As well as a shift of dissociation curve occurring in different species to suit the situation in which the animal lives, a young animal may possess two haemoglobins with different dissociation curves in its circulation at the same time. Foetal haemoglobin, which is a physiological pigment in early infancy, possesses a curve which resembles that of the haemoglobin of aquatic animals and lies to the left of that of adult haemoglobin. When the red cells containing the two haemoglobins are lysed, the curve of the haemolysate lies to the right of a similar solution of adult haemoglobin. If this solution is dialysed, the curve of the mixture of foetal and adult haemoglobin resembles that of adult haemoglobin. It appears that the corpuscular environment is responsible for the shift to the left of the foetal haemoglobin, and that the presence of a dialysable factor causes the reversal of this shift in haemoglobin solutions[12]. The environment in which a haemoglobin molecule functions appears therefore to have an influence over its properties, just as does the globin over the haem group itself.

An example of polymorphism for two varieties of adult haemoglobin has been described in sheep. Mountain sheep show a higher incidence of the haemoglobin with the high oxygen affinity, enabling the animals to acquire oxygen with greater ease at rarefied atmospheric conditions. The lowland animals show a greater frequency of the haemoglobin with lower affinity. If heterozygotes for the two haemoglobin genes become anaemic, which may occur because of a worm infestation, a greater proportion of the haemoglobin with the low affinity, which would therefore deliver more oxygen to the tissues, is produced in newly formed erythrocytes[13]. The position of the dissociation curve has to be suitable for a particular set of circumstances. A single fixed pigment would have been perhaps of value to particular animals occurring sporadically in nature. The value of haemoglobin and the reason why it has emerged as the dominant respiratory pigment is due to the ability of the protein portion of the molecule to adapt the haem to suit prevailing circumstances and thus to benefit animals in their struggle to survive in widely varying conditions.

4. The structure of myoglobin and haemoglobin

The invertebrate haemoglobin molecule is extremely variable in size and may have a molecular weight[14] from a few thousand to three million, each of the massive molecules then having over a hundred haem–oxygen linkages. The very large size of the molecule may be a means of preventing easy diffusion of the protein to the tissues. Certainly the life of free haemoglobin in man is very limited. It is either removed by the reticulo-endothelial system or via the kidneys or forms complexes with the haptoglobins of the α_2-globulin fraction of the plasma proteins, thereby increasing its molecular weight from 67,000 to about 310,000.

References p. 74

The molecular weight of vertebrate haemoglobin is less variable. The lamprey has a haemoglobin of only mol.wt. 17,000 and like myoglobin has only a single haem group, whilst some amphibia have a haemoglobin of mol.wt. 290,000. The high vertebrates have a fixed haemoglobin size; presumably there is an upper limit to the size of the molecule which is compatible with rapid transfer of oxygen from molecule to molecule within the depths of the red cell.

The horse haemoglobin molecule is an ellipsoid with a length of approx. 64 Å, a width of 55 Å and a height of 50 Å (one Ångström unit $= 10^{-8}$ cm). In all it has about 10,000 atoms and as has been stated before, has a mol.wt. of 67,000. The fact that myoglobin and lamprey haemoglobin are approximately one quarter of this size suggests that the completed mammalian molecule is formed of four subunits and this has been confirmed by the determination of the end groups of peptide chains in the human haemoglobin molecule and X-ray analysis of horse haemoglobin crystals.

(a) The haem group

The haem group comprises an iron atom inserted into the centre of a disc-shaped porphyrin constructed from four pyrrole rings linked by methene $(=CH-)$ groups. The side chains have four methyl, two vinyl and two propionic acid groups. The position of the single and double linkages in the written formula are misleading since the molecule is resonating and all the pyrrole rings are therefore similar. By interchanging the position of the side chains there are fifteen possible isomers, and the porphyrin present in haemoglobin has been labelled protoporphyrin 9. If one now confines oneself to a consideration of the position of the methyl groups, the number of isomers of a simpler compound containing only methyl or ethyl side chains (aetioporphyrin) is reduced to four and of these, only two, 1,3,5,7-tetramethyl or series one, and 1,3,5,8-tetramethyl or series three, are known in nature. The protoporphyrin of haemoglobin belongs to series three of the aetioporphyrins. Compounds of series one and series three are not interchangeable without breaking the ring and recreating a fresh porphyrin structure.

The iron of haemoglobin remains permanently in the ferrous state and functions by replacement of a water molecule attached to the iron atom by molecular oxygen. The molecule of water can also be replaced by hydrogen cyanide, carbon monoxide and nitric oxide. Pauling[15] has suggested that a linkage with these apparently unrelated substances is possible because they are capable of forming bonds without destroying the electrical neutrality of the iron atom.

When haemoglobin or myoglobin is thoroughly dried, its absorption spectrum becomes that of a haemochromogen. On rehydration the spectrum reverts to that of haemoglobin. The explanation may be that the molecule of water on the iron atom is replaced on dehydration by a nitrogenous group from the globin molecule which has been brought closer to the iron by drying.

If the iron atom of haemoglobin is oxidised to the ferric state then methaemoglobin is formed. This is in contrast to the attachment of molecular oxygen to the ferrous atom which is called oxygenation. Methaemoglobin forms linkages with different complexes such as hydroxyl, hydrosulphuric, fluoride or cyanide[16]. It is incapable of combining reversibly with oxygen and it is therefore valueless as a respiratory pigment. Methaemoglobin is formed *in vitro* by the addition of potassium ferricyanide to blood. *In vivo* it is present as a result of ingestion of a wide variety of drugs such as acetanilide, sulphon-amides, phenacetin or nitrites, or it may be due to congenital abnormalities. These are either deficiencies in reducing systems which restore small amounts of methaemoglobin arising normally to the physiologically active pigment, or they are inborn errors of globin formation which cause the production of a haemoglobin which can only exist in the ferric state (haemoglobin M). In artificial haemoglobin–methaemoglobin solutions, the resulting pigment gives up oxygen less freely for there is a shift of the oxygen dissociation curve to the left. This may be due to molecules containing both ferrous and ferric atoms in various proportions. This shift is not a constant feature when methaemoglobin occurs in disease.

The fact that normally oxygen fails to oxidise the ferrous atom of oxy-haemoglobin appears, at least in part, due to stabilisation produced by the linkage of haem with the globin portion of the molecule and this linkage becomes stronger after the displacement of water by oxygen. In the red cell, enzyme systems protect the essentially vulnerable ferrous atom from spontaneous oxidation to the ferric state. A flavoprotein links reduced coenzymes with methaemoglobin and it is this enzyme which appears reduced in congenital methaemoglobinaemia. As a result the physiological level of methaemoglobin (approx. 1%) rises to about 40%. Not all the haemoglobin becomes oxidised, and this is thought to be due to constant reduction by ascorbic acid in the blood stream. Ingestion of ascorbic acid (500 mg daily) reduces abnormal pigment to very near its physiological level.

The link between the iron atom of the haem and the underlying globin has been much studied and the position has been summarised by Keilin[17]. Four possible linkages have been suggested: (1) the imidazole group of histidine, (2) carboxyl group of aspartic and glutamic acid, (3) the sulphydryl group of cysteine, (4) no specific group.

The linkage may well involve both the iron atom and the porphyrin ring. Evidence for the latter is obtained by the alteration of the absorption spectrum of an alkaline solution of free porphyrin by native globin. Also, when globin recombines with haem, porphyrin is able to compete with haem for a position on the globin molecule.

By the formation of haemochromogens with varied nitrogenous compounds there appear to be only three likely iron–amino acid complexes—the imidazole group of histidine, the terminal α-amino acids and the ε-amino groups of lysine. The possibility of cysteine as a linkage is unlikely because a myoglobin has been found to be free of cysteine. The evidence for carboxyl groups binding the iron is based on the pH stability curves of methaemoglobin obtained by the oxidation of haemoglobin or by the reconstitution from haematin and globin showing ionising groups with pK 4.7. This lies closer to the pK of the carboxyl group than to the imidazole group of histidine.

The high degree of resolution obtained by Kendrew[18] in his examination of myoglobin succeeded in visualising an amino acid residue arising from the adjacent polypeptide chain and projected towards the iron atom of haem. This amino acid structure was highly suggestive of histidine. Some invertebrate myoglobin molecules of molecular weight 17,000 have been found to possess only one histidine molecule.

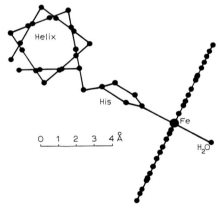

Fig. 2. Detail of the myoglobin molecule. It shows left to right a polypeptide helical chain in cross section, the histidine molecule, the haem group edge-on and finally what is presumably a water molecule. (From Kendrew et al.[18].)

The haem may be further bound by Van der Waals forces (physical forces of molecular attraction occurring between neighbouring non-polar molecules) which would bind the flat haem to the surface of the globin beneath.

The exact position occupied by the haem group is now known with some certainty for horse haemoglobin. The iron atoms lie at the corners of an

                  A – – – – – – – – – – – – – – A

α Val – Leu – Ser – Pro – Ala – Asp – Lys – Thr – Asp – Val – Lys – Ala – Ala – Try – Gly – Lys – Val – Gly – Ala –
    1   2   3   4   5   6   7   8   9   10   11   12   13   14   15   16   17   18   19

β Val – His – Leu – Thr – Pro – Glu – Glu – Lys – Ser – Ala – Val – Thr – Ala – Leu – Try – Gly – Lys – Val – Asp–
    1   2   3   4   5   6   7   8   9   10   11   12   13   14   15   16   17   18   19

γ Gly – His – Phe – Thr – Glu – Glu – Asp – Lys – Ala – Thr – Ileu – Thr – Ser – Leu – Try – Gly – Lys – Val – Asp–
    1   2   3   4   5   6   7   8   9   10   11   12   13   14   15   16   17   18   19

M   Val – Ala – Gly – Glu – Try – Ser – Glu – Ileu – Leu – Lys – ? – Try – ? –   Leu – ? – Leu – Glu – ?
      1   2   3   4   5   6   7   8   9   10   11   12   13   14   15   16   17
        A – – – – – – – – – – – – – – A

       B – – – – – – – – – – – – – B   C – – – – C

α – His – Ala – Gly – Glu – Tyr – Gly – Ala – Glu – Ala – Leu – Glu – Arg – Met – Phe – Leu – Ser – Phe – Pro – Thr – Thr –
   20   21   22   23   24   25   26   27   28   29   30   31   32   33   34   35   36   37   38   39

β – Val – Asp – Glu – Val – Gly – Gly – Glu – Ala – Leu – Gly – Arg – Leu – Leu – Val – Val – Tyr – Pro – Try – Thr –
   20   21   22   23   24   25   26   27   28   29   30   31   32   33   34   35   36   37   38

γ – Val – Glu – Asp – Ala – Gly – Gly – Glu – Thr – Leu – Gly – Arg – Leu – Leu – Val – Val – Tyr – Pro – Try – Thr –
   20   21   22   23   24   25   26   27   28   29   30   31   32   33   34   35   36   37   38

M– Leu – Val – Ala – Gly – His – Gly – Lys – Lys – Leu – Ileu – Ser – Phe – Lys – Ser – His – Pro – Glu – Thr –
   18   19   20   21   22   23   24   25   26   27   28   29   30   31   32   33   34   35   36   37
     B – – – – – – – – – – – – – B   C – – – – C

     – – – – CD   D – – – – D

α – Lys – Thr – Tyr – Phe – Pro – His – Phe – Asp – Leu – Ser – His – Gly – Ser – Ala –
   40   41   42   43   44   45   46   47   48   49   50   51   52   53

β – Glu – Arg – Phe – Phe – Glu – Ser – Phe – Gly – Asp – Leu – Ser – Thr – Pro – Asp – Ala – Val – Met – Gly – Asp – Pro –
   39   40   41   42   43   44   45   46   47   48   49   50   51   52   53   54   55   56   57   58

γ – Glu – Arg – Phe – Phe – Asp – Ser – Phe – Gly – Asp – Leu – Ser – Ser – Ala – Ser – Ala – Ileu – Met – Gly – Asp – Pro –
   39   40   41   42   43   44   45   46   47   48   49   50   51   52   53   54   55   56   57   58

M– Leu – Glu – Lys – Phe – Asp – Arg – Phe – Lys – His – Leu – Lys – Thr – Glu – Ala – Glu – Met – Lys – Ala – Ser – Glu –
   38   39   40   41   42   43   44   45   46   47   48   49   50   51   52   53   54   55   56   57
   – – – – CD   D – – – – D

Fig. 3. Part A.

```
        E - - - - - - - - - - - - - - - - - - - - - - - - - - - - - - - - - - - - - - - - - EF
α - Glu - Val - Lys - Gly - His - Gly - Lys - Lys - Val - Ala - Asp - Ala - Leu - Thr - Asp - Ala - Val - Ala - His - Val -
    54    55    56    57    58    59    60    61    62    63    64    65    66    67    68    69    70    71    72    73

β - Lys - Val - Lys - Ala - His - Gly - Lys - Lys - Val - Leu - Gly - Ala - Phe - Ser - Asp - Gly - Leu - Ala - His - Leu -
    59    60    61    62    63    64    65    66    67    68    69    70    71    72    73    74    75    76    77    78

γ - Lys - Val - Lys - Ala - His - Gly - Lys - Lys - Val - Leu - Thr - Ser - Leu - Gly - Asp - Ala - Ileu- Lys - His - Leu -
    59    60    61    62    63    64    65    66    67    68    69    70    71    72    73    74    75    76    77    78

M -(Asp- Leu)- Lys -(His)- Glu - Ileu- Val -Asp-(Glu)- Ala - Leu - Gly - Ala - Ileu- Asp - Arg - Lys - Lys -
    58          59          60    61    62    63    64    65    66    67    68    69    70    71    72    73    74    75    76    77
        E - - - - - - - - - - - - - - - - - - - - - - - - - - - - - - - - - - - - - - - - - EF
```

```
        F - - - - - - - - - - - - - - - - - - - - - - - - - - - - - - - - - - - - - - - - - FG
α - Asp - Asp - Met - Pro - Asp - Ala - Leu - Ser - Ala - Leu - Ser - Asp - Leu - His - Ala - His - Lys - Leu - Arg - Val -
    74    75    76    77    78    79    80    81    82    83    84    85    86    87    88    89    90    91    92    93

β - Asp - Asp - Leu - Lys - Gly - Thr - Phe - Ala - Thr - Leu - Ser - Glu - Leu - His - Cys - Asp - Lys - Leu - His - Val -
    79    80    81    82    83    84    85    86    87    88    89    90    91    92    93    94    95    96    97    98

γ - Asp - Asp - Leu - Lys - Gly - Thr - Phe - Ala - Glu - Leu - Ser - Glu - Leu - His - Cys - Asp - Lys - Leu - His - Val -
    79    80    81    82    83    84    85    86    87    88    89    90    91    92    93    94    95    96    97    98

M - Gly - Leu - His - Glu - Leu - Glu - Glu - Ala - Pro - Ala - Thr - Ala - His - Ser - His - Ala -  - Lys - Leu - Phe - Lys -
    78    79    80    81    82    83    84    85    86    87    88    89    90    91    92    93          94    95    96
        F - - - - - - - - - - - - - - - - - - - - - - - - - - - - - - - - - - - - - - - - - FG
```

```
        G - - - - - - - - - - - - - - - - - - - - - - - - - - - - - - - - - - - - - - - - - G
α - Asp - Pro - Val - Asp - Phe - Lys - Leu - Leu - Ser - His - Cys - Leu - Leu - Val - Thr - Leu - Ala - Ala - His - Leu -
    94    95    96    97    98    99    100   101   102   103   104   105   106   107   108   109   110   111   112   113

β - Asp - Pro - Glu - Asp - Phe - Arg - Leu - Leu - Gly - Asp - Val - Leu - Val - Cys - Val - Leu - Ala - His - His - Phe -
    99    100   101   102   103   104   105   106   107   108   109   110   111   112   113   114   115   116   117   118

γ - Asp - Pro - Glu - Asp - Phe - Lys - Leu - Leu - Gly - Asp - Val - Leu - Val - Thr - Val - Leu - Ala - Ileu- His - Phe -
    99    100   101   102   103   104   105   106   107   108   109   110   111   112   113   114   115   116   117   118

M - Ileu- Pro - Ileu- Lys - Tyr - ?  - Glu - His - Leu - Ser - ?  - Ala - Val - Ileu- His - Val - Arg - Ala - Thr - Lys -
    97    98    99    100   101   102   103   104   105   106   107   108   109   110   111   112   113   114   115   116
        G - - - - - - - - - - - - - - - - - - - - - - - - - - - - - - - - - - - - - - - - - G
```

Fig. 3. Part B.

H -

```
α – Pro –   | Ala – Glu – Phe – Thr – Pro – Ala – Val – His – Ala – Ser – Leu – Asp – Lys – Phe – Leu – Ala – Ser – Val –
      114    115   116   117   118   119   120   121   122   123   124   125   126   127   128   129   130   131   132

β – Gly –   | Lys – Glu – Phe – Thr – Pro – Pro – Val – Glu – Ala – Ala – Tyr – Glu – Lys – Val – Val – Ala – Gly – Val –
      119    120   121   122   123   124   125   126   127   128   129   130   131   132   133   134   135   136   137

γ – Gly –   | Lys – Glu – Phe – Thr – Pro – Glu – Val – Glu – Ala – Ser – Try – Glu – Lys – Met – Val – Thr – Gly – Val –
      119    120   121   122   123   124   125   126   127   128   129   130   131   132   133   134   135   136   137

M – His – Asp – Asp – Phe – Gly – Ala – Pro – Ala – Pro – Gly – Ala – Met – Gly – Lys – Ala – Leu – Glu – Leu – Phe –
      117   118   119   120   121   122   123   124   125   126   127   128   129   130   131   132   133   134   135   136
```

H - - - - - - - - -

- H

```
α – Ser – Thr – Val – Leu – Thr – Ser – Lys – Tyr – Arg
      133   134   135   136   137   138   139   140   141

β – Ala – Asp – Ala – Leu – Ala – His – Lys – Tyr – His
      138   139   140   141   142   143   144   145   146

γ – Ala – Ser – Leu – Ser – Ser – Arg – Tyr – His
      138   139   140   141   142   143   144   145   146

M – Arg – Lys – Asp – Ileu – Ala – Ala – Lys – Tyr – Lys – Glu – Leu – Gly – Tyr – Gly – Glu
      137   138   139   140   141   142   143   144   145   146   147   148   149   150   151
```

- - - - - - - - - - - HC

Fig. 3. The constitution of the α-, β- and γ-chains of the human haemoglobin and of the peptide chain of the whale myoglobin (M). All chains have almost identical helical structures, hence the helical twists as found in myoglobin are entered A—B—C—D—E—F—G—H. Abbreviations:

Ala	alanine	His	histidine
Arg	arginine	Ileu	isoleucine
Asp	aspartic acid	Leu	leucine
Cys	cysteine	Lys	lysine
Glu	glutamic acid	Met	methionine
Gly	glycine	Phe	phenylalanine

Pro	proline
Ser	serine
Thr	threonine
Tyr	tyrosine
Try	tryptophan
Val	valine

irregular tetrahedron with a distance of 33.4 and 36.0 Å between symmetrically related pairs. The closest approach between unrelated iron atoms is 25.2 Å.

Because the haem groups can be oxidised by relatively large molecules such as potassium ferricyanide and can also be removed and replaced on the globin they cannot be situated deep in the protein structure. Indeed Granick[19] has likened them to postage stamps stuck onto the surface of the underlying globin and their superficial situation has been confirmed by the use of X-ray crystallography which demonstrated the four haem groups in separate pockets on the surface of the haemoglobin molecule.

(b) The protein portion of the molecule

About 95% of the haemoglobin molecule is protein and the importance of this fraction goes beyond that of an inert carrier of the active haem.

There are four polypeptide chains in each molecule of mammalian haemoglobin. These polypeptide chains have been distinguished by recognition of their terminal amino acids, and by chromatographic analysis of their tryptic digests[20,21].

One type of peptide chain in human haemoglobin has the end group valyl–leucyl and has been called the α-chain, and another type has a valyl–histidyl–leucyl termination and has been labelled the β-chain. Normal adult haemoglobin has two α- and two β-chains in each molecule. Each foetal haemoglobin molecule has two α-chains but instead of the β-chains two others, which terminate in a glycyl residue called the γ-chain. The physiological change from foetal to adult haemoglobin therefore consists in changing the partners of the α-chain from γ to β. There exists besides adult and foetal haemoglobin yet a third human haemoglobin: A_2. It is present in adults at about 2% of the total haemoglobin, but is raised above that level in Mediterranean anaemia. Like normal adult haemoglobin (HbA) and foetal haemoglobin (HbF) HbA_2 is composed of one half of the α_2-subunit, the second pair of chains differs[22] from the β_2-γ_2-subunits and is designated δ_2.

The formula of the three physiological haemoglobins can thus be written:

$$HbA: \quad \alpha_2\beta_2$$
$$HbF: \quad \alpha_2\gamma_2$$
$$HbA_2: \quad \alpha_2\delta_2$$

Braunitzer and Rudloff[23] have summarised the latest knowledge of the three peptide chains of human haemoglobin α, β, γ, and of the myoglobin chain of the whale (M), which demonstrates the remarkable similarity in many places along these four chains (see Fig. 3).

The most recent advance in knowledge of protein structure has arisen from the use of X-ray diffraction techniques to investigate further the folding of the polypeptide chains within the molecules of myoglobin and of haemoglobin. This technique depends upon the interpretation of a photographic recording of the X-ray reflections from a crystal rotated in a beam of X-rays. Because the reflections result from the electrons of the atoms it becomes possible after complex mathematical calculations to plot the regions of high electron density within the molecule. Using this technique the position of the iron atoms are identified by their high electron density. Further reference points were mercury atoms, which were attached to two of the four sulphydryl groups of cysteine in the molecule prior to examination of the crystal. The results were finally plotted on contour maps, each plane representing the distribution of electron density at a distance of 2 Å within the molecule in that section. The effect produced when these two-dimensional maps were positioned over each other was likened by Perutz[24] to cylindrical clouds of high density like the vapour trails of an aeroplane curved to form intricate three-dimensional figures, which were the materialisation of the polypeptide chains of the molecule. These chains were four in number and consisted of two pairs of identical structures in each molecule, each chain being associated with an atom of iron. Perhaps the point of greatest interest is the almost

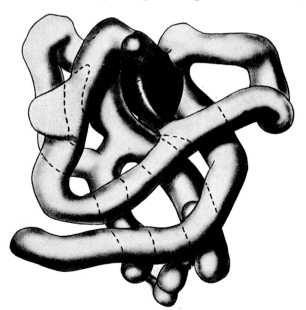

Fig. 4. The polypeptide chain of myoglobin established by Kendrew *et al.*[18] which is similar but not identical to the basic units of haemoglobin. (From Kendrew *et al.*[18].)

but not quite complete similarity of each chain to the unit of myoglobin, independently constructed by Kendrew *et al.*[18] (Fig. 4). The mode of construction of the haemoglobin molecule is shown by Figs. 5a and 5b. The β-chains carry the SH-groups[25].

Although there is little contact between identical chains (either black or white in the model) there is very close contact between unidentical chains. The position of the cysteine in the molecule (marked SH) suggests that it may play a part in linking the dissimilar chains together as well as being in close contact with, and having some influence, over the haem.

The final shape evolving from the complex pathways of the polypeptide chains is that of an ellipsoid and this may assist in the rapid transfer of oxygen within the red cell.

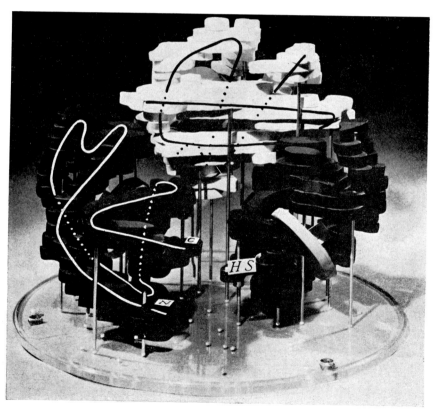

Fig. 5a. Partially assembled haemoglobin molecule showing two similar and one dissimilar chain. The disc-shaped haem and the position of a cysteine is shown (HS). (From Perutz *et al.*[24].)

Fig. 5b. The completed molecule after the addition of a fourth polypeptide chain.
(From Perutz *et al.*[24].)

5. The abnormal haemoglobins

Man possesses in addition to the three physiological haemoglobins (normal adult haemoglobin-A, foetal haemoglobin-F, and haemoglobin-A_2) some twenty abnormal pigments. There are two principal types of abnormality— one in which the combination of the polypeptide chains is altered, and the other in which the chains themselves are different.

To the first group belong the abnormal haemoglobin-H which consists of four β-chains—β_4—and haemoglobin "Bart's" which consists of four γ-chains—γ_4. H and Bart's can occur together and indeed it has been claimed that small amounts of Bart's are always found in persons with haemoglobin-H, though the reverse does not apply. The production of these haemoglobins is obviously due to an α-chain deficiency. Presumably a β-chain deficiency

References p. 74

might also occur, but this could be compensated by a greater production of γ-chains and a compensatory rise in haemoglobin-F ($\alpha_2\gamma_2$). For a haemoglobin-α_4 to be formed both β- and γ-chain production would have to be at fault, and this is less likely to arise because these two chains are under an independent genetic control. It is therefore not surprising that haemoglobin-α_4 has as yet not been described.

By far the most common abnormality of haemoglobin formation is a substitution of one amino acid by another in one of the two polypeptide chains. As there are α- and β-chains and as substitution can occur in either, two types of abnormal adult haemoglobins are known, abnormal α-chain haemoglobins (I, D_α, G_{Ibadan}, K, Norfolk, Q etc.) and abnormal β-chain haemoglobins (S (sickle-cell), C, D_β, D_γ, E, G_{Accra}, J, L, N, O, P etc.). In the M haemoglobins which cannot exist in the ferrous state (see p. 61) the amino acid substitution affects the histidine bridge from globin to haem or the amino acid near the water molecule of the haem. For example, in M_{Boston} the actual histidyl residue in the 58th position along the α-chain is replaced by a tyrosyl residue.

The analysis of these haemoglobins goes back to the ingenious work of Ingram on sickle-cell haemoglobin[26]. He digested the denatured globin with trypsin, thereby splitting the chains in places where an arginine or a lysine occurred. The resulting peptides were separated by a combination of chromatography and electrophoresis. It was found that haemoglobins A and S differed in only one single peptide. Within this peptide the differences could be narrowed down to one single amino acid which in the sixth position of the β-chain in A was glutamic acid, and in S was valine. In the allelic haemoglobin-C the same link of the peptide chain was taken up by lysine. These small differences could go far to explain the electrophoretic differences between the haemoglobins. They also illustrated how a small change in the nucleic acid template of the chromosome may result in the production of molecules which may not be very different chemically but are vastly different physiologically.

The most widespread abnormalities are the β-chain mutations which are S, C, E and to some extent $D_{\beta\ Punjab}$, and they affect many millions of the human race. This is presumably so because the normal α-chain allows a compensatory production of $\alpha_2\gamma_2$ (F) in the foetus and the anaemic child.

It is possible to separate the α_2- and β_2-subunits by incubation at acid pH. On recombination at neutral or slightly alkaline pH they recombine and, as one might expect, after the dissociation of a mixture of haemoglobins S and C ($\alpha_2\beta_2^S$ and $\alpha_2\beta_2^C$) into their α_2- and β_2-subunits on recombination again only haemoglobins S and C occur, although there may have been an exchange of α-chains (Itano and Robinson[27]). These authors showed however that the dissociation and recombination of a mixture of abnormal α- and abnormal β-chain haemoglobins resulted in two additional pigments: normal adult haemoglobin $(\alpha_2\beta_2)$ and a new, hitherto not known hybrid consisting of both abnormal α_2 and β_2.

A polymorphism for adult haemoglobins exists also in many mammals, notably in cows, sheep, mice. In the cow the polymorphism is restricted to the descendants of *Bos indicus*; the European breeds which are derived from *Bos taurus* are homozygous for the gene controlling bovine haemoglobin-A. It was of great interest that certain British breeds, Jersey, Guernsey, South Devon, which had always been supposed to be related to the Indian *Brachyceros*, possess both the bovine haemoglobins A and B.

The homozygous state for an abnormal haemoglobin is with one exception (G_{Accra}) always associated with anaemia; the same has been noted for heterozygotes for two abnormal haemoglobin genes (*e.g.* SC, SD etc.). This is primarily thought to be due to a diminished overall rate of haemoglobin production which results in a disproportion of stroma to haemoglobin. The cells are flat and their life span is shorter than the normal 120 days. There exists also an abnormality of haemoglobin-A production which results in poorly haemoglobinised red cells—thalassaemia. Here again the homozygote is severely affected and usually dies early. The heterozygote for the thalassaemia gene is usually able to compensate for the shorter life span of his red cells by increased production. He is, however, at risk when there is an additional strain such as infectious disease, or, in women, pregnancy. In sickle-cell anaemia there is, over and above the usual dyshaemopoiesis, additional cell destruction because of the formation of sickle cells. Sickle-cell haemoglobin is less soluble in the deoxygenated state[28] than reduced haemoglobin-A. Sickle-cell haemoglobin forms therefore tactoids in the reduced state, and these tactoids tend to distort the normal shape of the red cells. The spiked sickle cells block capillaries and small vessels which causes further deoxygenation and sickling. These blockages or crises may occur in all parts of the body and when they take place in vitally important regions will cause immediate death.

The haemoglobin content of the human red cell is about 38%. Under physiological conditions deoxygenation does not go far enough to cause sickling unless the percentage of S is well above 20%. In the sickle-cell trait carrier (AS) the proportion of A is greater than that of S and sickling will therefore not occur *in vivo* unless there is an abnormal oxygen lack as might occur in flying in an unpressurised aeroplane at high altitudes. The sickle-cell homozygote however will be subject to sickling crisis under normal conditions of life particularly if there is a slight decrease in oxygenation as it occurs in anaemia or infectious disease, notably pneumonia.

References p. 74

6. Haemoglobin in the red cell

The first attempt to localise haemoglobin within a cell occurs in the coelomic cavity of a few marine invertebrates. The red cells of the lower vertebrates are nucleated oval and biconvex and vary greatly in size. The tailed amphibians have cells of giant proportions compared with other species. The mammals are characterised by their non-nucleated biconcave red cells of fairly uniform size, but non-nucleated cells also occur in some American salamanders and are therefore not confined to the mammalian order.

The human red cell, although intensively studied, still presents many problems, one of the most interesting being the unknown mechanism which maintains the biconcave shape. Although to some degree still controversial, it now appears probable that the cell is surrounded by an envelope which is thickened over the biconcavities and to which stromal fibres are attached on the internal surface. The envelope should be considered as a dynamic part of the cell rather than an inert membrane because it is able to control selective absorption of metabolites and maintain energy gradients. The oxidation of glucose 6-phosphate has been found to be a key reaction in providing energy for the synthesis of fatty acids in the red cell envelope. The absence of glucose 6-phosphate dehydrogenase was found to be the cause of haemolysis in some American negroes treated with the anti-malarial drug primaquine[29], and has since been found in other populations, notably in the Mediterranean. This abnormality is genetically controlled and is sex linked. It may cause a haemolytic reaction as a manifestation of drug sensitivity and is responsible for the haemolytic crises in favism.

The interior of the cell must consist of extremely closely packed haemoglobin molecules because the red cell contains about 38% haemoglobin whereas wet horse haemoglobin crystals contain 55%.

Only 2% of the haemoglobin molecules are at the surface of the cell and Crosby[30] conceives transfer of oxygen by passage from one rapidly spinning ellipsoid haemoglobin molecule to another, reminiscent of the rollers of a printing press. The movement of the haem groups on oxygenation of the iron atoms may then be a mechanism to unlock the molecule from its neighbour.

Perutz (personal communication) has found that the β-chains of horse and human haemoglobin alter their configuration when haemoglobin is de-oxygenated. Such a change in the molecular shape may perhaps mechanically transmit itself throughout the red cell from one molecule to the other.

The red cell appears to be an advanced and highly efficient mechanism to carry haemoglobin, preserving it from injurious chemicals and possessing energy providing enzyme systems enabling it to function efficiently as an independent respiratory carrier.

7. Myoglobin in the muscle

The muscular flesh of a man constitutes about 40% of his weight. The muscle fibre is a multinucleated cell surrounded by a fine sheath called the sarcolemma which separates the potassium-rich interior from the sodium-rich extracellular fluids. In this respect it does not differ from the membrane of any other cell. The muscle fibre contains large numbers of contractile filamentous myofibrils separated by a sticky matrix of undifferentiated granular protoplasm called the sarcoplasm. In frog muscle, the sarcoplasm has been estimated as 40% of the total volume of the muscle and in general the constantly active muscles such as the respiratory muscles possess the most. The lightness and darkness of a muscle is related not only to the myoglobin content but also to the opacity of the myofibrils, which is governed by the lipid content.

The myoglobin in the sarcoplasm is probably in solution. Little is known about its formation or destruction but isotope studies have shown that it appears to be relatively stable and its reduction in iron deficiency anaemia shows that its formation is—as perhaps expected—dependent on the general availability of iron in the body.

The crystallisation of myoglobin by Theorell and De Duve[31] in 1934, and the demonstration of its structure by Kendrew et al.[18] in 1960, have given valuable information about its chemical and physical properties. Our present lack of knowledge concerns primarily its state in nature—rather than detail of its structure.

REFERENCES

[1] L. J. HENDERSON, quoted in J. BARCROFT, *Respiratory Function of the Blood*, Vol. II, Cambridge University Press, Cambridge, 1928.

[2] G. WALD, *Biochemical Evolution* in E. S. GUZMAN BARRON (Ed.), *Modern Trends in Physiology and Biochemistry*, Academic Press, New York, 1952.

[3] D. KEILIN, *Acta Biochem. Polon.*, 3 (1956) 439.

[4] J. BARCROFT, *Physiol. Revs.*, 5 (1925) 596.

[5] A. C. REDFIELD, *Quart. Rev. Biol.*, 8 (1933) 31.

[6] J. T. RUUD, *Nature*, 173 (1954) 848.

[7] H. M. FOX, *Nature*, 179 (1957) 148.

[8] G. BIORK, *Acta Med. Scand.*, 133 (1949) Suppl. 226.

[9] F. HAUROWITZ, *Progress in Biochemistry*, Interscience, New York, 1950.

[10] M. ADINOLFI, G. CHIEFFI AND M. SINISCALCO, *Nature*, 184 (1959) 1325.

[11] M. FLORKIN, *Biochemical Evolution*, Academic Press, New York, 1949.

[12] D. W. ALLEN, J. WYMAN JR. AND C. A. SMITH, *J. Biol. Chem.*, 203 (1953) 81.

[13] T. H. J. HUISMAN, H. J. VAN DER HELM, H. K. A. VISSER AND G. VAN VLIET, *Investigations on Different Haemoglobin Types in some Species of Animals* in J. H. P. JONXIS AND J. F. DELAFRESNAYE (Eds.), *Abnormal Haemoglobin*, Blackwell, Oxford, 1959.

[14] D. KEILIN AND E. F. HARTREE, *Nature*, 168 (1951) 266.

[15] L. PAULING in F. J. W. ROUGHTON AND J. C. KENDREW (Eds.), *Haemoglobin*, Barcroft Memorial Conference, Butterworth, London, 1949.

[16] D. KEILIN, *Nature*, 171 (1953) 922.

[17] J. KEILIN, *Nature*, 187 (1960) 365.

[18] J. C. KENDREW, R. E. DICKERSON, B. E. STRANDBERG, R. G. HART, D. R. DAVIES, D. C. PHILLIPS AND V. C. SHORE, *Nature*, 185 (1960) 422.

[19] S. GRANICK, *Ann. N.Y. Acad. Sci.*, 48 (1946) 657.

[20] W. A. SCHROEDER, *Fortschr. Chem. org. Naturstoffe*, 17 (1959) 371.

[21] C. J. MULLER AND J. H. P. JONXIS, *Nature*, 188 (1960) 949.

[22] A. O. W. STRETTON AND V. M. INGRAM, *Federation Proc.*, 19 (1960) 343.

[23] G. BRAUNITZER AND V. RUDLOFF, *Deut. med. Wochschr.*, 87 (1962) 959.

[24] M. F. PERUTZ, M. G. ROSSMAN, A. F. CULLIS, H. MUIRHEAD, G. WILL AND A. C. T. NORTH, *Nature*, 185 (1960) 416.

[25] A. RIGGS AND M. WELLS, *Federation Proc.*, 19 (1960) 78.

[26] V. M. INGRAM, *Brit. Med. Bull.*, 15 (1959) 27.

[27] H. A. ITANO AND E. ROBINSON, *Nature*, 183 (1959) 1799.

[28] M. F. PERUTZ, *Nature*, 161 (1948) 204.

[29] P. E. CARSON, C. L. FLANAGAN, C. E. ICKSES AND A. S. ALVING, *Science*, 124 (1956) 484.

[30] W. H. CROSBY, *Ann. Rev. Med.*, 8 (1957) 151.

[31] H. THEORELL AND C. DE DUVE, *Arch. Biochem.*, 12 (1947) 113.

Chapter II

Peptide and Protein Hormones

Section a

Thyroid Hormone

JEAN ROCHE AND RAYMOND MICHEL

Institute of General and Comparative Biochemistry, Collège de France,
Paris (France)

1. Thyroid uptake of iodine

The thyroid gland is an aggregate of closed vesicles, the follicles or acini.
Each follicle has the appearance of a microscopic spheroid and can be considered as the secretory unit. The average diameter[1,2] of the follicle of the
human thyroid gland, although it is variable, is estimated at 300–500 μ.
The thyroid gland of the rat has about 100,000 of these follicles, the sizes of
which vary, but their diameters range from 15 to more than 100 μ. The wall
of the follicle consists of a continuous epithelium composed of a single layer
of cubical cells, the average thickness[3] of which is 15 μ. They surround a
wide vesicle filled with a substance of gelatinous consistency called colloid,
which contains almost all the iodine of the thyroid gland. The human thyroid
gland contains about $^1/_5$th of the total iodine of the organism, although its
weight of about 20 g is not more than 0.03 % of the body weight[4]. The avidity
of this gland for iodine is considerable; in man it can retain up to 23 mg. The
uptake of the halogen takes place very rapidly, and one may say that the
specific feature of the thyroid gland is not so much to concentrate iodide,
which is done to a lesser degree by other tissues (salivary glands, intestinal
mucosa), but rather its ability to incorporate the halogen rapidly into the
proteins. Indeed, this "organification" of iodine is a practically instantaneous
phenomenon, since the iodine bound to the proteins can be detected as early
as 11 sec after intravenous injection of a tracer dose of radioactive iodine into
the mouse[5]. The proportion of protein-bound iodine subsequently increases.
The rate of its incorporation varies according to the species of the animal. In

the hamster 60% of the iodine retained by the thyroid after injection of [131]I
is present in the organic form within 15 sec; binding of iodine to the protein
is much slower in the monkey, guinea pig, and rabbit[6].

The thyroid gland can store not only iodides, but also other anions. The
use of [82]Br has shown that the radioactivity of the thyroid gland is higher
than that of an equivalent weight of blood, indicating a preferential binding
by the gland[7]. After administration of small doses of Br^- (1 μg), 0.5% is
retained by the gland between 6 and 8 h after injection, but no organic
bromine compound is formed[8]. The same applies to the element astatine
(No. 85, atomic weight 211) but the presence of organic compounds of this
element has not been proved[9,10]. The binding of elements of Group VII B,
manganese, technetium and rhenium, has also been established[11]. The
distribution of $KClO_4$ in the tissues is almost identical with that of I^- and
it is also taken up by the thyroid gland. Fluoride, on the contrary, is not so
fixed[12], but monofluorosulfonate, difluorophosphate, and fluoroborate are
concentrated by the gland[13]. All these ions, like the I^- ion, have an ionic
volume of about $4 \cdot 10^{-23}$ cm^3, hence one might ask whether the "trapping"
mechanism depends on the presence in the colloid of a special protein with a
particular spatial configuration which can chelate various ions of similar
electric charge and volume. The complex must be labile, however, since it is
decomposed by electrophoresis. With iodine, and only with this halogen, a
second almost simultaneous reaction occurs. It probably consists in the
conversion[14,15] by H_2O_2 of I^- into I° or I^+, which then combines immediately with protein at the site where oxidation occurs. The biphasic integra-
tion of the iodine seems to take place in the colloid. It has, indeed, been
shown by histoautoradiography that radioactive iodine forms a peripheral
ring around the colloid vesicle at an early stage[16].

2. Preparation and properties of thyroid iodinated proteins

The thyroid colloid contains almost all of the iodine, and most of it is in the
form of a soluble iodinated protein, thyroglobulin. A less abundant, insoluble
fraction is localized in the cellular "particulates". The preparation and
properties of normal and pathological thyroglobulin will first be described,
then those of the insoluble iodinated proteins.

(a) Normal thyroglobulin

(i) Preparations

The soluble iodinated protein was early identified as a globulin[17-22]. The
first preparations of thyroglobulin were obtained by extraction of the contents of the vesicle with a solution of 0.9% sodium chloride, followed by
precipitation with a half-saturated solution of ammonium sulfate[22]. The

protein was isolated after acidification with acetic acid. The thyroglobulin obtained was impure and denatured. Another technique consists in first removing the lipids with toluene and then by precipitation at pH 4.8 eliminating an insoluble nucleoprotein which accompanies thyroglobulin in thyroid extracts. In the course of this precipitation, however, the iodinated protein is partially denatured[23].

The greater part of the lipids can be eliminated by previously freezing the thyroid gland, and after cutting in thin sections, extracting the soluble proteins with isotonic salt solution. By fractionation of this extract with 35–40% saturation with ammonium sulfate, a relatively pure thyroglobulin can be obtained[24]. Extremely pure preparations have resulted from a systematic study of the factors controlling the precipitation of thyroid proteins by salting-out reagents (ammonium sulfate, mono- and di-potassium phosphates, sodium sulfate)[25].

It has been possible to follow the purification of thyroglobulin during salt fractionation by its iodine content or, when preparations were made from animals treated with ^{131}I, by its radioactivity[26]. As a result of studies in which the N/I ratio remained constant during salt fractionation, it has been possible to prepare thyroglobulin with a constant iodine content. Thus it has been possible to prepare thyroglobulin, free of nucleoproteins, of the ox, horse, dog, man and pig. Recently a method involving differential centrifugation at high speed has been recommended[27, 28].

Thyroglobulin marked with ^{131}I has been prepared after administration of tracer doses of ^{131}I to an animal 24 h before sacrifice. A solubility curve in the presence of salts is established on extracts of the gland by determining, for each salt concentration, the content of soluble nitrogen and [131]I. Estimation of the latter is made directly with a gamma-ray scintillation counter. It has also been possible to prepare human thyroglobulin labelled with ^{131}I by immersion of sections of the thyroid, obtained after accidental death, in an isotonic solution containing radioactive iodide[29]. The thyroid acini remained functional and incorporated the halogen into their thyroglobulin in a few hours.

In addition, preparations of thyroglobulin have been obtained from glands of sheep marked *in vivo* with ^{131}I, or from several glands marked *in vitro*[30]. Although each of these preparations was homogeneous by electrophoresis and ultracentrifugation, they seemed to be heterogeneous by chromatography and ultraviolet spectrophotometry.

(ii) Properties

The solubility characteristics of the thyroglobulins indicate the globulin nature of the protein. Preparations obtained by repeated *salting-out* are homogeneous to electrophoresis in liquid media as well as on paper. They show an average electrophoretic mobility of $4.54 \cdot 10^{-5}$ cm^2/V·sec at pH 7.68 in a buffered solution[31] (phosphate, ionic strength 0.2). No heterogeneity is evident between pH 6.2 and 7.7. The iodinated protein of the pig, prepared by salting-out, is highly purified and has a sedimentation constant of $s^{\circ}_{20} = 19.4$; its *partial specific volume* is 0.723. Bovine thyroglobulin has, after ultracentrifugation, a spatial specific volume of 0.714 and its *refractive index increment* is 0.1949. The *intrinsic viscosity* of thyroglobulin in 0.01 M KNO$_3$ is a function of pH and changes, between pH 7.0 and 11.0, from 0.47 to 0.144 (ref. 28). The molecular weight[32] of thyroglobulin determined by sedimentation, diffusion and diffraction is 650,000 to 670,000.

Bovine thyroglobulin shows a series of reversible changes which depend on the pH and the ionic strength of the solution. The first modification of this type is the appearance, between pH 6 and 8, of a particle with a smaller sedimentation rate, and which corresponds from diffusion and diffraction measurements to the dissociation of thyroglobulin into two units. Beyond pH 9.5 two new compounds appear, which have molecular weights lower than that of thyroglobulin. The latter is denatured at ordinary temperatures in the neighbourhood of pH 11.4.

A low concentration of dodecyl sulfate causes a dissociation of the thyroglobulin into two units without alteration of its symmetry[33]. It has also been found that thyroglobulin can dissociate reversibly[34, 35] under various conditions, such as changes in the dielectric constant of the medium and the presence of low concentrations of certain salts. The formation of aggregates may also take place in concentrated solutions of neutral salt, which may explain the fact that very highly purified preparations show three fractions well characterized by solubility curves, in spite of the fact that the N/I ratio is the same in these three fractions. This heterogeneity is also evident when the solubility is studied by Northrop's test (solubility at increasing protein concentration with the same salt content), or, further, by immunochemistry[36].

(b) Abnormal thyroglobulins and insoluble thyroid iodinated proteins

The use of radioactive iodine has made it possible to study the different compounds formed during biosynthesis under various experimental conditions and in certain pathological states. In this way it has been shown that thyroid extracts marked with ^{131}I derived from normal dogs, or from dogs treated with thyroid-stimulating hormone (thyrotrophin or TSH), contain a protein which, when isolated by salting-out, retains almost the whole of the radioactivity. In contrast, in animals with a goitre due to propylthiouracil treatment, the iodinated proteins include, in addition to normal thyroglobulin, another radioactive iodinated protein with different solubility and electrophoretic properties[26].

Relatively few studies of human thyroglobulin have been made. The solubility characteristics of extracts of the thyroids of normal or hyperthyroid patients seem to be identical[37]. An iodinated protein soluble in 0.15% NaCl, but different from thyroglobulin in its other physical properties, has been isolated from a case of follicular thyroid adenoma. This iodinated protein is more soluble in phosphate buffer than the normal protein; it sediments much more slowly and has a higher electrophoretic mobility[38-40].

The thyroglobulin of hypothyroid patients with over-fixation of the iodine and disorders of hormone synthesis, show solubility features which are normal in some cases and abnormal in others[41]. In the abnormal cases an important part of the iodinated protein remains in solution even at 70% saturation with ammonium sulfate, while all the normal protein is precipitated at 45% saturation. These abnormal iodinated proteins can be compared with those obtained experimentally in dogs given prolonged treatment with a synthetic antithyroid agent, and also with an iodinated protein present in the blood of some patients with carcinoma, which has a sedimentation coefficient of 4.25 (refs. 42–45). These abnormal iodinated proteins have an electrophoretic mobility and a solubility curve analogous to those of serum albumin[46,47]. It has been possible to detect, in certain instances, a similar iodinated protein in normal thyroid tissue and the name thyralbumin has been given to this[48].

Various insoluble constituents of an iodinated protein nature have also been defined[27,49]. They are associated with the cell particulates. The iodinated particles are not homogeneous. These iodinated proteins are soluble in a strongly alkaline medium at pH 13. Under these conditions they have solubility features in the presence of salts which are comparable to those of thyroglobulin, but these two proteins are nevertheless differentiated by their sedimentation constants, and the dissolved iodinated proteins seem to be heterogeneous by chromatography. Other attempts to dissolve them have been made by exposing them, for a very brief period, to the action of proteolytic enzymes. These iodinated proteins seem to have an origin different from that of thyroglobulin, and their quantity is increased only in tumours of the thyroid gland.

3. Chemical composition of thyroglobulin

Thyroglobulin is a glycoprotein; the carbohydrates it contains were detected by histochemical methods[50]. They are composed of galactose, mannose, glucosamine, and traces of fucose[51-55], and the high viscosity of thyroglobulin must be attributed to its glycoprotein structure. Yet the specific character of this protein is due to the presence of iodine in its molecule, in which three types of iodinated substances have been identified. Some of these are derived from L-tyrosine, others from L-thyronine, and finally others from L-histidine. Their formulas are given below (Fig. 1).

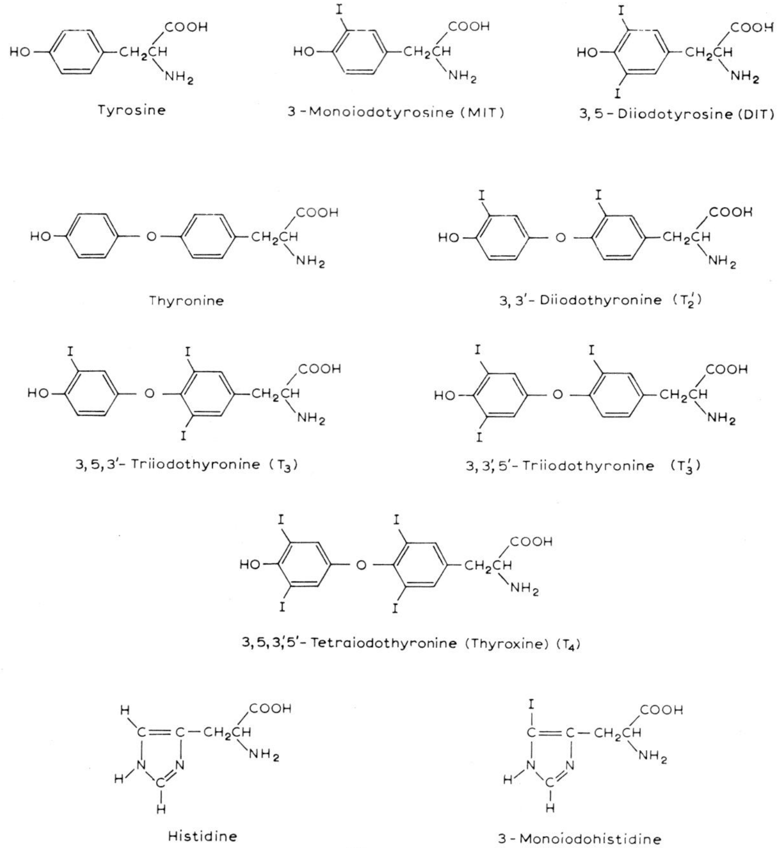

Fig. 1.

Only the iodinated amino acids derived from L-thyronine are hormonal constituents: the iodotyrosines are their precursors. Monoiodohistidine does not take part in hormonogenesis[56, 57]. We will examine in turn the characteristics of the iodinated derivatives of tyrosine and thyronine.

(a) Iodotyrosines

(i) 3-Monoiodo-L-tyrosine

The substitution of a single atom of iodine in the benzene ring of L-tyrosine takes place near the hydroxyl group, at the 3 (or 5) position.

Monoiodotyrosine (MIT), $C_9H_{10}O_3NI$ (iodine 41.4%), was first isolated in an impure state from products of the alkaline hydrolysis of iodocasein and iodopepsin[58, 59]. Later it was detected as an amino acid occurring naturally in the scleroproteins of some coelenterates (*Gorgonacea*)[60], in some of which it is very abundant (up to 8–9%), and in thyroglobulins[61, 62] and sclero-proteins of sponges[63]. Chromatographic technique and its application to labelled constituents of the thyroid proteins has made it possible to reveal amounts of 3-monoiodo-L-tyrosine too small to be measured by other means of analysis (0.1–0.2%).

The DL and L compounds have been prepared from the corresponding 3-mononitrotyrosine by reduction to the amine, diazotization, and treatment with iodide[64] (m.p. 204–206° decomp., $[\alpha]_D^{20} = -4.4°$ in N HCl; $pK_{OH} = 8.2$ in contrast to 10.07 for tyrosine[65]). MIT has also been prepared by partial iodination of tyrosine[62]. 3-Monoiodotyrosine is quantitatively extracted from acid solutions with n-butanol at a pH below 2. It is decomposed by the dehalogenase of the thyroid with formation of L-tyrosine and iodide[66].

(ii) 3,5-Diiodo-L-tyrosine

Treatment of L-tyrosine with an excess of halogen leads to the substitution of two atoms at positions 3 and 5 of the benzene ring; it gives rise to 3,5-di-iodo-L-tyrosine (DIT), $C_9H_9O_3NI_2$ (iodine 58.7%)[62].

This was isolated by Drechsel[67] in 1896 from the horny axis of a variety of the gorgonid *Eunicella verrucosa* Pallas, designated by Koch at that time as *Gorgonia cavolinii*. This explains the name iodogorgonine first given to this compound. Later it was extracted from various gorgonids and sponges[68], from thyroglobulins[69], and from numerous iodinated proteins[70]. It is present in minimal amounts in the proteins of algae of the genus *Laminaria*[71], in egg yolk proteins of birds[72], and in various scleroproteins of invertebrates[73].

The constitution of the natural amino acid, not well defined for a long time, has been established by synthesis[74]. The simplest technique for achiev-ing this is based on the action of iodine chloride on L-tyrosine at 60° in an acetic acid medium, the two reactants being used in stoichiometric propor-tions[75]. Iodine also reacts with L-tyrosine in an ammoniacal medium, giving rise to the 3,5-diiodo derivative[76].

3,5-Diiodotyrosine crystallizes in aqueous solutions with two molecules of water, which it loses[77] when dried over P_2O_5. Its isoelectric point is below that of L-tyrosine ($pH_i = 4.29$, instead of 5.66, at 25°), chiefly because of the more marked dissociation of the phenolic group. The pK values of the two amino acids are respectively: for tyrosine, 2.20 (COOH), 9.11 (NH_3^+), and 10.07 (OH); and for 3,5-diiodotyrosine, 2.11 (COOH), 7.82 (NH_3^+), and 6.48 (OH). The diiodo compound can be easily extracted with n-butanol from acid solutions at pH 2 or lower[78], but not on the other hand from alkaline solutions of $1 N$ NaOH or stronger[79]. On this basis it has been possible to separate iodothyronines and iodotyrosines in hydrolysates of iodinated proteins. It has been found possible to use the brown-orange colour (changing to orange in ammoniacal solution) of the o-diiodophenols under specific conditions for the estimation of 3,5-diiodotyrosine[80]. Thyroid dehalogenase degrades 3,5-diiodotyrosine to iodide and tyrosine, and the iodide formed may be re-utilized by the gland[81].

(b) Iodothyronines

(i) L-Thyroxine (T_4)

This was isolated in 1919 in crystalline form, from an alkaline hydrolysate of thyroid extract[82, 83]. Its structure was established some years later and then confirmed by synthesis[84, 85]. It corresponds to β-3,5-diiodo-4(3',5'-di-iodo-4'-hydroxyphenoxy)phenyl-α-aminopropionic acid. Thyroxine is obtained by 3',5'-iodination of 3,5-diiodothyronine. The first synthesis was achieved by Harington and Barger[85]. Since their original work, two new methods have been developed[86, 87]; although different in principle, both use L-tyrosine as the starting material and yield the natural L-thyroxine. The optical rotation of L-thyroxine $[\alpha]_{5461} = -5.7°$ in ethanol–NaOH solution.

T_4 crystallizes in microscopic needles united in sheaths or rosettes. It is practically insoluble at pH 4.5 and at this pH precipitates quantitatively from solution. This property is utilized in the estimation of T_4 in hydrolysates of thyroglobulin[88]. It can be extracted with n-butanol at pH 4 and remains in this solvent after washing with alkali, which distinguishes it from the iodotyrosines[79].

(ii) Di- and tri-iodo-L-thyronines $(T_2', T_3$ and $T_3')$

The detection of partially iodinated L-thyronines in thyroglobulin has been achieved by use of ^{131}I in conjunction with chromatography. 3,5,3'-Triiodo-thyronine, T_3, is prepared by partial iodination of 3,5- diiodothyronine in an ammoniacal medium, either with $KI–I_2$ (ref. 89) or with a solution of iodine in methanol[90]. T_3 is then purified by chromatography. It crystallizes in long needles and melts at 233° with decomposition. The ultraviolet spectrum shows a maximum absorption at 3173 Å in a weakly alkaline medium.

The two other iodothyronines, T_2' and T_3', identified in thyroglobulin, have been obtained by controlled iodination of 3-iodothyronine[91], of which various syntheses have been described[92–94].

The iodothyronines can be identified on chromatograms by the various colour reactions of the amino acids and phenols (see properties in Table I) and also by the presence of iodine[95].

Alkaline solvents lend themselves best to the separation of iodothyronine mixtures[96]. n-Butanol saturated with $2 N$ ammonia will satisfactorily resolve a mixture of T_4, T_3 and I^-, and also one of T_2', T_3' and I^-, but it will not on the other hand resolve a mixture of T_4, T_2' and T_3', nor a mixture of 3'-iodo-thyronine, T_1 and 3',5'-diiodothyronine. *n*-Butanol–dioxane (4:1) saturated with 2 *N* ammonia gives analogous results; it has the advantage that it

TABLE I

IDENTIFICATION REACTIONS OF THYROID HORMONES

Reactions	T_4	T_3	T_3'	T_2'
1. Ninhydrin reaction	+	+	+	+
2. Phenol group reactions				
Pauly	+	+	+	+
Millon	—	+	—	+
α-Nitroso-β-naphthol	—	+	—	+
Nitrite	+	—	+	—

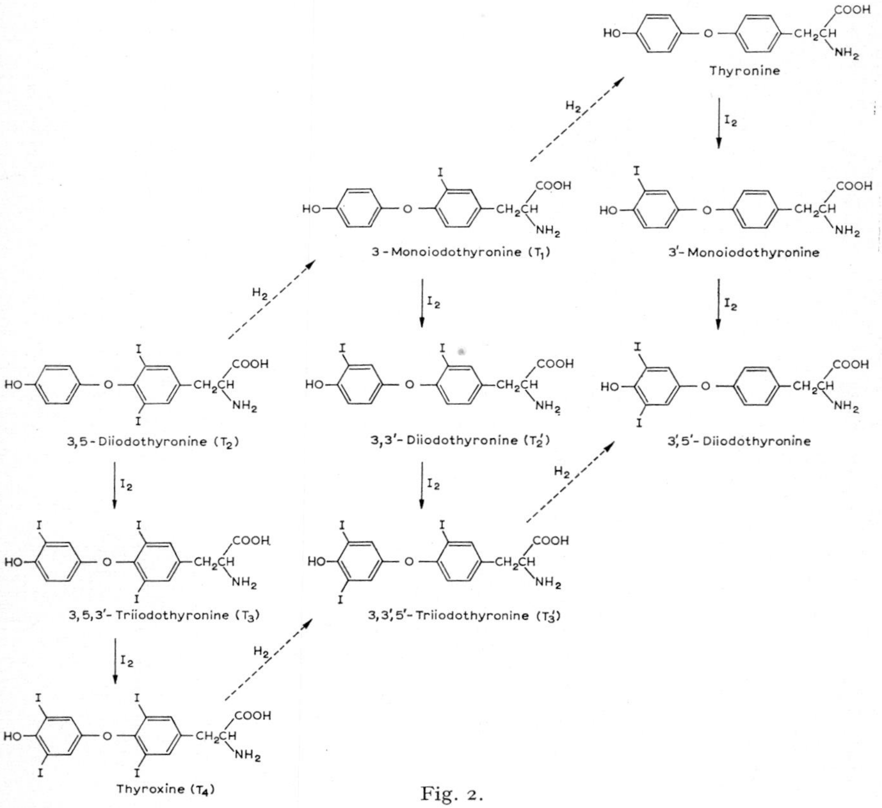

Fig. 2.

TABLE II

R_F VALUES OF IODOTHYRONINES

Product	1 n-Butanol-acetic acid-water (78:5:17)	2 n-Butanol saturated with 2N NH4OH	3 n-Butanol-dioxane (4:1) saturated with 2N NH4OH	4 Isopentanol saturated with 2N NH4OH	5 tert-Pentanol saturated with 2N NH4OH	6 Collidine-water (100:35.5) saturated with NH3	7 Methanol-0.2 M NH4Ac (1:2.5)
Thyronine	0.60	0.50	0.55	—	—	0.57	—
3'-Monoiodothyronine	0.68	0.41	0.40	—	—	0.58	—
3-Monoiodothyronine	0.70	0.60	0.65	0.70	0.46	0.65	0.00
3,5-Diiodothyronine	0.65	0.72	0.70	0.75	0.54	0.68	0.00
3,3'-Diiodothyronine	0.70	0.51	0.48	0.50	0.35	0.63	0.23
3',5'-Diiodothyronine	0.75	0.43	0.40	—	—	0.38	—
3,3',5'-Triiodothyronine	0.68	0.43	0.41	0.40	0.20	0.58	0.00
3,5,3'-Triiodothyronine	0.70	0.65	0.62	0.60	0.45	0.70	0.00
Thyroxine	0.75	0.48	0.46	0.50	0.25	0.59	0.00
Iodide	0.20	0.31	0.37	0.20	0.18	0.85	0.60

Systems 1,2,3: descending technique, 17°. System 4: descending, 13°. Systems 5,6: ascending, 17°. System 7: ascending, 3°.

produces smaller and better defined spots. In both these solvents T_3 and T_2' are almost indistinguishable, while the separation of T_4 and T_3' is generally not sufficient to identify T_3'. It is possible by using isoamyl alcohol saturated with ammonia at 13° to separate T_3' from T_4, T_2', I^- and T_3, but only after 72 h of migration time. Even this solvent, however, does not separate T_4 from T_3'. It has been possible to overcome this latter difficulty by using *tert.*-amyl alcohol saturated with 2 N ammonia (descending, 17°); T_2' is then separated from T_4, T_3, and T_3' and from iodide and other iodothyronines. Chromatographic properties of the iodothyronines are recorded in Table II.

To summarize the interconversions of the thyronines, two products, thyronine and 3,5-diiodothyronine (T_2), make it possible to prepare all the iodinated derivatives at one of the positions 3, 5, 3' or 5', or at several of these. The preparation of racemic thyronine has been described by various authors[97,98]. The L-isomer has been obtained by catalytic reduction of L-thyroxine[99]. Iodination, partial and progressive, of the thyronine yields 3'-monoiodothyronine and then 3',5'-diiodothyronine. Partial iodination of T_2 yields T_3, and further iodination gives 3,5,3',5'-tetraiodothyronine (T_4). Partial catalytic reduction of T_2 yields 3-monoiodothyronine (T_1) and, by further hydrogenation, thyronine. T_1 gives rise, by partial iodination, to T_2', which provides 3,3',5'-triiodothyronine (T_3') with an excess of iodine[100-102]. It is in fact possible to obtain all these derivatives from T_2, that is, two monoiodothyronines, three diiodothyronines, two triiodothyronines, and thyroxine. Fig. 2 summarizes the paths by which the different iodothyronines have been synthesized.

TABLE III

AMINO ACID CONTENT OF THYROGLOBULIN OF THE PIG

Amino acid	% of protein	Amino acid	% of protein
Arginine	12.7	Cystine	3.6
Histidine	2.2	Methionine	1.3
Lysine	3.4	Alanine	7.4
Phenylalanine	3.1	Glycine	3.7
Tryptophan	2.1	Leucine	12.8
Tyrosine	3.1	Valine	1.4
Diiodotyrosine*	0.5	Serine	10.8
Thyroxine*	0.2	Proline	14.0

* The contents of thyroxine and diiodotyrosine, like that of total iodine (0.48 % in the product studied) have no absolute significance since they vary from one preparation to another. The content of monoiodotyrosine can be indicated only by its order of magnitude, about 0.1 %. Variations in the contents of the various amino acids among preparations are too small to be reflected to an appreciable degree in the L-tyrosine value.

References p. 90

(c) Amino acid content of thyroglobulin

Table III shows the amino acid content of porcine thyroglobulin highly purified by salting-out, and Table IV the amino acid composition of sheep thyroglobulin as determined by chromatography on ion-exchange resins.

TABLE IV

AMINO ACID CONTENT OF EARLY- AND LATE-ELUTING
FRACTIONS OF OVINE THYROGLOBULIN

	I Fractions 18–20	II Fractions 21–27	III Fractions 28–31
Aspartic	7.8	9.0	8.4
Threonine	4.8	5.7	5.3
Serine	7.6	8.2	7.6
Glutamic	15.1	16.6	15.5
Proline	7.3	7.5	7.0
Glycine	5.0	5.3	4.9
Alanine	6.5	6.0	5.5
Cystine	1.1	0.9	0.8
Valine	9.5	5.7	5.3
Methionine	1.2	1.2	1.1
Isoleucine	2.6	2.6	2.4
Leucine	11.7	10.8	10.1
Hexosamine	0.0	1.9	1.8
Tyrosine	3.3	3.2	3.0
Phenylalanine	7.8	7.0	6.5
Lysine	4.2	3.5	3.2
Ammonia	2.2	2.5	2.3
Histidine	2.4	2.4	2.2

The compositions of these two iodoproteins are not markedly different, although there is considerably more valine in sheep thyroglobulin than in the porcine variety[30, 32]. Thyroglobulin of the dog contains 4.2% of tyrosine and 2.28% of tryptophan, a fact which implies a protein of rather different nature from that of the sheep and pig. The compositions of proteins isolated from various types of goitre are different from those of proteins derived from normal organs. In man, the proteins of colloid goitre are richer in tyrosine than those of hyperplastic goitre, although the amounts of the other amino acids are similar. The most remarkable feature of thyroglobulin is its high content of arginine, serine, proline, and of course the presence of iodinated amino acids.

Tyrosine and iodotyrosine are easily liberated from thyroglobulin on digestion with crystalline pepsin, which distinguishes this protein from most others[103]. Thyroglobulin appears to contain several N-terminal amino acids: leucine, valine, glycine, serine, threonine, aspartic and glutamic acids, alanine, and tyrosine[104].

A part of the diiodotyrosine and thyroxine is also N-terminal[105]. The fact that N-carbobenzyloxythyroxylated gelatin is an antigen, the antibodies to which precipitate thyroxine, is not sufficient to prove that thyroglobulin contains the hormone only in the thyroxyl residues[106]. This is a reflection of the great structural complexity of thyroglobulin and suggests the existence of several polypeptide chains. It is not possible to represent the structure of thyroglobulin in such a way that it will reflect the development of the processes of iodination and the oxidative mechanisms which lead to hormonogenesis.

The contents of diiodotyrosine and thyroxine have no absolute significance; they vary from one preparation to another and depend on the total iodine content of the protein[107]. The latter can vary from 0.2 to 1.2%, according to the species[108], food habits of the animal, and the time when the sample is collected. The ratio hormonal I/total I (approximately 0.3) varies little from one thyroid gland to another, in spite of considerable variation in the total halogen content of different preparations[109, 110]. The constancy of this ratio is probably related to the structure of the protein. The percentage of iodine is not constant in thyroglobulin and is not a criterion of purity.

3,5-Diiodo-L-tyrosine is the most abundant iodinated constituent and contains 50–60% of the total iodine. Other percentages represented are 10–15% as monoiodo-L-tyrosine, 20% in the form of T_4, smaller percentages in the form of 3,5,3'-triiodo-L-thyronine, 3,3'-diiodo-L-thyronine and 3,3',5-triiodo-L-thyronine, and finally a small amount of monoiodohistidine.

(d) Mechanism of thyroxine formation

(i) Chemical models of hormonogenesis

The simultaneous presence of T_4 and DIT in thyroglobulin, known since 1929, has led to the plausible hypothesis that a molecule of the former arises from two molecules of the latter[111]. An important series of studies devoted to chemical models of the genesis of thyroxine has corroborated this hypothesis. Traces of T_4 can be obtained by incubating weakly alkaline solutions of DIT at 37° for several weeks[112]. The yield of T_4 is increased to 4% by using a boiling-water bath and employing oxidants (H_2O_2, I_2) and continuous extraction with n-butanol[113]. If certain peptides of DIT (N-acetyl-3,5-diiodo-tyrosylglutamic acid, N-acetyl-DL-diiodotyrosyl-ε-N-[α-N-acetyl]-L-lysine) are substituted for free amino acid the yield[114,115] reaches or exceeds 30–35%.

Iodination of the proteins with solutions of $^{131}I_2$ has made it possible to construct a model of hormonogenesis which is probably close to that involved in thyroglobulin formation. Indeed, with the action of increasing amounts of the halogen on casein and on other proteins, there results the formation of MIT, DIT, and finally, complete saturation by iodine of positions 3 and 5 of all tyrosine residues.

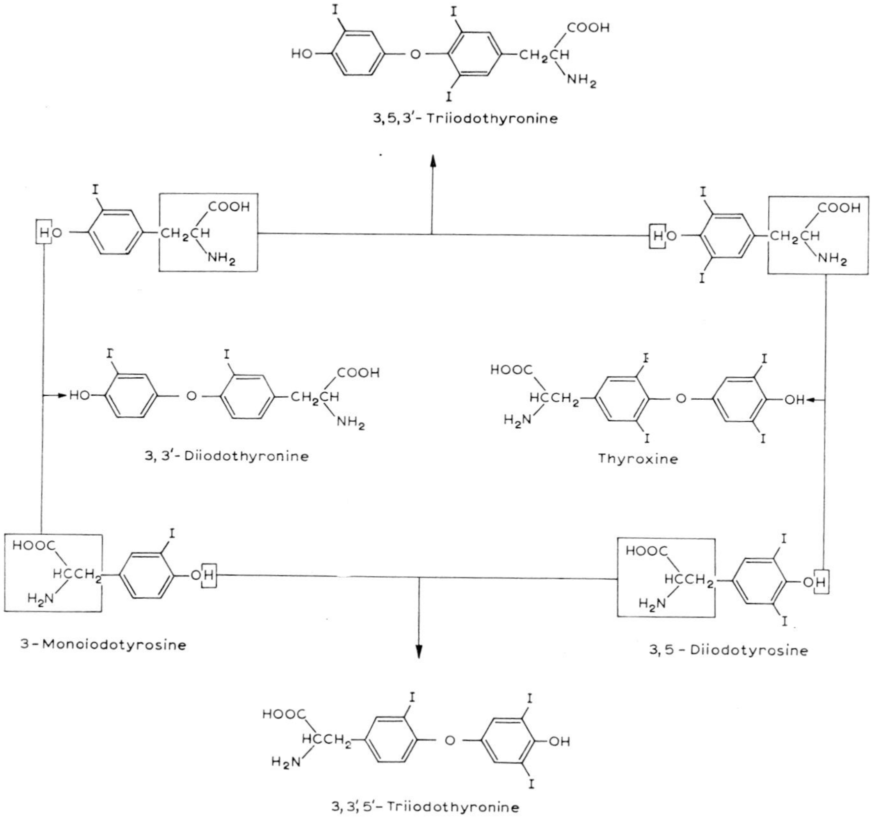

Fig. 3.

MIT and DIT arise by a substitution reaction $RH + I_2 \rightarrow RI + HI$, affecting only the carbons 3 and 5 of the hydroxylated benzene rings, the phenol group playing an orientation role. T_3 and T_4 appear as the result of a rather high degree of iodination, so that MIT and DIT can be regarded as their precursors, as well as those of T_3' and T_2'. These relations are illustrated in Fig. 3.

(ii) Biosynthesis of hormones and their precursors

The uptake of plasma iodide by the thyroid is quickly followed by the formation of iodinated organic compounds found in the thyroglobulin[116]. Most of the information on this subject has been achieved by the use of ^{131}I and will be summarized briefly.

A limited amount of data is available on the mechanism of oxidation of the iodide ions, which is generally ascribed to the activity of various peroxidases[117]. Recent studies[118] have shown that in the thyroid gland, I^- is catalytically oxidized by H_2O_2 and a peroxidase. The source of H_2O_2 is probably the autoxidation of a flavin. Thyroid peroxidase is specific for iodide; salivary gland enzyme acts on iodide and bromide. Cytochrome oxidase also catalyzes the oxidation of iodide[119]. The reality of this oxidation is inferred particularly by the products found. Tyrosine of proteins binds iodine by a substitution reaction, giving rise to MIT and DIT. Thyroglobulin behaves in this respect like all proteins, and when submitted to the action of I_2, enriches itself in T_4 and its homologues only at a stage subsequent to the substitution reaction[120].

Analysis of hydrolysates of thyroid glands of rats given successive doses of labelled iodide has shown that the specific activity of the iodotyrosine fraction increases progressively during the first 24 h, and then diminishes as the activity of the hormonal fraction increases. It follows from this that the iodothyronines appear to be formed at the expense of the iodotyrosines[121]. Since T_4 is, in animals, so predominant, it has not been possible to follow precisely the biosynthesis of its less iodinated homologues. It has been determined, however, that labelling of MIT occurs before that of DIT.

In general, the results of iodination of proteins *in vitro* show a close analogy with thyroid biosynthesis of the hormones. It has been possible to relate the *in vitro* and *in vivo* results. Thus it has been possible, by incubation of *N*-acetyldiiodotyrosylgelatin, prepared by the action of *N*-acetyl-diiodotyrosylazide on gelatin, to isolate a protein which is active in the metamorphosis of tadpoles and contains thyroxine[122]. Molecular rearrangements probably occur in the same way *in vivo* to yield various iodothyronines, but it is not known to what extent enzymes may be involved.

4. Conclusion

In this chapter we have considered chiefly the chemical problem of the thyroid hormones, the site at which concentration of halogen occurs, and something of the oxidation and incorporation of iodine into a protein. The preparation, physico-chemical properties and amino acid composition of thyroglobulin have been described. A review of the iodinated amino acids found in thyroglobulin has suggested the possible stages of hormonogenesis.

References p. 90

Some of the biological aspects of the problem have been pointed out, but the problems of hormone transport and metabolism, and the biological activities of the hormones and their analogues must be left to other chapters.

REFERENCES

1 J. H. MEANS, The Thyroid and its Diseases, 2nd ed., Lippincott, Philadelphia, 1948.
2 T. LEVITT, The Thyroid, Livingstone, Edinburgh and London, 1954.
3 N. J. NADLER AND C. P. LEBLOND, The Thyroid, Brookhaven National Laboratories, Associated Universities, Upton, L.I., N.Y., 1955, p. 40.
4 A. W. ELMER, Iodine Metabolism and Thyroid Function, Oxford University Press, London, 1938.
5 S. H. WOLLMAN AND I. WODINSKY, Endocrinology, 56 (1955) 9.
6 R. PITT-RIVERS, Brit. Med. Bull., 16 (1960) 118.
7 I. PERLMAN, M. E. MORTON AND I. L. CHAIKOFF, Am. J. Physiol., 134 (1941) 107.
8 Y. YAGI, R. MICHEL AND J. ROCHE, Bull. soc. chim. biol., 35 (1953) 289.
9 P. W. DURBIN, J. G. HAMILTON AND M. W. PARROTT, Proc. Soc. Exptl. Biol. Med., 86 (1954) 369.
10 C. J. SHELLABARGER, P. W. DURBIN, M. W. PARROTT AND J. G. HAMILTON, Proc. Soc. Exptl. Biol. Med., 87 (1954) 626.
11 R. MICHEL, Ann. Rev. Physiol., 18 (1956) 457.
12 P. C. WALLACE, The Metabolism of Fluorine in Normal and Chronically Fluorosed Rats, Univ. of Calif. (Berkeley) Radiation Lab. Rept. No. 2196, U.S. Atomic Energy Comm., Tech. Inform. Service, Oak Ridge, Tenn., 1953, 119 pp.
13 Z. LEWITUS, M. ANBAR AND S. GUTMAN, 4th Intern. Goitre Conference, London, 1960.
14 G. S. SERIF AND S. KIRKWOOD, J. Biol. Chem., 233 (1958) 109.
15 N. M. ALEXANDER, 4th Intern. Goitre Conference, London, 1960.
16 I. DONIACH, A. HOWARD AND S. R. PELC, Progr. Biophys. Biophys. Chem., 3 (1953) 1.
17 E. BAUMANN AND E. ROOS, Z. physiol. Chem., 21 (1896) 481.
18 N. A. BUBNOW, Z. physiol. Chem., 8 (1883) 1.
19 F. GOURLAY, J. Physiol. (London), 16 (1894) 23.
20 R. HUTCHISON, J. Physiol. (London), 20 (1896) 474.
21 R. HUTCHISON, J. Physiol. (London), 23 (1898) 178.
22 A. OSWALD, Z. physiol. Chem., 27 (1899) 14.
23 M. HEIDELBERGER AND W. W. PALMER, J. Biol. Chem., 101 (1933) 433.
24 J. W. CAVETT AND S. R. SELJESKÖG, J. Biol. Chem., 100 (1933) XXIV.
25 Y. DERRIEN, R. MICHEL AND J. ROCHE, Biochim. Biophys. Acta, 2 (1948) 454.
26 J. ROCHE, R. MICHEL, O. MICHEL, G. H. DELTOUR AND S. LISSITZKY, Biochim. Biophys. Acta, 6 (1951) 572.
27 J. E. RALL, J. ROBBINS AND H. EDELHOCH, Ann. N.Y. Acad. Sci., 86 (1960) 373.
28 H. EDELHOCH, J. Biol. Chem., 235 (1960) 1326.
29 J. ROCHE, O. MICHEL, G. H. DELTOUR AND R. MICHEL, Ann. Endocrinol. (Paris), 13 (1952) 1.
30 S. H. INGBAR, B. A. ASKONAS AND T. S. WORK, Endocrinology, 64 (1959) 110.
31 J. ROCHE AND R. MICHEL, Fortschr. Chem. org. Naturstoffe, 12 (1955) 349.
32 J. R. CHALMERS, G. T. DICKSON, J. ELKS AND B. A. HEMS, J. Chem. Soc., (1949) 3424.
33 H. EDELHOCH AND R. E. LIPPOLDT, J. Biol. Chem., 235 (1960) 1335.
34 H. P. LUNDGREN, J. Chem. Phys., 6 (1938) 177.
35 I. J. O'DONNELL, R. L. BALDWIN AND J. W. WILLIAMS, Biochim. Biophys. Acta, 28 (1958) 294.
36 I. M. ROITT AND D. DONIACH, Brit. Med. Bull., 16 (1960) 152.
37 J. ROCHE, S. LISSITZKY, O. MICHEL AND R. MICHEL, Methods Biochem. Anal., 1 (1954) 243.
38 J. WOLFF, J. ROBBINS AND J. E. RALL, Endocrinology, 64 (1959) 1.
39 J. ROBBINS, J. WOLFF AND J. E. RALL, Endocrinology, 64 (1959) 12.
40 J. ROBBINS, J. WOLFF AND J. E. RALL, Endocrinology, 64 (1959) 37.

[41] J. Roche, R. Michel and M. Tubiana, *Rev. franç. études clin. biol.*, 4 (1959) 1051.
[42] C. A. Owen and W. M. Mc Conahey, *J. Clin. Endocrinol. Metab.*, 16 (1956) 1570.
[43] A. M. DiGeorge and K. E. Paschkiv, *J. Clin. Endocrinol. Metab.*, 17 (1957) 645.
[44] L. J. DeGroot, S. Postel, J. Litvak and J. B. Stanbury, *J. Clin. Endocrinol. Metab.*, 18 (1958) 158.
[45] L. J. DeGroot and J. B. Stanbury, *Am. J. Med.*, 27 (1959) 586.
[46] J. Robbins, J. E. Rall and R. W. Rawson, *J. Clin. Endocrinol. Metab.*, 15 (1955) 1315.
[47] J. R. Tata, J. E. Rall and R. W. Rawson, *J. Clin. Endocrinol. Metab.*, 16 (1956) 1554.
[48] S. Shulman, N. R. Rose and E. Witebsky, *Federation Proc.*, 16 (1957) 433.
[49] G. H. Hogeboom, W. C. Schneider and G. E. Pallade, *J. Biol. Chem.*, 172 (1948) 619.
[50] E. R. Fisher, *Arch. Pathol.*, 56 (1953) 275.
[51] I. Werner, *Acta Soc. Med. Upsalien.*, 58 (1953) 1.
[52] G. J. M. Hooghwinkel, G. Smits and D. B. Kroon, *Biochim. Biophys. Acta*, 15 (1954) 78.
[53] N. F. Bods and J. B. Foley, *Endocrinology*, 56 (1955) 474.
[54] G. Lacombe and R. Michel, *Compt. rend. soc. biol.*, 149 (1955) 888.
[55] L. Ujeski and R. E. Glegg, *Can. J. Biochem. Physiol.*, 33 (1955) 199.
[56] J. Roche and R. Michel, *Biochim. Biophys. Acta*, 8 (1952) 339.
[57] R. J. Block, R. M. Mandl, S. Keller and S. C. Werner, *Arch. Biochem. Biophys.*, 75 (1958) 508.
[58] P. V. Mutzenbecher, *Z. physiol. Chem.* ,261 (1939) 253.
[59] R. M. Herriott, *J. Gen. Physiol.*, 25 (1941) 185.
[60] C. Fromageot, M. Jutisz, M. Lafon and J. Roche, *Compt. rend. soc. biol.*, 142 (1948) 785.
[61] K. Fink and R. M. Fink, *Science*, 108 (1948) 358.
[62] J. Roche, M. Jutisz, S. Lissitzky and R. Michel, *Biochim. Biophys. Acta*, 7 (1951) 257.
[63] J. Roche and Y. Yagi, *Compt. rend. soc. biol.*, 146 (1952) 288.
[64] C. R. Harington and R. Pitt-Rivers, *Biochem. J.*, 38 (1944) 320.
[65] R. M. Herriott, *J. Gen. Physiol.*, 31 (1947) 19.
[66] J. Roche, R. Michel, O. Michel and S. Lissitzky, *Biochim. Biophys. Acta*, 9 (1952) 161.
[67] E. Drechsel, *Z. Biol.*, 33 (1896) 85.
[68] J. Roche, *Experientia*, 8 (1952) 45.
[69] C. R. Harington and S. S. Randall, *Biochem. J.*, 23 (1929) 373.
[70] A. Oswald, *Z. physiol. Chem.*, 70 (1911) 310.
[71] J. Roche and M. Lafon, *Compt. rend.*, 229 (1949) 481.
[72] J. Roche, O. Michel, R. Michel and M. Marois, *Compt. rend. soc. biol.*, 145 (1951) 1833.
[73] J. Roche, G. Ranson and M. Eysseric-Lafon, *Compt. rend. soc. biol.*, 145 (1951) 1474.
[74] H. L. Wheeler and G. S. Jamiesson, *Am. Chem. J.*, 33 (1905) 365.
[75] P. Block Jr., *J. Biol. Chem.*, 135 (1940) 51.
[76] C. R. Harington, *Biochem. J.*, 22 (1928) 1429.
[77] C. R. Harington and R. Pitt-Rivers, *Nature*, 144 (1939) 205.
[78] J. P. Leland and G. L. Foster, *J. Biol. Chem.*, 95 (1932) 165.
[79] N. F. Blau, *J. Biol. Chem.*, 110 (1935) 351.
[80] J. Roche and R. Michel, *Biochim. Biophys. Acta*, 1 (1947) 335.
[81] J. Roche, R. Michel, O. Michel and S. Lissitzky, *Biochim. Biophys. Acta*, 9 (1952) 161.
[82] E. C. Kendall, *J. Biol. Chem.*, 39 (1919) 125.
[83] E. C. Kendall, *J. Biol. Chem.*, 40 (1919) 265.
[84] C. R. Harington, *Biochem. J.*, 20 (1926) 293.
[85] C. R. Harington and G. Barger, *Biochem. J.*, 21 (1927) 169.
[86] J. R. Chalmers, G. T. Dickson, J. Elks and B. A. Hems, *J. Chem. Soc.*, (1949) 3424.
[87] G. Hillmann, *Z. Naturforsch.*, 11b (1956) 419.

[88] C. H. Li, *J. Am. Chem. Soc.*, 66 (1944) 228.
[89] J. Roche, S. Lissitzky and R. Michel, *Biochim. Biophys. Acta*, 11 (1953) 215.
[90] J. Gross and R. Pitt-Rivers, *Biochem. J.*, 53 (1953) 645.
[91] J. Roche, R. Michel and W. Wolf, *Compt. rend.*, 239 (1954) 597.
[92] C. L. Gemmill, J. J. Anderson and A. Burger, *J. Am. Chem. Soc.*, 78 (1956) 2434.
[93] J. Roche, R. Michel, J. Nunez and C. Jacquemin, *Compt. rend.*, 244 (1957) 1507.
[94] J. Roche, R. Michel, J. Nunez and C. Jacquemin, *Compt. rend.*, 245 (1957) 77.
[95] C. H. Bowden, N. F. MacLagan and J. H. Wilkinson, *Biochem. J.*, 59 (1955) 93.
[96] J. Roche and R. Michel, *Recent. Progr. Hormone Res.*, 12 (1956) 1.
[97] C. R. Harington and R. Pitt-Rivers, *J. Chem. Soc.* (1940) 1101.
[98] C. R. Harington and R. Pitt-Rivers, *Biochem. J.*, 50 (1952) 438.
[99] J. R. Chalmers, G. T. Dickson, J. Elks and B. A. Hems, *J. Chem. Soc.*, (1949) 3424.
[100] J. Roche, R. Michel and W. Wolf, *Bull. Soc. Chim. France*, (1957) 462.
[101] J. Roche, R. Michel and W. Wolf, *Bull. Soc. Chim. France*, (1957) 464.
[102] J. Roche, R. Michel and W. Wolf, *Bull. Soc. Chim. France*, (1957) 468.
[103] J. Roche, R. Michel, S. Lissitzky and Y. Yagi, *Bull. soc. chim. biol.*, 36 (1954) 143.
[104] J. Roche, R. Michel, J. Nunez and G. Lacombe, *Bull. soc. chim. biol.*, 37 (1955) 219.
[105] J. Roche, R. Michel and J. Nunez, *Bull. soc. chim. biol.*, 37 (1955) 229.
[106] R. F. Clutton, C. R. Harington and M. E. Yuill, *Biochem. J.*, 32 (1938) 1119.
[107] W. T. Salter, *The Chemistry and Physiology of Hormones*, Amer. Assoc. Adv. Science, Washington, 1944, p. 104.
[108] A. S. Gorbman, S. Lissitzky, O. Michel, R. Michel and J. Roche, *Compt. rend. soc. biol.*, 145 (1951) 1642.
[109] J. W. Cavett, C. O. Rice and J. F. McClendon, *J. Biol. Chem.*, 110 (1935) 673.
[110] Y. Derrien, R. Michel, K. O. Pedersen and J. Roche, *Biochim. Biophys. Acta*, 3 (1949) 436.
[111] C. R. Harington, *Proc. Roy. Soc. (London)*, B, 132 (1944) 223.
[112] M. Henze, *Z. physiol. Chem.*, 51 (1907) 64.
[113] C. R. Harington and R. Pitt-Rivers, *Biochem. J.*, 39 (1945) 157.
[114] R. Pitt-Rivers, *Biochem. J.*, 43 (1948) 223.
[115] R. Pitt-Rivers and A. T. James, *Biochem. J.*, 70 (1958) 173.
[116] S. H. Wollman, *Ann. N.Y. Acad. Sci.*, 86 (1960) 354.
[117] E. W. Dempsey, *Ann. N.Y. Acad. Sci.*, 50 (1949) 336.
[118] N. M. Alexander, *4th Intern. Goitre Conference*, London, 1960, Abstract No. 88.
[119] A. Taurog and A. L. Franklin, *J. Biol. Chem.*, 151 (1945) 537.
[120] J. Roche and R. Michel, *Adv. Prot. Chem.*, 6 (1951) 253.
[121] A. Taurog and I. L. Chaikoff, *J. Biol. Chem.*, 169 (1947) 49.
[122] J. Roche, R. Michel, S. Lissitzky and S. Mayer, *Biochim. Biophys. Acta*, 7 (1951) 446.

Chapter II

Peptide and Protein Hormones

Section b

Parathyroid Hormone

HOWARD RASMUSSEN

Department of Biochemistry, University of Wisconsin, Madison Wis. (U.S.A.)

The parathyroid glands were described first in 1850 by Richard Owen[1]; but it was not until 1925 that a stable hormonally active extract of these glands was prepared by Collip[2]. Following Collip's work a great deal of progress was made in the understanding of parathyroid physiology, but little progress was made in the purification of this hormone until more rapid and economic assay methods were developed by Davies *et al.*[3] and by Munson[4], and more powerful separation procedures such as chromatography and countercurrent distribution were introduced. With these methods available, parathyroid polypeptides have been obtained in relatively pure form in the past few years[5-7].

The most striking changes observed following parathyroid hormone administration are hypercalcemia, hypercalciuria, hyperphosphatemia, and hypophosphaturia. Methods of assay have been developed which have used each of these parameters as the basis for assessing hormonal activity. Of them all, the most reliable, specific and widely used have been those based upon the so-called calcium-mobilizing activity of parathyroid extracts. The assay method of Munson[4] is the most widely used. In this method young rats are maintained on a low calcium diet for four days and then parathyroidectomized. Immediately after operation, the animals are injected with extract, six hours later a blood sample taken and the concentration of calcium in the plasma from this sample measured. The assay depends upon the fact that the injection of hormone prevents the fall in concentration of plasma calcium which occurs following parathyroidectomy. The assay has an accuracy of approximately ±25 %.

The only material from which parathyroid hormone has been extracted is defatted bovine parathyroid tissue. Three methods have been employed for this extraction. The first method used, that introduced by Collip[2], employs hot 0.2 N hydrochloric acid. More recently Davies and Gordon[8] have introduced the use of hot 80 % acetic acid, and Aurbach[9] the use of 70 % aqueous phenol. Each type of crude extract has been further purified and hormonally active polypeptides obtained from each type of extract. These polypeptides have been found to differ in chemical and biological properties. For sake of reference the polypeptide(s) obtained from hydrochloric acid extracts have been called parathormone A (PTH-A); those from the 80 % acetic acid extracts parathormone B (PTH-B); and those from the phenol extracts parathormone C (PTH-C)[7].

Each type of crude extract has been further purified by means of solvent or salt fractionation[8-11], chromatography[7,12], ultrafiltration[8,12], zone electrophoresis[13] and countercurrent distribution[5-7]. Of these various methods, countercurrent distribution has been found to be the most useful. Crude material from each of the three types of extracts has been partially purified by solvent or salt fractionation and then subjected to countercurrent distribution. Highly purified hormonal polypeptides have been obtained from each type of crude extract[5-7]. The countercurrent distribution pattern

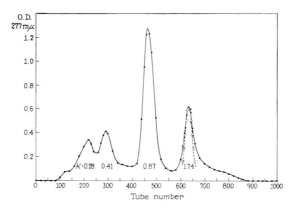

Fig. 1. The countercurrent distribution of PTH-A in NaCl–acetic acid *vs.* *n*-butanol–*n*-propanol for 1000 transfers. The material with K of 1.74 was the only peak having substantial biological activity. The ultraviolet absorption (●—●) and theoretical distribution (o - - - o) are plotted.

obtained following the distribution of crude PTH-A is illustrated in Fig. 1. The only material which had significant biological activity was that having a partition coefficient (K) of 1.74. The solvent system employed for this separation consisted of a mixture of *n*-propanol–*n*-butanol (1:1) as the organic phase and 6 % acetic acid and 1 % NaCl as the aqueous phase. Separation of both PTH-B and PTH-C have also been obtained in this system[7] and a similar system with a higher salt and acid concentration and no propanol has been used[7] successfully for the separation of PTH-C. Another type of solvent system has been used[5] successfully with PTH-C. This system is composed of pyridine, 0.1 % acetic acid, and n-butanol (3.5:12:5). The distribution of PTH-C in this system is demonstrated in Fig. 2. The purity of the various types of polypeptides has been tested by

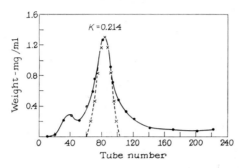

Fig. 2. Countercurrent distribution pattern of PTH-C after 471 transfers in system of pyridine–n-butanol–0.1 % acetic acid. The weight recovered (●—●) and theoretical distribution (×---×) are plotted[5].

either ultracentrifugation[5], paper chromatography[6,7] or column chromatography[7,14]. Solvent systems of butanol–H_2O–acetic acid have been found useful for the paper chromatographic separation or identification of parathyroid polypeptides[6,7,14].

The biological activities, molecular weights, and amino acid composition of the three types of hormonal polypeptides are recorded in Table I[7,14]. The data indicate that the largest polypeptide is obtained by phenol extraction, and the smallest by hydrochloric acid extraction. Also the largest polypeptide (PTH-C) is the most active biologically, being approximately twice as active and twice the size of PTH-A so that on a molar basis it is at least 4 times more potent. The data are consistent, except for minor discrepancies, with the concept that the hormone exists in the gland as a polypeptide of molecular weight 8447, that this is extracted intact by phenol, but that extraction with either hot acetic or hydrochloric acid results in partial hydrolysis of this large polypeptide. The results with hydrochloric acid are not too surprising, but the results with hot acetic acid are of interest and indicate that certain sensitive peptide bonds may be hydrolyzed by this reagent. It is also apparent that partial acid hydrolysis of PTH-C results in loss of biological activity. This can be explained in part by the fact that

TABLE I

THE AMINO ACID COMPOSITION*, MOLECULAR WEIGHT AND BIOLOGICAL
ACTIVITIES OF PARATHYROID POLYPEPTIDES

Amino acid	PTH-A	PTH-B	PTH-C
Lysine	2.90 (3)	5.70 (6)	7.06 (7)
Histidine	1.16 (1)	1.80 (2)	2.75 (3)
Arginine	1.78 (2)	3.27 (3)	3.98 (4)
Aspartic acid	3.06 (3)	6.44 (6)	7.71 (8)
Threonine	1.13 (1)	2.13 (2)	0.78 (1)
Serine***	2.82 (3)	4.87 (5)	6.79 (7)
Glutamic acid	3.84 (4)	7.42 (8)	9.99 (10)
Proline	1.18 (1)	2.10 (2)	2.82 (3)
Glycine	1.97 (2)	3.63 (4)	3.82 (4)
Alanine	2.91 (3)	5.96 (6)	6.11 (6)
½ Cystine	0.20 (0)	0.00 (0)	0.00 (0)
Valine	1.90 (2)	3.35 (4)	6.02 (6)
Methionine	0.71 (1)	1.49 (2)	1.66 (2)
Isoleucine	0.93 (1)	2.07 (2)	2.57 (3)
Leucine	2.80 (3)	5.64 (6)	6.93 (7)
Tyrosine	0.90 (1)	0.96 (1)	0.88 (1)
Phenylalanine	1.07 (1)	2.03 (2)	1.85 (2)
Tryptophan****	0.92 (1)	0.91 (1)	0.93 (1)
Total	33	62	75
Amide ammonia**	2.66 (2)	7.46 (6)	7.58 (7)
Molecular weight	3778	6943	8447
Calcium-mobilizing activity, U.S.P., units/mg	750–1000	1200–1600	2000–3000

* Determined by ion exchange chromatography[15].
** Corrected for gain during acid hydrolysis.
*** Corrected for loss during acid hydrolysis.
**** Determined spectrophotometrically.

the smaller parathyroid polypeptides are extremely labile and readily inactivated[7,16]. This inactivation has been shown to be due, in part at least, to an oxidative process. The oxidative inactivation of these polypeptides is completely or partially reversible depending upon the oxidative conditions and pH. Present evidence[7,14] indicates that the site of this oxidation–reduction center in the molecule involves a methionine residue. It has been postulated that oxidative inactivation is reversible if the

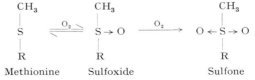

Fig. 3. The oxidation of methionine.

methionine sulfur is oxidized to the sulfoxides (1 oxygen) but irreversible if oxidized to the sulfone[7] (Fig. 3).

The smaller polypeptides, PTH-A and PTH-B, are much more readily inactivated by oxidizing agents (Table II), so it seems that although the *active center* of this hormone is contained in a polypeptide as small as 3800 (PTH-A) the remainder of the molecule stabilizes this center and protects certain reactive groups in it. This is of interest because the amino acid data (Table I) indicate that the hormone does not contain cystine and is therefore

TABLE II

BIOLOGICAL ACTIVITY OF PARATHYROID HORMONE AFTER
OXIDATION AND REDUCTION[16]

Preparation	Initial potency (U.S.P. units/mg)	pH at which* oxidation carried out	Potency after oxidation (% of initial)	Potency after reduction (% of initial)
PTH-A	300– 600	3.8	40–70	90–100
PTH-B	900–1200	3.8	35–65	110–160
PTH-B	900–1200	7.0	5–15	35– 75
PTH-C	2000–2500	3.8	60–85	95–110

* Oxidation carried out at 25° for 30 min with 0.1 M H_2O_2. The reaction was stopped with catalase. Reduction was carried out at 80° for 6 h with 0.1 M cysteine HCl.

presumably a single polypeptide chain. The small amount of cystine found in certain preparations (PTH-B, Table I) is thought to represent contamination by a small amount of non-hormonal polypeptide. However, after performic acid oxidation of the various parathyroid polypeptides there is always a small amount of material, approximately 0.15–0.20 of an amino acid residue, appearing at the cysteic acid position of the amino acid chromatogram, which is thought to represent homocysteic acid derived from methionine[14]. However, there is a slight possibility that the hormone contains a cysteine residue. This seems unlikely on the basis of the available data, but the possibility cannot be completely ruled out.

No data are available concerning the physico-chemical properties of these hormonal polypeptides. However, end group analysis, by the DNP method of Sanger, has revealed that a preparation of PTH-C has a single N-terminal amino acid, alanine, whereas a preparation of PTH-A was found to contain a single N-terminal valine. These data are independent evidence of the homogeneity of the various polypeptides, and indicate that the N-terminal alanine of the parent hormone is not essential to its biological activity.

Certain reports have suggested that the parathyroid hormone is partially lipid in character[17], but no lipid or other non-protein moiety has been found in the purified preparations[7,14].

References p. 98

REFERENCES

[1] R. Owen, *Trans. Zool. Soc. (London)*, 4 (1862) 31.
[2] J. B. Collip, *J. Biol. Chem.*, 63 (1925) 395.
[3] B. M. A. Davies, A. H. Gordon and M. V. Mussett, *J. Physiol. (London)*, 125 (1954) 383.
[4] P. L. Munson, *Ann. N.Y. Acad. Sci.*, 60 (1955) 776.
[5] H. Rasmussen and L. C. Craig, *J. Am. Chem. Soc.*, 81 (1959) 5003.
[6] G. D. Aurbach, *J. Biol. Chem.*, 239 (1959) 3179.
[7] H. Rasmussen in R. O. Greep and R. V. Talmage (Eds.), *The Parathyroids*, Thomas, Springfield, Ill., 1961.
[8] B. M. A. Davies and A. H. Gordon, *Biochem. J.*, 61 (1955) 646.
[9] G. D. Aurbach, *Arch. Biochem. Biophys.*, 80 (1959) 467.
[10] S. Friedman and P. L. Munson, *Biochem. Biophys. Acta*, 28 (1958) 204.
[11] M. V. l'Heureux, H. M. Tepperman and A. E. Wilhelmi, *J. Biol. Chem.*, 168 (1947) 167.
[12] H. Rasmussen and R. G. Westall, *Biochim. J.*, 67 (1957) 658.
[13] H. Rasmussen, *J. Biol. Chem.*, 229 (1957) 781.
[14] H. Rasmussen, unpublished data.
[15] D. H. Spackman, W. H. Stein and S. Moore, *Anal. Chem.*, 30 (1958) 1190.
[16] H. Rasmussen, *J. Biol. Chem.*, 234 (1959) 547.
[17] Y. Raoul, C. Marnay and M. Prelot, *Compt. rend.*, 240 (1955) 1151.
[18] P. J. Gaillard in R. O. Greep and R. V. Talmage (Eds.), *The Parathyroids*, Thomas, Springfield, Ill., 1961.
[19] A. R. Lavender, I. Aho, H. Rasmussen and T. Pullman, *J. Lab. Clin. Med.*, 54 (1959) 916.

Peptide and Protein Hormones

Section c

Adenohypophyseal Hormones*

CHOH HAO LI

Hormone Research Laboratory,
University of California, Berkeley, Calif. (U.S.A.)

1. Introduction

Of all the endocrine glands, the anterior lobe of the hypophysis occupies the prime place. In addition to its influence on general body growth and metabolic processes, the adenohypophysis exercises direct control on the functions of the adrenal cortex, the thyroid and the gonads. Hence, the hormones secreted by the anterior pituitary (except the growth hormone) are called *tropic* hormones; *i.e.*, their function is the stimulation of a specific target organ, an endocrine gland, whose activity is thereby enhanced or awakened. There are six known adenohypophyseal hormones whose existence has been firmly established. These six hormones may be classified into two groups, *metabolic* and *gonadotropic*. The metabolic hormones are thyrotropic hormone (thyroid-stimulating hormone, TSH), adrenocorticotropic hormone (ACTH), and growth hormone (somatotropin, STH). The gonadotropic hormones are follicle-stimulating hormone (FSH), interstitial cell-stimulating hormone (ICSH, luteinizing hormone, LH) and lactogenic hormone (prolactin, luteotropic hormone, LTH, mammotropic hormone, MH). Since the hypophysis of some species (*i.e.*, chicken, whale, etc.) has no intermediate lobe and since melanocyte-stimulating activity is found in the anterior lobe, this chapter will include a discussion of the melanocyte-stimulating hormone (MSH, melanotropin, intermedin).

---

* Written and submitted on February 7, 1961. No developments, after this date are included in this chapter.

2. Gonadotropic hormones*

In the female, FSH stimulates the development of immature ovarian follicles, bringing them to maturity. ICSH in turn stimulates the mature follicles to form estrogens and gives the follicle impetus for further development as a corpus luteum. An earlier review by this writer[1] on the chemistry of the gonadotropic hormones marked the close of an active period in research on the gonadotropic hormones from ovine and porcine pituitaries, to be followed by more than half a decade of relative quiescence as investigators in this field turned their attention to other studies. Recently, attention has once more been directed to the problem of purification and characterization of the gonadotropic hormones from several species including man; indeed, the number of publications which have appeared, especially in the last three years, demonstrate that the gonadotropic hormones have once again become an active field of investigation. For other reviews on the chemistry and biology of FSH and ICSH see refs. 2–6.

(a) ICSH

Early work on the purification and characterization of hypophyseal ICSH yielded highly active products from sheep and swine pituitary glands[1], preparations which appeared to be homogeneous according to the physical and biological criteria of purity then available. More recent advances in the methodology of the purification and characterization of proteins have stimulated the re-examination of this problem by various investigators. As a result, a new purification procedure[7] was developed involving fractional precipitation with alcohol, sulfosalicylate, and ammonium sulfate, column chromatography on the cation exchanger IRC-50 resin, and zone electrophoresis on starch. In the course of the chromatographic experiments, two distinct fractions, designated α- and β-ICSH, were detected; one of these, β-ICSH, was obtained in a state of high molecular homogeneity as evidenced by column chromatography, zone electrophoresis on starch and sedimentation velocity analysis. The molecular weight calculated from sedimentation velocity and diffusion measurements was approximately 30,000 and the isoelectric point was found to be between 7.0 and 7.5 in mono-monovalent buffers. Bioassays designed to detect contamination by any of the known pituitary hormones other than ICSH indicated no contamination at the 0.1 % contamination level.

The existence of more than one ICSH component in ovine pituitary extracts received additional support from electrophoretic studies[8] on cellulose

---

* The writer wishes to thank Dr. P. G. Squire for the assistance in preparing this section.

columns and chromatography on hydroxylapatite[9]. More recently, Ward et al. have also obtained from ovine glands[10] two ICSH components which are presumably similar to α- and β-ICSH.

Attempts to purify ICSH from human pituitaries have been seriously hampered by the difficulty of obtaining human pituitary glands in quantity. Certain side fractions obtained during the purification of human pituitary growth hormone serve as suitable starting materials for the purification of ICSH (and FSH, vide infra)[11-13]. One of these fractionation procedures[12] is based upon fractional precipitation with ammonium sulfate, chromatography on IRC-50 resin in 0.45 M ammonium sulfate, chromatography on the same resin in 0.2 M phosphate buffer and zone electrophoresis on cellulose columns. The other[13] involves chromatography on carboxymethylcellulose (CM-cellulose). Even though the products obtained by these procedures are by no means pure by physical, chemical or biological criteria, marked physicochemical and biological differences between human and ovine ICSH are already quite apparent[12]. The critical pH value above which the ICSH activity is no longer adsorbed by IRC-50 resin from 0.2 M phosphate buffers is located at pH 5.6 for human ICSH and 6.2 for the ovine hormone. Furthermore, the biological behavior of the two in stimulating the ventral prostate glands in hypophysectomized rats is different.

(b) FSH

A comprehensive scheme for the purification of ovine FSH on a large scale has been outlined by Ellis[14]. Woods and Simpson[15] have reported the purification of ovine FSH on diethylaminoethyl-cellulose (DEAE-cellulose) following ammonium sulfate fractionation; the product showed a high specific follicle-stimulating potency and a very low ICSH activity. The observation of some ICSH activity in the purest fractions of FSH has been very common, but Woods and Simpson[15] pointed out that any conclusions about an intrinsic ICSH activity in the FSH molecule must be made with caution so long as new fractionation methods for FSH are available and are being applied in the laboratory.

Studies of the electrophoretic behavior of sheep pituitary FSH on starch[16] have revealed the presence of an inert protein contaminant with the same isoelectric point, pH 4.5, as the FSH, but with a different mobility at higher pH values. A 10-fold purification of the FSH could be achieved by zone electrophoresis on starch in a borate buffer of pH 7.9.

Purification of FSH from porcine glands has been described[5]; the preparation was claimed to be homogeneous in the ultracentrifuge and in paper electrophoresis. The molecular weight of porcine FSH was reported to be 29,000. The purification procedure for human FSH is still in the developmental stage. A partial purification of this hormone has been reported[11-13], by methods similar to those used for human ICSH, including chromatography on DEAE-cellulose.

The presence of a carbohydrate moiety in preparations of ICSH and FSH[1] has been abundantly confirmed by recent investigations of preparations obtained by the newer procedures[10,17]. Moreover, quantitative data on the content of hexose, fucose, hexosamine and sialic acid in human and sheep pituitary ICSH and FSH have been reported[18]. Gottschalk *et al.*[19] demonstrated that the enzymic release of sialic acid by a highly purified receptor-destroying enzyme resulted in the complete inactivation of a sample of purified sheep FSH; considerations of the enzyme's specificity led these investigators also to conclude that the sialic acid residues are terminal, linked α-ketosidically to their partner, and are accessible to the enzyme.

The action of periodate on ICSH and FSH diminishes markedly their biological activity[20]; this treatment causes oxidative destruction of the carbohydrate moiety as well as of N-terminal hydroxyamino acids if present. It is of interest, however, that 5-10 % of the gonadotropic activity is retained after this treatment with periodate even when the periodate concentration is increased or the reaction is prolonged; this may mean that a residual inherent activity remains after the removal of carbohydrate residues by periodate oxidation.

(c) Lactogenic hormone

After the early studies of Stricker and Grueter[21] had demonstrated that the administration of an anterior pituitary extract elicited lactation in the pseudopregnant rabbit, the first direction of subsequent research was to identify a hormone from the anterior pituitary that was responsible for this effect. Because of this first observation of its action, *lactogenic hormone* or *prolactin* or *lactogen* have figured among the suggested terms for this pituitary principle. We now know, however, not only that this hormone is both mammogenic and lactogenic (and may be called with equal appropriateness *mammotropin* or *mammotropic hormone*, which is preferred by some investigators), but also that it is not the sole factor implicated in these processes. Nonetheless, notwithstanding its interaction with other hormonal factors, it is evident that lactogenic hormone is one of the most important factors controlling the growth of the mammary glands and the initiation of the process of milk production. The chemistry and biology of the hormone have recently been reviewed[22-24].

(i) A simplified procedure of isolation

Until recently all the published methods for the isolation of lactogenic hormone[25] involved fractional precipitation, which always necessitated

(i) Physicochemical characterization

There are now growth hormone preparations from the pituitary glands of six different species, namely, ox, sheep, whale, pig, monkey and man[11, 39], that can be obtained in a high degree of purity for physicochemical characterization. These preparations have been examined for homogeneity according to their behavior in the ultracentrifuge and in electrophoresis and chromatography, as well as by N-terminal group analysis. In a few cases, immunological purity has also been established. Some physical and chemical data for the six pituitary growth hormones are summarized in Table II.

TABLE II

SOME PHYSICOCHEMICAL PROPERTIES OF PITUITARY GROWTH HORMONE
FROM VARIOUS SPECIES

Physicochemical characteristics*	Ox	Sheep	Pig	Whale (Humpback)	Monkey (Macacus)	Man
Sedimentation coefficient, $s_{20,w}$	3.19	2.76	3.02	2.84	1.88	2.47
Molecular weight, M	45,000	48,000	42,000	39,000	25,000	29,000
Isoelectric point, pI	6.85	6.8	6.3	6.2	5.5	4.9
Cystine	4	5	3	3	4	3
Tyrosine	12	13	13	12	10	9
Tryptophan	3	3	3	3	1	1

* $s_{20,w}$ (in S) determined in pH 9.9 borate buffer; $D_{20,w}$ ($\times 10^7$ cm^2/sec) in pH 9.9 borate buffer; cystine, tyrosine and tryptophan, as residues per mole.

Recently, Squire and Pedersen[40] examined in detail the sedimentation behavior of human somatotropin in the ultracentrifuge. It was noted that the hormone protein undergoes association in pH 2.38 phosphate buffer; the best value for the molecular weight of the hormone was obtained from studies of approach to sedimentation equilibrium and was calculated to be 29,000 ± 1,000.

Although amino acid analysis has disclosed differences among the six somatotropins in chemical composition, all have the same amino acid residue (phenylalanine) at both termini. The bovine and ovine hormones, however, have two N-terminal residues and the other four somatotropins have only one. Further investigations on the sequences adjacent to the C- and N-termini have revealed that these hormones manifest further differences as chemical entities. The known NH$_2$-terminal sequences for the hormones from various species are as follows: bovine somatotropin, alanyl-phenylalanyl-alanyl... and phenylalanyl-threonyl-alanyl..., and human, phenylalanyl-prolyl-threonyl... The known COOH-terminal sequences are: bovine somatotropin, ...leucyl-alanyl-phenylalanyl-phenylalanine;

ovine, ... alanyl-leucyl-phenylalanine; cetacean, ... leucyl-alanyl-phenyl-alanine; simian, ... alanyl-glycyl-phenylalanine, and human, ... leucyl-phenylalanine. From these physical and chemical data, it is evident that even the protein hormones isolated from species as closely related as man and monkey are not identical.

(ii) Immunological behavior

Immunological studies conducted with bovine[41] and human[42] growth hormones have demonstrated that the protein hormones form antibodies that are specific to the species, as evidenced by results of precipitin ring tests with rabbit antiserum and of anaphylactic shock experiments in guinea pigs. It has been further demonstrated in hypophysectomized rats that the rabbit antiserum possesses specific anti-hormone activity. In addition, the immunological homogeneity of the rabbit antiserum to human growth hormone has also been indicated by agar-gel diffusion tests performed by the Ouchterlony technique. Production of hemagglutinating antibodies to human growth hormone has also been reported by other investigators[43,44].

Furthermore, it was shown by the Ouchterlony technique that antibodies to human somatotropin cross-react almost completely with the simian hormone but give no reaction with the bovine, ovine, porcine or cetacean hormones[45,46]. Similar studies with rabbit antiserum to bovine somato-tropin indicated that the bovine and ovine somatotropins appear to be closely related antigenically, whereas bovine somatotropin and the primate hormones are very different in this respect. These observations on the species specificity of immunological reactions were further supported by a demonstration that antibodies to bovine somatotropin can completely neutralize the biological activity of bovine somatotropin but not that of the human hormone.

(iii) Biological specificity

It is of considerable interest that growth is elicited in the rat by the administration of pituitary somatotropin from practically all the species studied so far, including ox, sheep, whale, pig, monkey and man, the only exception being the hormone from fish glands[47,48]. In view of the fact that there are marked differences among these various growth hormones in chemical structure and physicochemical characteristics, it is remarkable that the rat is capable of such a wide response. On the other hand, although it has been demonstrated that man can respond to the growth-promoting activity in primate somatotropins, practically all attempts to obtain a response in man with the bovine hormone have hitherto failed. The question has been raised whether a common biologically active core[49] or nucleus[47] might possibly exist in the somatotropin molecules derived from various species, and, further, whether the rat may possess the necessary enzyme system to utilize the whole hormone protein from non-primate sources whereas man does not[49]. In order to explore this hypothesis, it is necessary to establish the primary assumption that the complete integrity of the protein molecule is not necessary for the hormonal action. This was earlier found to be the case for bovine somatotropin[50], when the hormone was partially hydrolyzed with the enzymes chymotrypsin, trypsin and carboxypeptidase. Similar studies with ovine, porcine, cetacean, simian and human somatotropins have also shown that limited digestion of the hormone with chymotrypsin does not cause loss of growth-promoting potency[39,49]. Indeed, a fraction (alpha core) prepared from a chymotryptic digest of bovine somatotropin[51] was shown in preliminary studies to produce nitrogen retention in human subjects[52]. It should be pointed out that these observations are not sufficient to verify the assumption that the same active core is present in various somatotropins, but they do encourage further investigation along the lines of the *common core* hypothesis.

(b) Adrenocorticotropic hormone

The removal of the anterior pituitary, in almost all the species that have been studied, brings about a pronounced atrophy of the cortex of the adrenal glands, whereas the medulla is affected scarcely at all[53]. On the other hand a marked hypertrophy of the adrenal cortex occurs after implantation of anterior pituitary tissue or injection of pituitary extracts into normal animals. Hence, the name adrenocorticotropic hormone (ACTH, adrenocorticotropin) has been employed to designate the active principle in pituitary extracts that accomplishes repair of adrenal-cortical atrophy following hypophysectomy. In both experimental animals and human subjects, injections of ACTH accelerate the synthesis and secretion of adrenal hormones, including cortisol and aldosterone.

(i) Isolation and structure

Polypeptides possessing ACTH activity have been isolated in a highly purified state from sheep[54], pig[55], beef[56] and human[57] pituitaries. Although all these ACTH preparations possess similar biological properties, there are slight differences among them in amino acid composition and in chemical structure. The adrenocorticotropins from sheep, pig and beef pituitary glands are single-chain polypeptides composed of 39 amino acids with a molecular weight of approximately 4,500 and with serine and phenylalanine as NH_2- and COOH-terminal residues, respectively[58-60].

The only difference in amino acid composition between the pig and sheep hormones appears to be one more leucine in the former and one more

TABLE III

STRUCTURAL DIFFERENCES AMONG ADRENOCORTICOTROPINS ISOLATED
FROM PIG, SHEEP AND BEEF PITUITARY GLANDS

Structure of ACTH: Ser-Tyr-Ser-Met-Glu-His-Phe-Arg-Try-Gly-Lys-Pro-Val-Gly-Lys-Lys-Arg-Arg-Pro-Val-Lys-Val-Tyr-Pro
            1 2 3 4 5 6 7 8 9 10 11 12 13 14 15 16 17 18 19 20 21 22 23 24

                    -Ala-Phe-Pro-Leu-Glu-Phe
                     34 35 36 37 38 39

                                  NH_2
                                  |
Beef: Asp-Gly-Ala-Glu-Asp-Ser-Ala-Glu
      25 26 27 28 29 30 31 32 33

                                  NH_2
                                  |
Sheep: Ala-Gly-Glu-Asp-Asp-Glu-Ala-Ser-Glu

                                  NH_2
                                  |
Pig: Asp-Gly-Ala-Glu-Asp-Glu-Leu-Ala-Glu

serine in the latter; this difference occurs at positions 31 and 32 of the amino acid sequence, where alanine and serine appear in the ovine hormone and leucine and alanine in the porcine. Although there are no differences in amino acid composition between the sheep and beef hormones, a difference in amino acid sequence occurring in a small portion of the polypeptide chain seems to support the conclusion that sheep and beef adrenocortico-tropins are distinct chemical entities. Table III summarizes the structural differences that exist among these adrenocorticotropins[6,50,61].

From these structural data, it may be inferred that the removal of that portion of the COOH-terminal sequence which includes positions 25–39 does not impair the adrenal-stimulating activity. Indeed, it has recently been demonstrated that a synthetic nonadecapeptide[62] with a structure identical to the first nineteen NH$_2$-terminal amino acid sequence, namely:

H-Ser-Tyr-Ser-Met-Glu-His-Phe-Arg-Try-Gly-Lys-Pro-Val-Gly-Lys-Lys-Arg-Arg-Pro-OH
  1   2   3   4   5   6   7   8   9 10 11 12 13 14 15 16 17 18 19

possesses not only adrenal-stimulating potency but also other biological activities of the natural hormone. It will be of importance to obtain a synthetic peptide which possesses either minimal activity or none at all but which exhibits other physiological activities.

(ii) Biological activity

The biological potency of ACTH peptides has been estimated to be in the range of 80–150 I.U. per mg on the basis of the capacity of these peptides to deplete ascorbic acid in the adrenals of hypophysectomized rats[50]. Forsham et al.[63] reported that when α_s-ACTH (the main component of sheep ACTH) was assayed in man on the basis of steroidogenesis elicited by intravenous injections, an activity equivalent to 150 I.U. per mg of the peptide was obtained. The adrenocorticotropic activity of α_p-ACTH (the main component of porcine ACTH) as determined by the in vitro corticoido-genesis assay procedure was found to be 95 U.S.P. units per mg[64].

It is now well known that ACTH possesses melanocyte-stimulating (MSH) activity, although the MSH potency of this hormone is only a fraction of that possessed by highly purified MSH preparations[50]. Since the synthetic nonadecapeptide[62] has both ACTH and MSH activities, it is now established beyond doubt that the melanocyte-stimulating activity of ACTH is an intrinsic property of the hormone.

The effect of ACTH in darkening frog skins in vitro is clearly an extra-adrenal property of the hormone. However, this is not the only extra-adrenal effect of ACTH. Lipolytic activity exerted by adrenocorticotropin on rat adipose tissue in vitro[65] and the in vitro release of nonesterified fatty acids from adipose tissues of adrenalectomized rats under the stimulation of ACTH[66] provide additional evidence that ACTH is biologically active in the absence of adrenal glands. This points to a misconception that has been prevalent, arising from the name originally coined for the major biological activity of the hormone, *i.e.*, adrenocorticotropic hormone. It has been assumed for a long time that any ACTH preparation which can elicit a biological response in adrenalectomized animals is contaminated with some active component or components other than the ACTH itself. A similar confusion arising from terminology has recently been discussed in connection with pituitary growth hormone[67].

(iii) Functional groups and biological function

One of the most fruitful ways to investigate the relationship of structure of proteins or polypeptides to biological behavior is to study the effect of the chemical modification of a certain functional group or groups in the molecule by means of reaction with certain specific agents. The adreno-corticotropins furnish the ideal molecule for this type of study, since they have the form of a random coil with no secondary or tertiary structures[50, 68] to complicate the interpretation of results. One such study was the effect of guanidination on the adrenocorticotropic molecule. In preliminary studies, it was found that under none of the conditions employed could this protein hormone be completely guanidinated, since only 3 of the 4 lysine residues present in the hormone were converted to homoarginine[33]. Albeit incomplete, guanidination of ACTH produced a derivative whose biological activity was similar to that of the control preparation. As is the case with most of the other pituitary hormones, acetylation of adrenocorticotropin resulted in complete loss of activity. However, unlike the results obtained with other hormones, acetylation of the guanidinated derivative of ACTH also resulted in complete loss of activity. These results are consonant with the findings of other investigators that the NH_2-terminal serine of the hormone is necessary for its activity[6,50].

Another such investigation was on the effect of esterification of the free carboxyl groups in α_b-ACTH with acid methanol[69]. It was found that esterification of adrenocorticotropin does not reduce its melanophore-stimulating activity but it does diminish its adrenocorticotropic potency. This means that the free carboxyl groups in adrenocorticotropin are essential for its ACTH activity but are not implicated in its intrinsic melanocyte-stimulating effect. It makes it quite clear that the structural requirements for these two biological activities in ACTH peptides are different. Oxidation of adrenocorticotropin with periodate was also shown to destroy the adrenal-stimulating activity of this hormone, although its melanocyte-stimulating activity was unaltered by the treatment[6,50].

(c) Thyrotropic hormone *

Any discussion of the pituitary hormone TSH (thyrotropic-stimulating hormone, thyrotropin) must necessarily be of a provisional nature. A TSH in pure form is yet to be isolated, and consequently, the chemical and physiological data obtained thus far may be subject to revision in the future. This may be especially true of the biological data which attribute more than one action to the hormone. This short survey can but highlight the tremendous amount of work published on various aspects of TSH. Several recently published reviews may be consulted for more detailed information[70-72].

(i) Biological studies

Although there were suggestions as early as the nineteenth century that there was a relationship between the pituitary and the thyroid, it was not until the early part of the present century that this relationship was demonstrated unequivocally by systematic studies. Studies with tadpoles showed that hypophysectomy not only prevented metamorphosis but also caused an atrophy of the thyroid gland. Since thyroidectomy also results in the prevention of metamorphosis, this seemed to suggest that the pituitary action was mediated by the thyroid. Further studies demonstrating that pituitary transplants reverse the involution of the thyroid following hypophysectomy and that anterior pituitary extracts give rise to thyroid changes established the hormonal nature of the process.

Among the thyroid changes elicited by TSH preparations are increased cell height, increase in size of nuclei, vacuolization and subsequent decrease in colloid, increase in mitoses and hypertrophy of the Golgi apparatus. These observed histological changes are supported by changes in the organism which are similar to those evoked by the thyroid hormone treatment. Thus, TSH preparations increase the basal metabolism and the blood iodine level while decreasing the level of iodine in the thyroid gland. With the more recent radiological techniques, it can be shown that hypophysectomy will result in a decreased uptake of ^{131}I while TSH treatment will accelerate its release by the thyroid.

A multitude of techniques for the bioassay of TSH[70, 72] have appeared in the literature. In general, assays have been of either a gravimetric or a chemical nature. Among the former are found histological procedures designed to measure increases in cell height, relative percentage of cells and colloid, and the occurrence of colloid droplets in the thyroid. Increase in thyroid weight has also found use as an assay procedure both by *in vivo* and *in vitro* techniques.

---

* The assistance of Dr. H. Papkoff in preparing this section is gratefully acknowledged.

Assays employing radiological techniques have found wide acceptance in recent years; for example, ^{32}P uptake by the thyroid has been studied as an index of TSH activity. More pertinent, perhaps, have been assays based upon the uptake or release by the thyroid of [131]I. The most commonly used experimental animals for these assays have been the rat, chick, guinea pig, and tadpole. Accurate comparisons between the results of various laboratories have been greatly facilitated by the establishment[73] of an international unit (I.U.).

(ii) Purification and chemical properties

Thyrotropin has been detected in the pituitaries of the frog, sole, rat, mouse, dog, pig, sheep, toad, beef, turkey, man, horse, rabbit, cat, pigeon, chick, and guinea pig[74]. The body of evidence would indicate the basophile cell as the site of production, or at least storage, of TSH in the anterior pituitary. For the most part, ox pituitaries have been used in purification studies.

Earlier studies by Ciereszko[75] employing organic solvent and isoelectric precipitation led to a product with a potency of about 5 I.U./mg. Following the observation of Heideman[76] in 1953 that TSH could be further purified by chromatography on Amberlite IRC-50, purification studies of this sort have been carried out by Pierce, Carsten, Bates, Condliffe and their collaborators[71, 72]. By means of cellulose ion-exchangers, such as diethyl-aminoethyl-cellulose, crude TSH preparations have been chromatographed and fractions obtained with potencies of 30–40 I.U./mg. The active material, however, emerges from the column as a complex peak, and when examined by the technique of starch-gel electrophoresis, a multitude of components are evident, many of which possess TSH activity. Indeed, it has been shown that at least six closely related components all possess thyrotropic activity.

Ultracentrifugation experiments as well as membrane electrodialysis carried out with these highly potent TSH preparations support the conclusion that the molecular weight of the hormone is in the range of 26,000–30,000, rather than 10,000 which was proposed by earlier workers for much cruder preparations. Chemical analyses indicate that TSH contains the usual amino acid components with an unusually high content of cystine. Thyrotropin has long been thought to be a glycoprotein; carbohydrate analysis of the most potent fractions indicate the presence of glucosamine, galactosamine, mannose, and fucose. Sialic acid could not be detected.

A word on species variations may be pertinent here. Pierce et al.[71] have compared TSH preparations from beef, sheep, and humpback whale pituitary glands and found them to be similar with respect to their chromatographic and starch-gel properties. On the other hand, Bates and Condliffe[72] have shown differences between beef TSH and mouse tumor-produced TSH as well as human circulating TSH.

4. Melanocyte-stimulating hormones

In 1916, Smith[77] reported a striking change in the pigmentation of the tadpole following hypophysectomy. Subsequently, it was shown by numerous studies that transplantation of the intermediate lobe of adult frogs into normal or hypophysectomized tadpoles causes a marked expansion of the melanocytes and that extracts of the intermediate lobes of the bovine pituitary exercised the most marked influence on the pigmentation of the hypophysectomized tadpole, although suspensions of the anterior lobes were also effective in this regard. These investigations left no doubt that the pituitary gland possesses a principle or principles which regulate the pigmentation of amphibia.

In 1932, Zondek and Krohn[78] studied the effect of bovine pituitary extracts on the appearance of erythrophores and concluded that a principle elaborated in the intermediate lobe was responsible for an increased formation of red pigment in the skin of *Phoxinus*. These investigators proposed the name *intermedin* for the principle. Various other names have since been coined for the hormone, including melanophore hormone, melanophore-dilating or -expanding hormone, chromatophorotropic hormone, melano-phore-stimulating hormone, the B-hormone, the melanosome-dispersing hormone, melanocyte-stimulating hormone and melanotropin.

(*i*) *Isolation and structure*

It is now well established that two melanocyte-stimulating peptides are present in pituitary extracts[79]: α-MSH and β-MSH; the former is more basic in nature than the latter. The isolation and structure of α-MSH from pig pituitaries have been achieved by Lerner and his coworkers[79, 80]; it is a 13-amino acid polypeptide with an *N*-acetylserine and valine amide as N- and C-terminal residues respectively:

$$CH_3CO-Ser-Tyr-Ser-Met-Glu-His-Phe-Arg-Try-Gly-Lys-Pro-Val-NH_2$$
$$1 \quad 2 \quad 3 \quad 4 \quad 5 \quad 6 \quad 7 \quad 8 \quad 9 \quad 10 \quad 11 \quad 12 \quad 13$$

It was subsequently shown that α-MSH isolated from beef and horse pituitaries[81] has the same composition and structure as the pig hormone.

Since 1955, four groups of investigators[22] have published methods for the purification and isolation of melanotropins from beef and pig pituitary glands. All the published procedures for the preparation of MSH concentrates from posterior-intermediate lobes of pituitary glands incorporate the acetic acid extraction technique first introduced by Kamm *et al.*[82] for posterior pituitary hormones. In addition, oxycellulose is employed to adsorb the MSH activity from the acetic acid extract according to the technique of Astwood *et al.*[83] for ACTH. From this concentrate and by means of a combination of zone electrophoresis on starch and countercurrent distribution, β-MSH was obtained[84] in a form which fulfills various criteria of homogeneity, such as zone electrophoresis, countercurrent distribution, ultracentrifugation, N- and C-terminal amino acid analysis and quantitative data on the constituent amino acids. Recently, the isolation of β-MSH from horse pituitaries has also been achieved[85].

The structure of pig β-MSH (β_p-MSH) was elucidated independently in two laboratories[22, 86] and both groups of investigators obtained the following amino acid sequence for the β-MHS of this species:

H - Asp·Glu·Gly·Pro·Tyr·Lys·Met·Glu·His·Phe·Arg·Try·Gly·Ser·Pro·Pro·Lys·Asp-OH
  1   2   3   4   5   6   7   8   9   10   11   12   13   14   15   16   17   18

The amino acid sequence[87] for bovine β-MSH (β_b-MSH) differs from that proposed for the porcine β-MSH only at position 2, where a seryl residue replaces a glutamyl. Because of this difference, the isoelectric point of the bovine hormone (pH 7.0) is higher than that of porcine β-MSH (pH 5.8). The latter was found to migrate faster on starch in a veronal buffer of pH 8.5 than does the bovine melanotropin. Electrophoretically, the equine β-MSH (β_e-MSH) behaves like β_b-MSH; however, it has a glutamyl residue in position 2 (like β_p-MSH) in place of the seryl residue found in β_b-MSH at that position and an arginyl residue in position 16, which carries a positive charge, in place of the neutral prolyl residue found at this position in all other β-MSH preparations[85].

β-MSH has also been prepared from human pituitary glands (β_h-MSH) and its structure has been reported[86]. The human hormone differs distinctly from the non-primate hormones with respect to NH_2-terminal sequence, although the remaining portion of the hormone peptide from human glands is identical with other preparations of β-MSH.

(ii) The relationship between MSH and ACTH

The speculation that MSH and ACTH might be identical[88], which recently has given a new impetus to the studies on the former hormone, probably originally had its source in clinical observations that pigmentation of the skin and mucous membrane occurs in patients who have been subjected to prolonged treatment with commercially available ACTH, and also in observations of the pigmentation characteristic of Addison's disease. Furthermore, it has been observed that long-term injections of cortisone, which is known to depress the secretion of ACTH from the pituitary, result in a decrease of melanocyte-stimulating activity in the serum, with pigmentation at the same time decreasing markedly. Furthermore, it has been observed that melanocyte-stimulating and adrenal-stimulating activities are both always present together in ACTH preparations.

Even before the isolation of adrenocorticotropins and melanotropins in highly purified form, there was good evidence against the hypothesis that these two hormones were identical. For example, a partial separation of the two activities can be obtained by zone electrophoresis on paper and chromatographic procedures[22]. It has now been established beyond any doubt that melanotropins and adrenocorticotropins are chemically distinct from each other; however, it is also well established that adrenocorticotropins possess intrinsic MSH activity[50].

A comparison of the amino acid sequences of melanotropins and adrenocorticotropins (Table IV) reveals that there is a central heptapeptide sequence common to all these hormone molecules: H — Met·Glu·His·Phe·Arg·Try·Gly — OH. It may also be noted that if it were not for a transposition of the order of the serines and lysines on either side of the heptapeptide core, the area of identity between the two hormones would extend to 11 amino acids. It appears likely that the presence of this heptapeptide sequence in the adrenocorticotropins explains their intrinsic melanocyte-stimulating activity and furthermore, that it is by virtue of an arrangement of a different sequence of amino acids on each side of the heptapeptide core that the molecule acquires adrenal-stimulating as well as melanocyte-stimulating activity. The fact that the N-terminal serine present in the adrenocorticotropins is outside of the heptapeptide sequence probably explains the observation that alteration of this residue by oxidation with periodate fails to modify the melanocyte-stimulating activity; however, its integrity is essential for the adrenocorticotropic activity[50]. Table V summarizes the melanocyte-stimulating activity of melanotropins and adrenocorticotropins from various species as estimated by the *in vitro* frog skin assay method[89].

The disclosure of a sequence common to two different hormones is highly reminiscent of the finding in connection with oxytocin and vasopressin[90]. In the case of the latter hormones, two variations occur in a basic nonapeptide structure, and each hormone is endowed with some of the major activities characteristic of the other. Both of these hormones are produced by the hypothalamus and stored in the posterior pituitary. On the other hand, the adrenocorticotropins are produced by a group of the cells of the anterior lobe of the pituitary, whereas the melanotropins originate from an entirely different group of cells, those of the intermediate lobe of the pituitary. This latter lobe, however, is derived embryologically from the same anlage as the anterior lobe.

(iii) Synthetic peptides and MSH activity

Guttmann and Boissonnas have achieved the complete synthesis of α-MSH[91] and shown that the synthetic product possesses an activity comparable to that of the naturally occurring hormone. Subsequently, Hofmann *et al.*[92]

TABLE IV

THE RELATION OF THE PARTIAL STRUCTURE OF ADRENOCORTICOTROPINS (ACTH) TO THE STRUCTURE OF MELANOTROPINS (MSH)

ACTH:
(Pig, Sheep, Beef)

Ser	Tyr	Ser	Met	Glu	His	Phe	Arg	Try	Gly	Lys	Pro	Val	Gly	Lys	Lys	Arg	Arg	Pro
1	2	3	4	5	6	7	8	9	10	11	12	13	14	15	16	17	18	19

α-MSH:
(Pig, Beef, Horse)

CH₃CO	Ser	Tyr	Ser	Met	Glu	His	Phe	Arg	Try	Gly	Lys	Pro	Val	NH₂
	1	2	3	4	5	6	7	8	9	10	11	12	13	

β-MSH:
(Pig)

Asp	Glu	Gly	Pro	Tyr	Lys	Met	Glu	His	Phe	Arg	Try	Gly	Ser	Pro	Pro	Lys	Asp
1	2	3	4	5	6	7	8	9	10	11	12	13	14	15	16	17	18

β-MSH:
(Beef)

Asp	Ser	Gly	Pro	Tyr	Lys	Met	Glu	His	Phe	Arg	Try	Gly	Ser	Pro	Pro	Lys	Asp
1	2	3	4	5	6	7	8	9	10	11	12	13	14	15	16	17	18

β-MSH:
(Horse)

Asp	Glu	Gly	Pro	Tyr	Lys	Met	Glu	His	Phe	Arg	Try	Gly	Ser	Pro	Arg	Lys	Asp
1	2	3	4	5	6	7	8	9	10	11	12	13	14	15	16	17	18

β-MSH:
(Human)

Ala	Glu	Lys	Lys	Asp	Glu	Gly	Pro	Tyr	Arg	Met	Glu	His	Phe	Arg	Try	Gly	Ser	Pro	Pro	Lys	Asp
1	2	3	4	5	6	7	8	9	10	11	12	13	14	15	16	17	18	19	20	21	22

reported the synthesis of glutaminyl and formyl–lysyl analogues of α-MSH which possess melanocyte-stimulating activity ranging from $0.6 \cdot 10^{10}$ to $2.2 \cdot 10^{10}$ MSH units per gram. The synthesis of a β_b-MSH carrying various protecting groups has also been described[93]; the activity of this product was shown to be $1.4 \cdot 10^7$ units per gram as compared with $2 \cdot 10^9$ for β_b-MSH. A synthetic nonadecapeptide[62] identical with the first 19 amino acids of ACTH was found, by the *in vitro* assay method[89], to have an MSH activity of $1.4 \cdot 10^7$ units per gram, a potency very close to that of native adrenocorticotropins (see Table V).

TABLE V

MELANOCYTE-STIMULATING ACTIVITY OF MELANOTROPINS AND
ADRENOCORTICOTROPINS FROM VARIOUS SPECIES

Hormone	Species	Melanocyte-stimulating activity (units/g)
$\alpha_{s,p,b}$-ACTH	Sheep, pig, beef	$0.3 \cdot 10^8$
β_b-MSH	Beef	$2.0 \cdot 10^9$
β_p-MSH	Pig	$3.0 \cdot 10^9$
β_e-MSH	Equine	$1.2 \cdot 10^9$
$\alpha_{p,b,e}$-MSH	Pig, beef, equine	$1.0 \cdot 10^{10}$

A number of peptides related to the heptapeptide sequence present in both MSH and ACTH preparations have been synthesized, to gain a further understanding of the structural and biological significance of this phenomenon of a common core. The smallest synthetic peptide that exhibits MSH activity is a pentapeptide[94–96] with the composition: H — His·Phe· Arg·Try·Gly — OH.

REFERENCES

[1] C. H. Li, *Vitamins and Hormones*, 7 (1949) 223.

[2] E. E. Hays and A. L. Steelman, in G. Pincus and K. V. Thimann (Eds.), *The Hormones*, Vol. III, Academic Press, New York, 1955, p. 201.

[3] C. H. Li, in H. Neurath and K. Bailey (Eds.), *The Proteins*, Vol. 2A, Academic Press, New York, 1954, p. 595.

[4] R. Acher, *Ann. Rev. Biochem.*, 29 (1960) 547.

[5] A. Segaloff and S. L. Steelman, in *Recent Progr. in Hormone Research*, 15 (1959) 127.

[6] O. K. Behrens and W. W. Bromer, *Ann. Rev. Biochem.*, 27 (1958) 57.

[7] P. G. Squire and C. H. Li, *J. Biol. Chem.*, 234 (1959) 520.

[8] M. Jutisz and P. G. Squire, *Bull. soc. chim. biol.*, 40 (1958) 1875.

[9] M. Jutisz and P. G. Squire, *Acta Endocrinol.*, 37 (1961) 96.

[10] D. N. Ward, R. McGregor and A. C. Griffin, *Biochim. Biophys. Acta*, 32 (1959) 305.

[11] C. H. Li, *Ciba Colloq. Endocrinology*, 13 (1960) 46.

[12] C. H. Li, P. G. Squire and U. Gröschel, *Arch. Biochem. Biophys.*, 86 (1960) 110.

[13] S. L. Steelman, A. Segaloff and R. N. Andersen, *Proc. Soc. Exptl. Biol. Med.*, 101 (1959) 452.

[14] S. Ellis, *J. Biol. Chem.*, 233 (1958) 63.

[15] M. C. Woods and M. E. Simpson, *Endocrinology*, 66 (1960) 575.

[16] I. D. Raacke, A. J. Lostroh and C. H. Li, *Arch. Biochem. Biophys.*, 77 (1958) 138.

[17] S. L. Steelman, T. L. Kelly, H. Segaloff, G. F. Wever, *Endocrinology*, 59 (1956) 256.

[18] U. Gröschel and C. H. Li, *Biochim. Biophys. Acta*, 37 (1960) 375.

[19] A. Gottschalk, W. K. Chittin, E. R. B. Graham, *Biochim. Biophys. Acta*, 38 (1960) 183.

[20] I. I. Geschwind and C. H. Li, *Endocrinology*, 63 (1958) 449.

[21] P. Stricker and F. Grueter, *Compt. rend. soc. biol.*, 99 (1928) 1978.

[22] C. H. Li, *Advances in Protein Chem.*, 12 (1957) 269.

[23] A. T. Cowie and S. J. Folley, in G. Pincus and K. V. Thimann (Eds.), *The Hormones*, Vol. III, Academic Press, New York, 1955, p. 309.

[24] W. R. Lyons, *Proc. Roy. Soc. (London), B*, 149 (1958) 303.

[25] A. White, *Vitamins and Hormones*, 7 (1949) 253.

[26] R. D. Cole and C. H. Li, *J. Biol. Chem.*, 213 (1955) 197.

[27] C. H. Li, R. D. Cole and M. J. Coval, *J. Biol. Chem.*, 229 (1957) 153.

[28] C. H. Li, W. R. Lyons and H. M. Evans, *J. Biol. Chem.*, 140 (1941) 43.

[29] R. D. Cole, I. I. Geschwind and C. H. Li, *J. Biol. Chem.*, 224 (1957) 399.

[30] C. B. Anfinsen and R. R. Redfield, *Advances in Protein Chem.*, 11 (1956) 1.

[31] C. H. Li, *J. Biol. Chem.*, 229 (1957) 157.

[32] C. H. Li and J. T. Cummins, *J. Biol. Chem.*, 233 (1958) 73.

[33] I. I. Geschwind and C. H. Li, *Biochim. Biophys. Acta*, 25 (1957) 171.

[34] H. Cushing, *Harvey Lectures*, 28 (1934) 90.

[35] H. M. Evans, *Harvey Lectures*, 19 (1925) 212.

[36] C. H. Li, *Harvey Lectures*, 46 (1952) 181.

[37] C. H. Li, H. M. Evans and M. E. Simpson, *J. Biol. Chem.*, 159 (1945) 353.

[38] A. E. Wilhelmi, J. B. Fishman and J. A. Russell, *J. Biol. Chem.*, 176 (1948) 737.

[39] C. H. Li, in A. Neuberger (Ed.), *Symposium on Protein Structure*, Methuen, London, 1958, p. 302.

[40] P. G. Squire and K. O. Pedersen, *J. Am. Chem. Soc.*, 83 (1961) 476.

[41] T. Hayashida and C. H. Li, *Endocrinology*, 63 (1958) 487.

[42] T. Hayashida and C. H. Li, *Science*, 128 (1958) 1276.

[43] C. H. Read and G. T. Bryon, *Ciba Colloq. Endocrinology*, 13 (1960) 68.

[44] J. Fishman, E. E. McGarry, J. C. Beck, *Proc. Soc. Exptl. Biol. Med.*, 102 (1959) 446.

[45] T. Hayashida and C. H. Li, *Endocrinology*, 65 (1959) 944.

[46] C. H. Li, N. R. Moudgal and H. Papkoff, *J. Biol. Chem.*, 235 (1960) 1038.

[47] J. A. Russell and A. E. Wilhelmi, *Ann. Rev. Physiol.*, 20 (1958) 43.

[48] E. Knobil and R. O. Greep, *Recent Progr. in Hormone Research*, 15 (1959) 1.

[49] C. H. Li, *Federation Proc.*, 16 (1957) 775.

[50] C. H. Li, *Advances in Protein Chem.*, 11 (1956) 101.

[51] C. H. Li, H. Papkoff and T. Hayashida, *Arch. Biochem. Biophys.*, 85 (1959) 97.

[52] P. H. Forsham, C. H. Li, V. DiRaimondo, F. O. Kolb, D. Mitchell and S. Newman, *Metabolism, Clin. and Exptl.*, 7 (1958) 762.
[53] P. E. Smith, *Am. J. Anat.*, 45 (1930) 205.
[54] C. H. Li, I. I. Geschwind, A. L. Levy, J. I. Harris, J. S. Dixon, N. G. Pon and J. O. Porath, *Nature*, 173 (1954) 251.
[55] P. H. Bell, *J. Am. Chem. Soc.*, 76 (1954) 5565.
[56] C. H. Li and J. S. Dixon, *Science*, 124 (1956) 934.
[57] T. H. Lee, A. B. Lerner and V. Buettner-Jamusch, *J. Am. Chem. Soc.*, 81 (1959) 6084.
[58] C. H. Li, I. I. Geschwind, R. D. Cole, I. R. Raacke, J. I. Harris and J. S. Dixon, *Nature*, 176 (1955) 687.
[59] K. S. Howard, R. G. Shepherd, E. A. Eigner, D. S. Davis and P. H. Bell, *J. Am. Chem. Soc.*, 77 (1955) 3419.
[60] C. H. Li, J. S. Dixon and D. Chung, *J. Am. Chem. Soc.*, 80 (1958) 2587; *Biochim. Biophys. Acta*, 46 (1961) 324.
[61] C. H. Li, *Science*, 129 (1959) 969.
[62] C. H. Li, J. Meienhofer, E. Schnabel, D. Chung, T. B. Lo and J. Ramachandran, *J. Am. Chem. Soc.*, 82 (1960) 5760.
[63] P. H. Forsham, V. DiRaimondo, D. Island, A. P. Rinfret and R. H. Orr, *Ciba Colloquia Endocrinology*, 8 (1955) 279.
[64] R. Guillemin, *Endocrinology*, 66 (1960) 819.
[65] E. Lopez, J. E. White and F. L. Engel, *J. Biol. Chem.*, 234 (1959) 2254.
[66] M. C. Schotz, G. M. C. Masson, I. H. Page, *Proc. Soc. Exptl. Biol. Med.*, 101 (1959) 159.
[67] C. H. Li, *Science*, 123 (1956) 617.
[68] J. Léonis and C. H. Li, *J. Am. Chem. Soc.*, 61 (1959) 415.
[69] C. H. Li, *J. Biol. Chem.*, 235 (1960) 1383.
[70] S. M. Sonenberg, *Vitamins and Hormones*, 16 (1958) 205.
[71] J. G. Pierce, M. E. Carsten and L. K. Wynston, *Ann. N.Y. Acad. Sci.*, 86 (1960) 612.
[72] R. W. Bates and P. G. Condliffe, *Recent Progr. in Hormone Research*, 16 (1960) 309.
[73] M. V. Musset and W. L. M. Perry, *Bull. World Health Organization*, 13 (1955) 917.
[74] A. E. Adams, *Quart. Rev. Biol.*, 21 (1946) 1.
[75] L. S. Ciereszko, *J. Biol. Chem.*, 160 (1945) 585.
[76] M. L. Heideman, *Endocrinology*, 53 (1953) 640.
[77] P. E. Smith, *Science*, 44 (1916) 280.
[78] B. Zondek and H. Krohn, *Klin. Wochschr.*, 11 (1932) 405.
[79] T. H. Lee and A. B. Lerner, *J. Biol. Chem.*, 221 (1956) 943.
[80] J. I. Harris and A. B. Lerner, *Nature*, 179 (1957) 1346.
[81] J. S. Dixon and C. H. Li, *J. Am. Chem. Soc.*, 82 (1960) 4568.
[82] O. Kamm, T. B. Aldrich, I. W. Grote, L. W. Rowe and E. P. Bugbee, *J. Am. Chem. Soc.*, 50 (1928) 573.
[83] E. B. Astwood, M. S. Raben, R. W. Payne and A. B. Grady, *J. Am. Chem. Soc.*, 73 (1951) 2969.
[84] I. I. Geschwind and C. H. Li, *J. Am. Chem. Soc.*, 79 (1957) 615.
[85] J. S. Dixon and C. H. Li, *Gen. Comp. Endocrinol.*, 45 (1962) 169.
[86] J. I. Harris, *Brit. Med. Bull.*, 16 (1960) 189.
[87] I. I. Geschwind, C. H. Li and L. Barnafi, *J. Am. Chem. Soc.*, 79 (1957) 1003.
[88] S. Johnsson and B. Hogberg, *Acta Endocrinol.*, 13 (1953) 325.
[89] K. Shizume, A. B. Lerner and T. B. Fitzpatrick, *Endocrinology*, 54 (1954) 553.
[90] V. du Vigneaud, *Harvey Lectures*, 50 (1956) 1.
[91] S. Guttmann and R. A. Boissonnas, *Helv. Chim. Acta*, 42 (1959) 1257.
[92] K. Hofmann, H. Yajima and E. T. Schwartz, *J. Am. Chem. Soc.*, 82 (1960) 3782.
[93] R. Schwyzer, H. Kappeler, B. Iselin, W. Rittel and H. Zuber, *Helv. Chim. Acta*, 42 (1959) 1703.
[94] R. Schwyzer and C. H. Li, *Nature*, 182 (1958) 1669.
[95] K. Hofmann, T. A. Thompson, M. E. Woolner, G. Spuhler, H. Yajima, J. D. Cipera and E. T. Schwartz, *J. Am. Chem. Soc.*, 82 (1960) 3721.
[96] E. Schnabel and C. H. Li, *J. Biol. Chem.*, 235 (1960) 2010.

Peptide and Protein Hormones

Section d

Neurohypophyseal Hormones

ROGER ACHER

Laboratory of Biological Chemistry, University of Paris (France)

The name *neurohypophyseal hormones* given to the hormones isolated from the post-pituitary is not entirely satisfactory as it tends to suggest that these hormones are actually made in the neurohypophysis. It is generally admitted that the active principles are synthesized by the hypothalamus and then transported into the neurohypophyseal reservoir where they accumulate. To the present time in the vertebrate Phylum, four substances have been isolated: oxytocin, arginine-vasopressin, lysine-vasopressin and vasotocin*. These hormones, peptide in nature, have very similar amino acid compositions, and this chemical likeness is reflected in their biological properties; that is, they have several hormonal activities in common, the difference between them being a matter of the degree of each of these activities.

1. Biological activities

The activities are measured by reference to an international standard which is that of an acetone powder of beef post-pituitary, set by convention at 2 units/mg. Several detailed reviews have been devoted to the physiology and pharmacology of these hormones (Scharrer and Scharrer[1], Heller[2], Landgrebe *et al.*[3] and Van Dyke *et al.*[4]).

(*a*) *Oxytocic activity*, contraction of the uterine muscle. The uterus of the rat, usually employed for this assay[5] is submerged in a small bowl containing a physiological solution of the proper composition, kept at 32°.

---

* A fifth hormone, called isotocin, has been now isolated from fish pituitaries[66].

When the hormone is added to this solution, the muscle contracts and the extent of contraction is recorded on a kymograph by means of a lever attached to the muscle.

(*b*) *Depressor activity*, lowering of the blood pressure in the anesthetized fowl[6]. The hormone is injected in the crural vein and the blood pressure is measured in the sciatic artery; this latter is relayed to a mercury manometer, whose variations are registered on a kymograph.

(*c*) *Milk-ejecting activity*. In the suckling female, the injection of the hormone provokes an ejection of milk, following the contraction of the mammary muscle. The assay is performed in the rabbit; the hormone is injected into the ear vein and the variations in pressure within the mammary gland are registered through the manometer attached to one of the nipples[7].

(*d*) *Pressor activity*, increase in blood pressure in the anesthetized mammal. Generally this action is measured in the rat. The hormone is injected into a thigh vein and the increase in pressure is determined in the carotid artery[8].

(*e*) *Antidiuretic activity*. In the hydrated animal, the hormone causes a decrease in the flow of urine. This action is assayed in the rat[9], or in the dog[4] after intravenous injection of the active principle.

(*f*) *Natriferic activity*, action on the active transport of sodium across frog skin. In the absence of an osmotic gradient, there is a net flux of sodium across the skin, the intensity of which is measured by the current which traverses this skin[10,11].

(*g*) *Hydro-osmotic activity*, action on water transport across the wall of the frog urinary bladder. The movement of water depends on the osmotic gradient, and the hormone acts only to increase the permeability[12].

Table I presents the degree of these different activities for oxytocin, vasotocin and vasopressin (arginine-vasopressin).

TABLE I

BIOLOGICAL ACTIVITIES OF THE NEUROHYPOPHYSEAL HORMONES
(units/mg calculated according to refs. 4, 11–13a)

	Oxytocic	Depressor	Milk-ejecting	Pressor	Anti-diuretic	Natri-feric	Hydro-osmotic
Oxytocin	500	500	500	7	3	500	500
Vasotocin*	75	150	—	125	—	900	15,000
Vasopressin**	30	85	100	600	600	20	40

* Values determined with synthetic vasotocin[13].
** Arginine-vasopressin.

2. Purification

The procedures employed until 1955 made great use of countercurrent distribution; they have been reviewed by Acher and Fromageot[14]. More recently the use of electrophoresis, column chromatography and specific adsorption have rendered the purification less laborious.

(a) Countercurrent distribution procedures

Du Vigneaud and collaborators have used countercurrent distribution to isolate oxytocin and vasopressin from beef and hog. Pierce et al.[15] separated oxytocin and vasopressin by fractional precipitation with ether and hexane and then purified oxytocin by two distributions in a sec.-butanol–0.05 % acetic acid system ($K = 0.4$). These authors obtained a crystalline oxytocin flavianate. Du Vigneaud et al. have purified beef[16] and hog[17] vasopressin by two distributions in an n-butanol–0.09 M p-toluenesulfonic acid system ($K = 1.25$ and 0.66 respectively). More recently hog vasopressin has been obtained by a combination of zone electrophoresis and counter-current distribution[18]. Beef vasopressin has a pressor activity of about 600 units/mg, while that of the hog hormone is of the order of 300 units/mg.

Fromageot et al.[19,20] have also isolated the post-pituitary hormones in highly purified states by countercurrent distribution techniques. Oxytocin and vasopressin are adsorbed on silica and eluted, the former with hot 0.5 % acetic acid and the latter with a 2.5 % solution of sodium sulfate containing a detergent. Oxytocin is then purified by distribution in a sec.-butanol–0.05 % acetic acid system, and vasopressin by adsorption on salicylic acid followed by distribution in an n-butanol–salicylic acid–water system.

(b) Chromatographic and electrophoretic procedures

Porath[21] purifies hog oxytocin and vasopressin by combining chromatography on cellulose derivatives and electrophoresis on a cellulose column. After fractionation of the extracts with acetone and ether, oxytocin is purified by chromatography on trimethylaminoethyl-cellulose, followed by lengthy electrophoresis at pH 2.35. Vasopressin is obtained after two consecutive chromatographic steps on diethylaminoethyl-cellulose and on sulfomethyl-cellulose, followed by electrophoresis. The activities of these preparations are similar to those of the pure hormones, but their homogeneity was not checked.

Schally et al.[22] also start with a product obtained by a fractional precipitation with ether (protopituitrin). A separation of oxytocin and vasopressin is obtained by chromatography on carboxymethyl-cellulose using a gradient of pH and of ionic strength. The oxytocic fraction is rechromatographed on carboxymethyl-cellulose under similar conditions but with an initial pH of 4.5 instead of 6. The oxytocin thus isolated is still impure (286 units/mg), but the lysine-vasopressin has an activity close to maximum (290 units/mg).

(c) Specific adsorption procedure

Oxytocin and vasopressin attach to a protein of the post-pituitary, *neurophysin*, to form a stable complex[23]. This property provides the basis for a rapid general method of purifying the hormones[24,25]. As a first step, the neurophysin–hormones complex is precipitated with sodium chloride at pH 3.9 from a glandular extract. In those species possessing little or no neurophysin, the protein from beef, sheep, or horse is added to the extract which is then treated under the usual conditions[25]. The complex can be dialyzed and consequently freed of peptide contaminants. In the second step, the protein support is eliminated by precipitation with trichloroacetic acid. In the third step, the hormones are separated by chromatography on Amberlite IRC-50, with a pH and ionic strength gradient. This procedure, developed with the hog and beef hormones, has been applied to the isolation of the hormones from man[26], horse[27], sheep[28], whale[29], chicken[30,31] and frog[32].

Table II presents the oxytocic and pressor activities of post-pituitary acetone powders of different species and Figs. 1 and 3 demonstrate the separation of the hormones from sheep and frog.

TABLE II

BIOLOGICAL ACTIVITIES OF POST-PITUITARY ACETONE-POWDERS

Species	Oxytocic activity (units/mg)	Pressor activity (units/mg)
Beef	1.0	1.1
Hog	1.4	1.4
Horse	0.9	0.8
Sheep	0.8	0.8
Whale	0.5	2.5
Chicken	0.4	0.4
Frog	1.2	1.0

3. Amino acid composition and structure

(a) Mammalian hormones

The amino acid composition of oxytocin and vasopressin has been determined quantitatively by Du Vigneaud *et al.*[15,16], using chromatography on starch. The results obtained, listed in Table III, indicate that: (*1*) oxytocin and vasopressin each contain 8 amino acids in stoichiometric quantities, and (*2*) 6 of the 8 amino acids are identical in the two hormones, the difference being that isoleucine and leucine are present in oxytocin and phenylalanine and arginine in vasopressin. In both cases, per peptide molecule, there are 3 molecules of ammonia from 3 amide groups. The calculated molecular weight is 1007 for oxytocin and 1084 for vasopressin.

TABLE III

AMINO ACID COMPOSITION OF BEEF OXYTOCIN AND VASOPRESSIN[15,16]

Amino acid	Number of residues*	
	Oxytocin	Vasopressin
Cystine	1.05	0.90
Tyrosine	0.89	0.92
Isoleucine	1.00	—
Phenylalanine	—	1.01
Glutamic acid	1.04	1.09
Aspartic acid	1.10	1.02
Proline	1.10	1.10
Leucine	1.00	—
Arginine	—	1.00
Glycine	1.17	1.09
Ammonia	3.35	3.52

* Leucine in the case of oxytocin and arginine in vasopressin were arbitrarily chosen as unity.

The structure of beef oxytocin has been established independently by Du Vigneaud et al.[33] and by Tuppy and Michl[34]. The former authors first showed that the peptide had only one N-terminal group, that of cystine. Then, by application of the Edman technique of step-wise degradation to oxidized oxytocin, they determined the sequence of the first four residues. The rest of the sequence was deduced after the characterization of short peptides resulting from partial acid hydrolysis and isolated by column chromatography. The C-terminal end has an amide group, as have the β- and γ-carboxyl groups of aspartic and glutamic acids. The results are in accord with the known isoelectric point of oxytocin, 7.7, as the peptide contains one free amino group but no free carboxyls. Finally, the position of the intrachain disulfide bridge was determined by the localization of the two cysteic acid residues obtained from the oxidation of cystine.

Tuppy and Michl[34] studied the peptides produced by partial acid and enzymatic (subtilisin) hydrolysis of oxidized oxytocin. These fragments are fractionated by electrodialysis and purified by paper chromatography. The characterization of the different fragments permits the identification of the complete sequence of oxytocin. The isolation of glycinamide after enzymatic hydrolysis shows it to be the C-terminal residue and also furnishes a direct proof of the presence of an amide C-terminal end. The structure of oxytocin arrived at by the concordant results of the two groups of workers is the following:

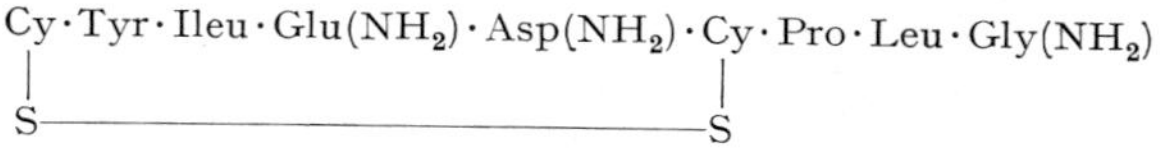

$$Cy \cdot Tyr \cdot Ileu \cdot Glu(NH_2) \cdot Asp(NH_2) \cdot Cy \cdot Pro \cdot Leu \cdot Gly(NH_2)$$

$$\begin{array}{ccc} | & & | \\ S & \rule{6cm}{0.4pt} & S \end{array}$$

The structure of vasopressin has been established by the independent work of Du Vigneaud et al.[35] and by Acher and Chauvet[36]. For this purpose, the Cornell group used the Edman degradation technique on oxidized vasopressin, partial acid hydrolysis and hydrolysis by trypsin and papain.

Acher and Chauvet determined the sequence of 4 residues on the N-terminal end using the Sanger and the Edman techniques on the oxidized hormone, and the sequence of 2 residues on the C-terminal end from the results of the action of trypsin, which split the arginyl–glycinamide bond. The central part of the sequence was obtained from the identification of fragments produced by partial acid hydrolysis. The presence of 3 molecules of ammonia per mole of peptide indicates that the aspartic and glutamic acid residues are amidated, an observation in agreement with the high isoelectric point (10.9) of beef vasopressin. Finally, the position of the intrachain disulfide bridge was established by the localization of the two cysteic acid residues obtained after oxidation of cystine. The ensemble of results lead to the following structure for beef vasopressin:

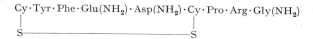

$$Cy \cdot Tyr \cdot Phe \cdot Glu(NH_2) \cdot Asp(NH_2) \cdot Cy \cdot Pro \cdot Arg \cdot Gly(NH_2)$$

Among other mammalian species, the oxytocin and vasopressin of pork[17], man[26], horse[27], sheep[28] (Fig. 1), and whale[29] have been isolated. The amino acid composition and in certain cases the structure has been determined. It appears that the same oxytocin is present in all of the species studied. Vasopressin too is always the same (arginine-vasopressin), with one exception—that of hog, in which a lysine residue replaces the arginine residue in the peptide chain (lysine-vasopressin)[17]. This substitution results in a decrease in the pressor activity measured in the rat (300 units instead of 600 units) and especially of the antidiuretic activity measured in the dog (50 units instead of 600 units)[37]. However, lysine-vasopressin possesses in the species from which it is extracted (hog) an antidiuretic activity equal to or greater than that of arginine-vasopressin[38]. On the basis of pharmacological observations, Van Dyke et al.[37] have suggested that arginine-vasopressin is present also in the monkey, dog, rat and camel. These hormones have not yet been isolated, but certain chromato-graphic data appear to confirm this suggestion in the case of the dog[39] and rat[40]. Thus in the mammals with the exception of the hog, the two hormones are apparently always the same.

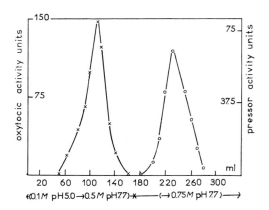

Fig. 1. Chromatography of sheep neurohypophyseal hormones on Amberlite IRC-50. The hormones are adsorbed on the top of a resin column of form H (0.9×10 cm). The column is then equilibrated with a $0.1\ M$ ammonium acetate buffer at pH 5.0, and a gradient is established by the successive addition of solutions of ammonium acetate, $0.5\ M$ and $0.75\ M$, at pH 7.7 (mixing chamber = 50 ml). $\times$—$\times$, oxytocic activity; o—o, pressor activity.

(b) Avian hormones

To the present time, only the neurohypophyseal hormones of the chicken have been isolated[30, 31]. A total of 10,000 chicken post-pituitaries furnished 6 g of acetone powder. In the purification of the hormones, the adsorption procedure of Acher et al.[24] was utilized. It was necessary, however, to add an extraneous neurophysin, in this case horse neurophysin[25]. The final separa-tion of the active principles was obtained by chromatography on Amberlite IRC-50. When the oxytocic and pressor activities of the fractions are measured, the presence of three substances is revealed. The first eluted from the column possesses practically only oxytocin and corresponds both by its position on the chromatogram and by its amino acid composition to mammalian oxytocin. The second substance has to an appreciable extent both oxytocic and pressor activity: from its amino acid composition and its pharmacological properties, especially the action on the transport of water and of sodium, it corresponds to synthetic arginine-vasotocin[13]. Nevertheless, the identity of the natural hormone must await the deter-mination of its structure. Finally, the last substance exhibits only pressor activity and it corresponds to mammalian arginine-vasopressin by its place on the chromatogram and its amino acid composition.

Chemically, vasotocin is a *hybrid* between oxytocin and vasopressin (Fig. 2). The differences between the hormones are to be found in residues 3

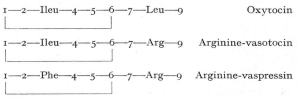

1—2—Ileu—4—5—6—7—Leu—9   Oxytocin

1—2—Ileu—4—5—6—7—Arg—9   Arginine-vasotocin

1—2—Phe—4—5—6—7—Arg—9   Arginine-vaspressin

Fig. 2. Comparison of the structures of oxytocin, vasotocin and vasopressin.

and 8. The presence of vasotocin in the chick post-pituitary had been suggested by Sawyer[12] on the basis of pharmacological observations. It is interesting to note that in this animal, vasotocin has a greater antidiuretic effect than arginine-vasopressin, which is the antidiuretic hormone of mammals[12].

(c) Amphibian hormones

The study of the neurohypophyseal hormones of the frog (*Rana esculenta L.*) has recently been undertaken[32]. 2 g of acetone powder were obtained from 20,000 post-pituitaries and the hormones were purified using conditions similar to those used in the isolation of the chicken hormones. Upon chromatography on Amberlite IRC-50, it was found that three active substances were present (Fig. 3). One of these possesses both oxytocic and pressor

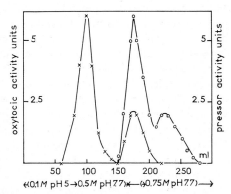

Fig. 3. Chromatography of frog neurohypophyseal hormones on Amberlite IRC-50 (experimental conditions identical to those of Fig. 1). ×—×, oxytocic activity; o—o, pressor activity.

activity and by its position on the chromatogram corresponds to chicken vasotocin. The two other substances have not yet been isolated.

In the lower vertebrates, the regulation of the hydromineral metabolism presents problems different from those in mammals and birds. The active transport of sodium across the skin of the batrachia, in particular, is apparently under hormonal control. For this effect, vasotocin is more active than oxytocin, but the former's most striking activity is that on the passive transport of water, resulting from an increased permeability of the biological membrane (Table I).

4. Synthesis of the hormones and of their analogues

Because of the relative simplicity of the neurohypophyseal hormones, it has been possible not only to synthesize the natural substances and a large variety of analogues, but also to a certain extent to determine the importance of the nature and the position of the constituent residues. Du Vigneaud et al. made the first steps in this direction. The discovery on the one hand that oxytocin could be reduced without loss of activity[41], and on the other hand that the reduced benzylated product upon debenzylation yielded the active substance[42], simplified the problem to that of the synthesis of a nonapeptide containing two residues of benzylated cysteine by use of the general method for the synthesis of cysteine peptides (introduced by Du Vigneaud and Miller[43] in the synthesis of glutathione).

(a) Synthesis of oxytocin

The Cornell group first synthesized two protected cysteine peptides: the N-terminal peptide, N-carbobenzoxy-S-benzyl-L-cysteinyl-L-tyrosine[44] and the C-terminal peptide, S-benzyl-L-cysteinyl-L-prolyl-L-leucyl-glycinamide[45] and then synthesized the central peptide tosyl-L-isoleucyl-L-glutaminyl-L-asparagine[46]. The central and the protected C-terminal peptide were condensed by use of tetraethylpyrophosphite; then after the elimination of the tosyl and benzyl radicals with sodium in liquid ammonia and re-benzylation of cysteine, the heptapeptide was condensed with the N-terminal peptide to yield the nonapeptide. The carbobenzoxyl and benzyl radicals were eliminated by reduction, and the sulfhydryl nonapeptide thus obtained was oxidized to yield oxytocin[47]. This substance purified by countercurrent distribution is identical to the natural product in its biological (degree of oxytocic, depressor and milk-ejecting activities), physical (melting point, optical rotation, distribution coefficient, infrared spectrum, electrophoretic mobility) and chemical (amino acid composition, sensitivity to reagents and to enzymes) properties. Boissonnas et al.[48] in Switzerland, Rudinger et al.[49]

in Czechoslovakia and Velluz *et al.*[50] in France have since developed different synthetic pathways. Recently, Bodanszky and Du Vigneaud[51] have used a procedure of step-wise synthesis, using *p*-nitrophenyl esters of the acylamino acids; the residues are strung together starting from the C-terminal end with a yield of 90 %. This method avoids racemization.

(*b*) *Synthesis of the vasopressins*

The synthesis of arginine- and of lysine-vasopressin has been performed by Du Vigneaud *et al.*[52,53]. Arginine-vasopressin was formed by coupling the azide of the N-terminal tripeptide, *S*-benzyl-*N*-tosyl-L-cysteinyl-L-tyrosyl-L-phenylalanine, with the C-terminal hexapeptide, L-glutaminyl-L-asparaginyl-*S*-benzyl-L-cysteinyl-L-prolyl-L-arginyl-glycinamide. The protecting groups are removed by treating with sodium in liquid ammonia, and the peptide is oxidized in a stream of air. The product is purified by countercurrent distribution followed by zone electrophoresis. The synthetic hormone is identical to the natural product in its pressor activity, partition coefficient, electrophoretic mobility, amino acid composition and chromatographic behavior on Amberlite IRC-50 (ref. 52).

Lysine-vasopressin was synthesized by coupling the N-terminal pentapeptide *S*-benzyl-*N*-tosyl-L-cysteinyl-L-tyrosyl-L-phenylalanyl-L-glutaminyl-L-asparagine with the C-terminal tetrapeptide *S*-benzyl-L-cysteinyl-L-prolyl-*N*-ε-tosyl-L-lysylglycinamide, in the presence of *N*,*N'*-dicyclohexyl-carbodiimide. The protecting groups are eliminated and the peptide is then oxidized. The hormone is finally purified by countercurrent distribution and zone electrophoresis. The biological, chemical and physical properties of the synthetic and natural product are identical[53]. Boissonnas and Huguenin[54] have recently obtained lysine-vasopressin by the coupling of the azide of the N-terminal tripeptide with the C-terminal hexapeptide.

(*c*) *Synthesis of vasotocin*

Katsoyannis and Du Vigneaud[55] have synthesized arginine-vasotocin by a procedure similar to that used for the synthesis of arginine-vasopressin. The azide of the N-terminal tripeptide, *S*-benzyl-*N*-tosyl-L-cysteinyl-L-tyrosyl-L-isoleucine, is coupled to the C-terminal hexapeptide L-glutaminyl-L-asparaginyl-*S*-benzyl-L-cysteinyl-L-prolyl-L-arginyl-glycinamide, and the protecting groups are then removed by treatment with sodium in liquid ammonia. The product is oxidized by aeration and purified by countercurrent distribution and zone electrophoresis. The pharmacological properties of the synthetic substance (Table I) are like those of the natural hormone.

TABLE IV

BIOLOGICAL ACTIVITIES OF SOME ANALOGUES OF NEUROHYPOPHYSEAL HORMONES

$$\begin{array}{ccccccccc}
1 & 2 & 3 & 4 & 5 & 6 & 7 & 8 & 9 \\
\text{Cy} & \text{Tyr} & \text{Ileu} & \text{Glu(NH}_2) & \text{Asp(NH}_2) & \text{Cy} & \text{Pro} & \text{Leu} & \text{Gly(NH}_2)
\end{array}$$

Cy—Tyr—Ileu—Glu(NH$_2$)—Asp(NH$_2$)—Cy—Pro—Leu—Gly(NH$_2$)

S———————————————————S

Oxytocin

	Analogue	Other name	Oxytocic activity (units/mg)	Pressor activity (units/mg)
	oxytocin		500	7
2 {	Phe^2-oxytocin		31	0.4
	Ser^2-oxytocin		< 0.01	< 0.01
	Val^3-oxytocin	Valyl-oxytocin	(170)	—
	Leu^3-oxytocin		(15)	—
3 {	Phe^3-oxytocin	Oxypressin	20	3
	Tyr^3-oxytocin		0.1	0.01
	Try^3-oxytocin		0.04	0
4	Iglu(NH$_2$)^4-oxytocin	Isoglutamine-oxytocin	0.01	0
5 {	Iasp(NH$_2$)^5-oxytocin	Isoasparagine-oxytocin	0	0
	Glu(NH$_2$)^5-oxytocin		—	—
8 {	Lys^8-oxytocin	Lysine-vasotocin	20	39
	Arg^8-oxytocin	Arginine-vasotocin	75	125
	Phe^3–Lys^8-oxytocin	Lysine-vasopressin	5	300
	Phe^3–Arg^8-oxytocin	Arginine-vasopressin	30	600
3–8 {	Phe^3–His^8-oxytocin	Histidine-vasopressin	1.5	1.5
	Tyr^3–Lys^8-oxytocin		0.01	1.6
	Try^3–Lys^8-oxytocin		< 0.01	0.07
	Ser^3–Lys^8-oxytocin		< 0.01	< 0.01
2–3–8 {	Phe^2–Phe^3–Lys^8-oxytocin		0.06	79
	Phe^2–Tyr^3–Lys^8-oxytocin		< 0.01	0.14

(d) Synthesis of analogues

Numerous analogues of the hormones have been synthesized by the American[56-60], Swiss[54, 61-64] and Czech[65] workers. It is convenient to consider all of the hormones and their analogues, about thirty substances, as derivatives of a basic molecule, that of oxytocin, by substitution of one or several residues. The different substances belonging to the oxytocin family can then be classified by indicating in the prefix the nature and the position of the substituted residues. Table IV presents several of these derivatives and their oxytocic and pressor activities.

It can be seen from Table IV that out of 7 possible substitutions, 5 have been studied. In all cases these changes have some effect. The *natural* substitutions are in positions 3 and 8. The oxytocic activity is controlled by the nature of each of the 7 residues, the best tolerated changes being in 3 and 8. For the pressor activity, the replacement of leucine in position 8 by a basic residue increases activity, but a simultaneous change in positions 3 and 8 ($Phe^3 Lys^8$ or $Phe^3 Arg^8$) increases the activity yet further. Molecules relatively close to vasopressin in structure ($Tyr^3 Lys^8$) or in charge ($Phe^3 His^8$) have no pressor activity. Therefore, the presence of a basic residue in position 8 is indispensable, and the variations possible in the cycle are very limited: Tyr or Phe in position 2, and Ileu or Phe in 3. Thus there is a rather strict correlation between the structure of the neurohypophyseal hormones and their biological functions.

REFERENCES

[1] E. Scharrer and B. Scharrer, *Recent Progr. in Hormone Research*, 10 (1954) 183.

[2] H. Heller, *J. Pharm. and Pharmacol.*, 7 (1955) 225.

[3] F. W. Landgrebe, B. Ketterer and H. Waring, *Hormones*, 3 (1955) 389.

[4] H. B. van Dyke, K. Adamson Jr. and S. L. Engel, *Recent Progr. in Hormone Research*, 11 (1955) 1.

[5] P. Holton, *Brit. J. Pharmacol.*, 3 (1948) 328.

[6] J. M. Coon, *Arch. intern. pharmacodynamie*, 62 (1939) 79.

[7] B. A. Cross and G. W. Harris, *J. Endocrinol.*, 8 (1952) 148.

[8] F. W. Landgrebe, M. H. F. Macaulay and H. Waring, *Proc. Roy. Soc. Edinburgh*, Sect. B, 62 (1946) 202.

[9] J. H. Burn, *Quart. J. Pharm. and Pharmacol.*, 4 (1931) 517.

[10] H. H. Ussing, *Symposium No. 8 of the Soc. Exptl. Biol.*, (1954) 407.

[11] F. Morel, J. Maetz and Cl. Lucarain, *Biochim. Biophys. Acta*, 38 (1960) 266.

[12] W. H. Sawyer, *Endocrinology*, 66 (1960) 112.

[13] P. G. Katsoyannis and V. du Vigneaud, *J. Biol. Chem.*, 233 (1958) 1352.

[13a] S. Jard, J. Maetz and F. Morel, *Compt. rend.*, 251 (1960) 788.

[14] R. Acher and C. Fromageot, *Ergeb. Physiol. biol. Chem. u. exptl. Pharmakol.*, 48 (1955) 286.

[15] J. G. Pierce, S. Gordon and V. du Vigneaud, *J. Biol. Chem.*, 199 (1952) 929.

[16] R. A. Turner, J. G. Pierce and V. du Vigneaud, *J. Biol. Chem.*, 191 (1951) 21.

[17] E. A. Popenoe, H. C. Lawler and V. du Vigneaud, *J. Am. Chem. Soc.*, 74 (1952) 3713.

[18] D. N. Ward and V. du Vigneaud, *J. Biol. Chem.*, 222 (1956) 951.

[19] H. Maier-Huser, H. Clauser, P. Fromageot and R. Plongeron, *Biochim. Biophys. Acta*, 11 (1953) 252.

[20] P. Fromageot, R. Acher, H. Clauser and H. Maier-Huser, *Biochim. Biophys. Acta*, 12 (1953) 424.

[21] J. Porath, *Arkiv Kemi*, 11 (1957) 259.

[22] A. V. Schally, H. S. Lipscomb and R. Guillemin, *Biochim. Biophys. Acta*, 31 (1959) 252.

[23] R. Acher, J. Chauvet and G. Olivry, *Biochim. Biophys. Acta*, 22 (1956) 421.

[24] R. Acher, A. Light and V. du Vigneaud, *J. Biol. Chem.*, 233 (1958) 116.

[25] J. Chauvet, M. T. Lenci and R. Acher, *Biochim. Biophys. Acta*, 38 (1960) 266.

[26] A. Light and V. du Vigneaud, *Proc. Soc. Exptl. Biol. Med.*, 98 (1958) 692.

[27] R. Acher, J. Chauvet and M. T. Lenci, *Bull. soc. chim. biol.*, 40 (1958) 2005.

[28] R. Acher, J. Chauvet and M. T. Lenci, *Compt. rend.*, 248 (1959) 1435.

[29] R. Acher, J. Chauvet and M. T. Lenci, unpublished data.

[30] R. Acher, J. Chauvet and M. T. Lenci, *Biochim. Biophys. Acta*, 38 (1960) 344.

[31] J. Chauvet, M. T. Lenci and R. Acher, *Biochim. Biophys. Acta*, 38 (1960) 571.

[32] R. Acher, J. Chauvet, M. T. Lenci, F. Morel and J. Maetz, *Biochim. Biophys. Acta*, 42 (1960) 379.

[33] V. du Vigneaud, C. Ressler and S. Trippett, *J. Biol. Chem.*, 205 (1953) 949.

[34] H. Tuppy and H. Michl, *Monatsh. Chem.*, 84 (1953) 1011.

[35] V. du Vigneaud, H. C. Lawler and E. A. Popenoe, *J. Am. Chem. Soc.*, 75 (1953) 4880.

[36] R. Acher and J. Chauvet, *Biochim. Biophys. Acta*, 12 (1953) 487.

[37] H. B. van Dyke, S. L. Engel and K. Adamsons, *Proc. Soc. Exptl. Biol. Med.*, 91 (1956) 484.

[38] R. A. Munsick, W. H. Sawyer and H. B. van Dyke, *Endocrinology*, 63 (1958) 688.

[39] H. Sachs, *Biochim. Biophys. Acta*, 34 (1959) 572.

[40] H. Heller and K. Lederis, *Nature*, 182 (1958) 1231.

[41] R. R. Sealock and V. du Vigneaud, *J. Pharmacol. Exptl. Therap.*, 54 (1935) 433.

[42] S. Gordon and V. du Vigneaud, *Proc. Soc. Exptl. Biol. Med.*, 84 (1953) 723.

[43] V. du Vigneaud and G. L. Miller, *J. Biol. Chem.*, 116 (1936) 469.

[44] C. W. Roberts and V. du Vigneaud, *J. Biol. Chem.*, 204 (1953) 871.

[45] C. Ressler and V. du Vigneaud, *J. Am. Chem. Soc.*, 76 (1954) 3107.

[46] P. G. Katsoyannis and V. du Vigneaud, *J. Am. Chem. Soc.*, 76 (1954) 3113.

[47] V. DU VIGNEAUD, C. RESSLER, J. M. SWAN, C. W. ROBERTS AND P. G. KATSOYANNIS, *J. Am. Chem. Soc.*, 76 (1954) 3115.

[48] R. A. BOISSONNAS, S. GUTTMANN, P. A. JAQUENOUD AND J. P. WALLER, *Helv. Chim. Acta*, 38 (1955) 1491.

[49] J. RUDINGER, J. HONZL AND M. ZAORAL, *Collection Czechoslov. Chem. Communs.*, 21 (1956) 202.

[50] L. VELLUZ, G. AMIARD, J. BARTOS, B. GOFFINET AND R. HEYMES, *Bull. soc. chim. France*, (1956) 1464.

[51] M. BODANSZKY AND V. DU VIGNEAUD, *J. Am. Chem. Soc.*, 81 (1959) 5688.

[52] V. DU VIGNEAUD, D. T. GISH, P. G. KATSOYANNIS AND G. P. HESS, *J. Am. Chem. Soc.*, 80 (1958) 3355.

[53] V. DU VIGNEAUD, M. F. BARTLETT AND A. JOHL, *J. Am. Chem. Soc.*, 79 (1957) 5572.

[54] R. A. BOISSONNAS AND R. L. HUGUENIN, *Helv. Chim. Acta*, 43 (1960) 182.

[55] P. G. KATSOYANNIS AND V. DU VIGNEAUD, *J. Biol. Chem.*, 233 (1958) 1352.

[56] P. G. KATSOYANNIS, *J. Am. Chem. Soc.*, 79 (1957) 109.

[57] M. BODANSZKY AND V. DU VIGNEAUD, *J. Am. Chem. Soc.*, 81 (1959) 1258.

[58] C. RESSLER AND V. DU VIGNEAUD, *J. Am. Chem. Soc.*, 79 (1957) 4511.

[59] W. B. LUTZ, C. RESSLER, D. E. NETTLETON JR. AND V. DU VIGNEAUD, *J. Am. Chem. Soc.*, 81 (1959) 167.

[60] P. G. KATSOYANNIS AND V. DU VIGNEAUD, *Arch. Biochem. Biophys.*, 78 (1958) 555.

[61] R. A. BOISSONNAS, S. GUTTMANN, P. A. JAQUENOUD AND J. P. WALLER, *Helv. Chim. Acta*, 39 (1956) 1421.

[62] P. A. JAQUENOUD AND R. A. BOISSONNAS, *Helv. Chim. Acta*, 42 (1959) 788.

[63] R. A. BOISSONNAS AND S. GUTTMANN, *Helv. Chim. Acta*, 43 (1960) 190.

[64] S. GUTTMANN AND R. A. BOISSONNAS, *Helv. Chim. Acta*, 43 (1960) 200.

[65] J. RUDINGER, J. HONZL AND M. ZAORAL, *Collection Czechoslov. Chem. Communs.*, 21 (1956) 770.

[66] R. ACHER, J. CHAUVET, M. T. CHAUVET AND D. CREPY, *Biochim. Biophys. Acta*, 58 (1962) 624.

Chapter II

Peptide and Protein Hormones

Section e

Insulin and Glucagon*

WILLIAM W. BROMER and OTTO K. BEHRENS

The Lilly Research Laboratories, Indianapolis, Ind. (U.S.A.)

1. Introduction

By 1920 the concept was well established that the pancreas played an important role in the regulation of carbohydrate metabolism and in the control of diabetes mellitus. Numerous, almost frantic, attempts were made to prepare extracts of the pancreas with the objective of developing a practical treatment for diabetes. The early attempts were frustrated largely by inadequate means of testing, by lack of knowledge of the nature and stability of the active hypoglycaemic agent, and by uncertainty regarding the best route of administration of the extracts. Finally, in 1921 and 1922, Banting and Best surmounted these obstacles and succeeded in preparing pancreas extracts that consistently produced hypoglycaemia following injection. The name insulin, which had been suggested earlier, was adopted for the active principle in the extracts.

The world-renowned feat of Banting and Best is memorable not only as a dramatic medical discovery, but also for the stimulation it provided to the field of protein chemistry. The intensive effort to further purify and characterize insulin led in 1923 to the discovery by Murlin and coworkers and by Fisher that pancreatic extracts caused a rapid transient hyperglycaemia; the following year Kimbal and Murlin named the unknown hyperglycaemic factor glucagon. However, many workers believed that the hyperglycaemic effect was related somehow to insulin. In 1926 Abel succeeded in crystallizing insulin; this represented the first crystallization of a protein that exhibited

---

* A number of reviews covering the chemistry of insulin[1–8] and of glucagon[4,6,9,10] are available.

a specific hormonal activity. These early insulin crystals elicited little or no hyperglycaemic response, and although the finding appeared to be largely ignored, the data supported the concept that insulin and glucagon were separate entities. In 1934 when Scott introduced a more practical method of crystallization for insulin, a hyperglycaemic response was again noted and the controversy was renewed. For almost two decades the hyperglycaemic effect of insulin preparations was considered variously to be caused by (a) insulin, (b) a substance separate from insulin, or (c) a compound very closely related to insulin, such as a degradation or association product. Finally in 1953, Staub, Sinn and Behrens, following a continued interest in insulin and its contaminants, purified and crystallized glucagon and demonstrated its manifold differences from insulin.

After a decade of pioneering work, Sanger and colleagues in 1955 completed the arduous task of establishing the amino acid sequence of insulin, thereby opening, through insulin, a new area in protein chemistry. The amino acid sequence of glucagon has since been elucidated by Bromer, Sinn, Staub and Behrens. Thus, insulin and glucagon are among the most carefully studied of proteins.

2. Assay

When the isolation of a natural product proves to be an extremely difficult task, it is reasonable to presume that one reason for the slow progress lies in an inadequate method of assay. Such was the case with both pancreatic hormones. The classical means of assay for insulin and glucagon was based on measurement of the fall and of the rise, respectively, of blood sugar in animals following the parenteral administration of the hormones. Over the years more precise *in vitro* biochemical assay techniques have been developed; neither hormone differs sufficiently from other proteins to permit a straightforward chemical assay.

(a) Assay of insulin[11]

(i) In vivo assay systems

Insulin is still often tested for biologic potency by measuring the fall in blood sugar of rabbits after subcutaneous injection of the hormone. Another method is based on the production of convulsions in mice through lowering of the blood sugar to a critical level. Generally the quantity of insulin injected is adjusted so that about half the animals convulse. Solutions containing as little as about 5 μg of insulin per ml may be tested. Both methods are simple and can be used in the routine standardization of crystalline or highly purified insulin. On the other hand, probably neither procedure is as specific, sensitive, and precise as some of the newer *in vitro* techniques.

(ii) Isolated tissue assay systems

In recent years both rat diaphragm and epididymal fat tissue slices have been used in the assay of insulin. The hormone enhances the uptake of glucose by the tissue, allowing either a measure of glycogen formation or of glucose removal from the media. The methods require considerable technical skill and are not completely specific for insulin; however, concentrations of insulin as small as 0.4–4 mμg per ml may be measured.

(iii) Immunochemical assay systems

Antisera produced in animals by administration of insulin also react with insulin-[131]I. The antiserum is incubated with a solution containing an unknown amount of insulin and a known amount of insulin-[131]I. The amount of labelled insulin that combines with the antiserum varies in an inverse manner to the quantity of insulin present in the test solution. The immunochemical method appears to be potentially more sensitive, specific, and precise than other assay methods, and for these reasons is being used extensively in the study of insulin in blood and tissues.

(iv) Fibril assay

Insulin after exposure to warm acid solutions elongates by polymerization to form fibrils. Seed fibrils thus obtained may be added to cold, acid insulin solutions to initiate fibril formation. The hormone may be quantitatively removed from solution in this manner and may be separated and weighed.

(v) Paper chromatographic assay[12]

Insulin may be measured in relatively purified samples by chromatography on paper, by location of the hormone with a dye, and by quantitative colorimetric determination of the eluted product.

(b) Assay of glucagon[13]

(i) In vivo systems

A variety of species has been used to measure the hyperglycaemia produced by injection of glucagon. A method currently in use that employs anaesthetized cats may be cited as simple, reproducible, and sensitive to about 0.04 μg of glucagon per ml; however, it suffers from the usual disadvantages of in vivo tests, as discussed in the case of insulin.

(ii) Isolated tissue assay systems

In liver slices or homogenates glucagon promotes the activation of phosphorylase which leads to a conversion of liver glycogen to glucose. The measurement of either the activation of phosphorylase or the release of glucose provides a basis for an assay of glucagon in quantities as small as 0.001–0.004 μg. Such methods are generally more precise and specific than the *in vivo* tests.

(iii) Immunochemical assay system

A method has been devised based on principles similar to those described for insulin. As little as 50–100 $\mu\mu g$ of glucagon can be detected.

3. Isolation

Glucagon was first observed in crude pancreatic extracts of insulin and was isolated from a side fraction from the crystallization of insulin. Clearly both small proteins behave in a rather similar fashion in certain conventional extraction and isolation procedures. Only after each hormone was crystallized and subjected to structural analysis was it certain that glucagon was a separate entity rather than a degradation product of insulin or a closely related protein.

(a) Insulin[1–3,14–16]

(i) Extraction

Although many different methods of isolation of insulin have been employed, the initial step in most cases is an acid–alcoholic extraction of pancreas. Extraction procedures utilizing aqueous solutions at high or low pH and/or organic solvents such as lower alcohols or acetone are desirable to help prevent the destruction of insulin by the proteolytic enzymes of the pancreas.

(ii) Intermediate purification

A crude insulin precipitate may be obtained from the extract by the addition of ether or by removal of the alcohol followed by salt precipitation. Various combinations of salts, alcohol, acetone, and isoelectric precipitations (pH 5.2–5.4) have been employed to obtain an amorphous product of 15–20 I.U. per mg. A method based on the formation of insulin fibrils provides a product of higher purity.

(iii) Crystallization

Scott in 1934 observed that insulin crystals contain zinc; thus, it has been found advantageous to add zinc in the form of a soluble salt prior to crystallization. Insulin has been crystallized under a variety of conditions from aqueous salt solutions, generally at pH 5.8–6.3. Yields of 80–150 μg of insulin (*ca.* 25 I.U. per mg) per g of pancreas are usually obtained.

(b) Glucagon[6, 9, 17]

A side fraction of the insulin process, containing about 4% glucagon, has been used as starting material for glucagon purification. After an acetone precipitation and repeated precipitations during dialysis under acidic conditions, glucagon preparations of about 50% purity were obtained. The amorphous glucagon was crystallized from slightly alkaline solutions containing salts and urea.

4. Homogeneity[6,9,17,18]

As is typical of proteins, preparations of either insulin or glucagon may be recrystallized many times, yet exhibit evidence of a small degree of heterogeneity. In the biologic sense impurity is perhaps not the proper word for these components since most of them possess hormonal activity. The components are not readily detectable by classical physicochemical means nor by measurements of biologic potency. The most definitive evidence for chemical heterogeneity has been obtained with some of the newer methods of characterization.

For example, Harfenist and Craig subjected five times recrystallized beef insulin to countercurrent distribution; a major component A, varying amount of a second component B, and other minor components were observed. The main component comprised about 90% of the original sample. Component B, which exhibited full biologic potency, was found later to differ from A through the absence of a single amide grouping. Extensive column chromatographic analyses of recrystallized insulin have also indicated the existence of minor impurities.

In the case of glucagon, Staub, Sinn and Behrens reported separation of the crystalline hormone into two components by electrophoresis using starch as a supporting medium. In all preparations examined the minor component represented about 10% of the starting preparation. The lesser component exhibited about 50% of the specific biologic activity of the major fraction, and had the same qualitative amino acid composition. Since re-electrophoresis of the major component again resulted in separation of two components, the minor fraction was considered to be an association product of the major fraction.

With both pancreatic hormones, chemical end group and structural analyses corroborated the high degree of purity.

5. Properties

(a) Crystal properties[1 – 3,19]

Rhombohedral crystals of zinc insulin are commonly obtained from solutions at pH 5.8–6.3; these were the first protein crystals that were studied carefully by vector analysis. More recently orthorhombic crystals of insulin were obtained by crystallization (without zinc) from sulfuric acid solutions at pH 2–3.5.

Glucagon crystals obtained from mildly alkaline solutions conform to the isometric system and appear as rhombic dodecahedra.

(b) Physicochemical properties

(i) Molecular weight[3,4,6,7,20,21]

The molecular weight of insulin in solution has been estimated by light-scattering, osmotic pressure, sedimentation and diffusion methods to be from 12,000 to 48,000, depending upon the conditions of measurement. X-ray data were consistent with an insulin monomer of 12,000. Subsequent sedimentation, diffusion and osmotic pressure studies of very dilute insulin solutions at low pH, and countercurrent distribution studies with partially substituted insulin, provided evidence for a molecular weight of about 6000. The structural analysis of insulin by Sanger and colleagues gave a formula weight of 5733, in good agreement with the concept of an insulin monomer of about 6000.

However, insulin readily aggregates in solution, and the 12,000 molecular weight dimer is the smallest unit ordinarily observed. The hexamer is most prevalent in solutions of neutral pH. Lindley and Rollett offered a possible explanation for the dimerization phenomenon through the linkage of one atom of zinc between the histidine residues in two insulin monomers. Waugh[4], drawing on his experience with fibrils, suggested that stabilization of the dimer and its association products may result from the interaction forces provided by the large non-polar side chains.

Preliminary ultracentrifugal studies of crystalline glucagon provided evidence for a molecular weight of about 4000. These data were confirmed by structural and amino acid analyses which showed the molecular weight to be 3485.

(ii) Solubility[1,2,3,9,10,17]

Electrophoretic data have located the isoelectric point of insulin at pH 5.3–5.4; preliminary measurements suggest an isoelectric region for glucagon of pH 7.5–8.5. As expected from these data, insulin and glucagon are soluble in dilute aqueous acid and alkali. Insulin has low solubility in the pH range of 4.5–6.5 while glucagon is relatively insoluble in solutions of pH 4–8.5. The hormones, nevertheless, are soluble in the above pH ranges to the extent of about 10 μg/ml at room temperature. Both exhibit a marked increase in solubility at elevated temperatures and at pH values on either side of their isoelectric regions; aqueous hormone solutions of 5–10% may be obtained under such conditions. The pancreatic hormones are also soluble in aqueous methanol and ethanol solutions, in glacial acetic acid, and in formamide.

(iii) Stability[1,2,9,10,17]

Both insulin and glucagon are remarkably stable small proteins. A sterile aqueous solution of either hormone is stable at pH 2–4, and 4° for several years. Insulin is more stable than glucagon in such solutions at the higher temperatures of 30–40°. The best explanation for the instability of glucagon under these conditions is the ease of fibril formation, leading eventually to irreversible inactivation. Probably because of lack of disulfide bonds glucagon is somewhat more stable to alkali than is insulin. Dilute glucagon solutions at pH 10.5–11.5, or solutions in 0.1 N NaOH, may be kept at room temperature for several hours without noticeable loss of potency. On the other hand, insulin, after treatment for three hours with 0.033 N NaOH at 34°, is almost completely inactivated, with a concomitant release of ammonia and loss of sulfur. An analogous situation exists concerning the stability of the hormones to the reducing action of cysteine or H_2S; insulin, with three disulfide bonds, is readily inactivated, while glucagon, lacking such bonds, is quite stable. Insulin is not inactivated by concentrated urea or by formation of monomolecular films.

(iv) Fibril formation[3,4,6,7,9,10,16,17]

Insulin and glucagon have the similar interesting property of conversion into fibrils in aqueous, acid solutions at elevated temperatures. A 1% solution of glucagon in dilute HCl (pH 1.5), warmed to 40° for several minutes, will readily form fibrils upon cooling. The formation of insulin fibrils appears to require the more rigorous treatment of heating in acid solution at 100° for 30 min.

Insulin fibrils formed by the hot acid treatment may be used to seed cool acid solutions of insulin, resulting in quantitative removal of insulin from solution. Glucagon probably behaves in a similar manner. Fibril formation has been used in the case of insulin as a basic for an assay method and also for a method of isolation.

Under the above conditions of heating in acid, both hormones form stable, birefringent thixotropic gels, which, if treated promptly with cold 0.05 N NaOH, will revert to the original soluble proteins. Preliminary data indicate that glucagon fibrils, unlike insulin fibrils which are inactive, retain biological activity for at least a few hours. After standing several months in solution at temperatures of 30–40°, the glucagon fibrils appear to become inactive and cannot be regenerated with alkali.

The formation of insulin fibrils has been studied extensively by Waugh[4]. Fibril formation occurs with acetylated or esterified insulins, and even in concentrated acids or 6 M urea at pH 7.0. Since conventional bonds do not appear to be operable under such conditions, Waugh has proposed that the numerous, large, non-polar side chains in insulin provide the necessary interaction energy for the molecular association. Insulin fibrils are quite stable from pH 1–10. Ionization of the phenolic functions above pH 10 may be involved in the breakdown of the fibrils. Schematically, fibril formation appears to consist of end-to-end binding of molecular units with a lateral, staggered binding of additional units. The small fibrils are of the order of 50 Å in diameter; the longer ones extend about 16,000 Å in length.

(c) Chemical properties[1, 2, 6, 22, 23]

Insulin and glucagon can be crystallized in biologically active forms in the absence of metals; however, both hormone molecules show a high affinity for metal ions and generally crystallize with varying amounts of zinc, nickel, cobalt, or cadmium. Insulin crystallizes with difficulty in the absence of metal ions and is most readily crystallized from zinc salt solutions. Such crystals have a zinc concentration of about 0.5 %, corresponding to approximately one gramatom of zinc per two moles of insulin. Glucagon, as usually prepared, contains less than 0.01 % zinc, and crystallization is readily induced in the absence of free metal ions.

Aside from metals, neither insulin nor glucagon contains constituents other than amino acids (cf. Table I).

On the basis of enzymic hydrolysis data, the residues of both hormones are of the L-configuration.

Both hormones exhibit the customary protein color reactions (e.g. ninhydrin, biuret) and undergo precipitation with high concentrations of salts and with the usual protein precipitating agents, as trichloroacetic and phosphotungstic acids.

6. Structure

(a) Covalent structure

(i) Insulin[20, 24–29]

The classical elucidation of the structure of insulin by Sanger and his colleagues, Tuppy, Thompson, Ryle, Kitai, and Smith, has been rightfully lauded and reviewed many times. Suffice it to say that this outstanding contribution played a vital role in the stimulation of research on the structure of proteins. Methods of structural analysis and specific amino acid sequence studies are treated extensively in Vol. 7, Chapter II.

TABLE I

THE AMINO ACID COMPOSITION OF INSULIN AND GLUCAGON

Amino acid	Number of residues per mole	
	Insulin[22]	Glucagon[23]
Aspartic acid	3	4
Threonine	1	3
Serine	3	4
Glutamic acid	7	3
Proline	1	0
Glycine	4	1
Alanine	3	1
Cystine	3	0
Valine	5	1
Methionine	0	1
Isoleucine	1	0
Leucine	6	2
Tyrosine	4	2
Phenylalanine	3	2
Histidine	2	1
Lysine	1	1
Arginine	1	2
Tryptophan	0	1
Ammonia (amide)	6	4
Totals (less amide)	48	29
Molecular weight	5733	3485

Determination of the structure was complicated by many factors, not the least of which was the misleading belief that the molecular weight of insulin was 12,000. Undaunted by the realization that insulin must contain about 100 amino acid residues (per 12,000 molecular weight), Sanger began laying the groundwork in 1945 by devising the now famous method of end group analysis using fluorodinitrobenzene (FDNB). Interestingly, Sanger's new reagent and his ingenuity and perseverance were probably the most decisive factors in the successful elucidation of the structure. When applied to insulin the new method demonstrated two glycine and two phenylalanine residues in amino-terminal positions, and two lysine residues within the peptide chains. By 1947 Sanger had split the disulfide bridges of insulin using performic acid oxidation; in 1949 he described the separation, using salt and pH precipitations, of the oxidized peptides into Fraction A (glycyl chain) and Fraction B (phenylalanyl chain). Sanger and Tuppy in 1951, using a partial hydrolysis method and extensively employing FDNB, described the complete amino acid sequence in the phenylalanyl chain. This exciting news was followed closely by the 1953 publications of Sanger and Thompson covering the structure of the glycyl chain. Sanger, Thompson, and Kitai determined the location of the six amide groupings in the molecule. Probably the most troublesome aspect of the entire problem was the final step, the unequivocal location of the disulfide bridges. After several failures and after much painstaking work, Ryle, Sanger, Smith and Kitai in 1955 succeeded brilliantly in solving the disulfide locations, and thus were able to present the complete covalent structure of beef insulin (Fig. 1).

Insulins from a variety of species have been studied, and, with one exception, they differ only in sequence 8 to 10 in the disulfide loop, as:

$$
\begin{array}{c}
\overset{\displaystyle{\underset{8\ \ \ 9\ \ \ 10}{\text{—S———————S—}}}}{} \\
\text{beef} \quad —\text{Cy}\cdot\text{Cy}\cdot\text{Ala}\cdot\text{Ser}\cdot\text{Val}\cdot\text{Cy}— \\[4pt]
\text{pig} \quad —\text{Cy}\cdot\text{Cy}\cdot\text{Thr}\cdot\text{Ser}\cdot\text{Ileu}\cdot\text{Cy}— \\[4pt]
\text{sheep} \quad —\text{Cy}\cdot\text{Cy}\cdot\text{Ala}\cdot\text{Gly}\cdot\text{Val}\cdot\text{Cy}— \\[4pt]
\text{horse} \quad —\text{Cy}\cdot\text{Cy}\cdot\text{Thr}\cdot\text{Gly}\cdot\text{Ileu}\cdot\text{Cy}— \\[4pt]
\text{sperm-whale} \quad —\text{Cy}\cdot\text{Cy}\cdot\text{Thr}\cdot\text{Ser}\cdot\text{Ileu}\cdot\text{Cy}— \\[4pt]
\text{sei-whale} \quad —\text{Cy}\cdot\text{Cy}\cdot\text{Ala}\cdot\text{Ser}\cdot\text{Thr}\cdot\text{Cy}—
\end{array}
$$

Interestingly, human insulin stands as the single exception, being identical with pig insulin except for the replacement in the C-terminus of the B chain of alanine by threonine[29].

(ii) Glucagon[6, 9, 30]

Porcine glucagon was found to contain single N- and C-terminal residues, histidine and threonine, respectively, which clearly indicated a single chain polypeptide. Further structural information was obtained by cleavage with proteolytic enzymes, resolution of the fragments on columns of Dowex 50, characterization of the small peptides, and location of the amide groups. The data allowed the structural formula for porcine glucagon to be written:

$$
\overset{\displaystyle \text{NH}_2}{\underset{}{\text{|}}}
$$

His·Ser·Glu·Gly·Thr·Phe·Thr·Ser·Asp·Tyr·Ser·Lys·Tyr·Leu·Asp·Ser·Arg·Arg·-

$$
\overset{\text{NH}_2}{|} \qquad\qquad \overset{\text{NH}_2}{|} \qquad\qquad \overset{\text{NH}_2}{|}
$$

Ala·Glu·Asp·Phe·Val·Glu·Try·Leu·Met·Asp·Thr

With the elucidation of the structures of insulin and glucagon, and with recent progress in methodology of organic peptide synthesis, there is reasonable optimism that the structures may be confirmed by chemical synthesis.

References p. 151

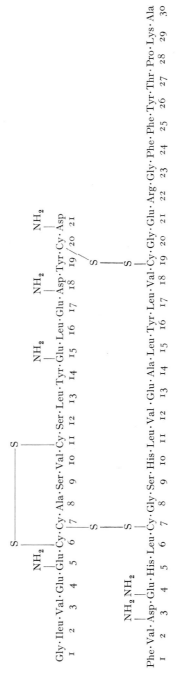

Fig. 1. Structure of beef insulin.

(b) Three-dimensional structures

(i) Insulin[4, 6, 7, 19, 21, 31, 32]

Through X-ray studies of air-dried crystals of insulin sulfate, Low has calculated the complete three-dimensional vector structure of the insulin crystal. Extensive X-ray studies on rhombohedral zinc insulin crystals indicate the occurrence of cylindrical rods of high density in close-packed array, parallel to the a-axis. These results, coupled with earlier work, indicate that the rhombohedral unit cell contains three parallel dimers of about 44 Å in length. Recently, Low and Einstein showed that the insulin dimer is composed of two monomer units related by a two-fold axis of rotation. The dimer symmetry appears to be invariant among the various crystal structures.

Various insulin models have been made on the basis of X-ray data and the known covalent structure. Most workers interpret the rotatory dispersion, deuterium exchange, and X-ray data to indicate that at least half the insulin molecule exists in some form of the familiar Pauling–Corey α-helix. The model studies showed that the free disulfide bridges do not readily fit into a simple two-chain α-helix. To accommodate the disulfide links, Hodgkin and Oughton[4] speculated on a *folded sheet* configuration for insulin. Others favored helical configurations, with appropriate adjustments for the disulfide positions. Thus, Lindley and Rollett constructed a model in which a left-handed α-helix exists on the N-terminal side of position 9 in the disulfide loop, and a right-handed α-helix is found on the C-terminal side of position 9. As dictated in part by the location of the interchain disulfide bridges, the B chain was pictured as a right-handed α-helix. The resulting molecular unit may associate with another unit to form a close-packed dimer that allows reasonable agreement with accepted unit cell dimensions. The model, along with physical data, permits the possibility that the insulin dimer exists with one zinc atom linked between the same two histidine residues (*cf.* Fig. 1; position 10, phenylalanyl chain) in each molecule.

On the basis of the results of deuterium exchange studies with insulin, Linderstrøm-Lang proposed that the A and B chains exist as right- and left-handed helices, respectively, except for the portions lying outside the interchain disulfide structure, which are considered to be more or less unfolded.

The proposed models are based on, and are not in apparent contradiction to, the known facts; nevertheless, a definitive answer to the problem of three-dimensional structure awaits further data.

(ii) Glucagon[33, 34]

On the basis of X-ray crystallographic data, King concluded that the unit cell is comprised of 12 glucagon molecules. The observed space group requires an arrangement of molecular triads about a three-fold axis. If the molecules assume an α-helical configuration, cylindrical rods of about 43 Å in length would be obtained. The data may be interpreted that the unit cell could contain four triads of glucagon helices in skew orientation.

However, optical rotatory dispersion measurements by Kay and Marsh suggest that glucagon, in solution at pH 10, is mostly in a random-coil configuration. Studies at lower pH, where glucagon might assume a higher degree of helical configuration, are hampered by lack of solubility.

7. Structure–activity relationships

One of the basic motivations for structural analyses of proteins involves a desire to better understand the relationship of structure to biological activity. Prior to the protein structure era the hope was often expressed that biologic activity was associated with some particular short sequence of amino acids as an *active core*. This concept has been partially realized in the case of a few enzymes; but with the protein hormones, and particularly with insulin, knowledge of the covalent structure is not sufficient in itself. Apparently more knowledge of the substrate and of the three-dimensional structure of insulin is required before an understanding of the structure–activity relationship can be reached. Despite the fact that insulin has again been in the forefront of research, comparatively little is known about the precise manner in which chemical structure governs biologic function.

Most of the work on structure–activity relationships of proteins is based on determining the effects of chemical modification and on obtaining the smallest active fragment through degradation. Also, species differences emphasize portions of the molecule that can be altered without destroying activity.

(a) Species differences[5, 6]

As previously described, nearly all structural differences among insulins from six species occur in the disulfide loop, positions 8 to 10 in the A chain. Therefore, the amino acid sequence in the loop may vary to some extent without marked effect on biological activity *per se*, although it is probably important to the formation of different antibodies.

On the basis of preliminary data pig and beef glucagon appear to be similar; other species have not been studied.

(b) Chemical modifications[6,35]

From the extensive chemical modifications of insulin a few generalizations can be drawn about the chemical groups involved in the structure that are necessary for biological activity. Modification of virtually all free amino and aliphatic hydroxyl groups does not destroy activity, nor does partial substitution of amide, guanidyl, phenolic, and imidazole functions. Biological activity is lost on rupture of the disulfide bridges, on esterification of the carboxyl groups, and on extensive modification of the phenolic and imidazole functions. Glucagon has not been sufficiently studied to permit generalizations.

(c) Degradations[6, 8]

Insulin activity is destroyed by long incubations with relatively high concentrations of pepsin, trypsin, papain, leucine aminopeptidase, or chymotrypsin. Limited digestions with carboxypeptidase and trypsin liberate mostly a C-terminal alanine residue, with no loss in activity. Prolonged digestion with carboxypeptidase splits the asparagine from the C-terminus of the A chain, completely destroying the activity. Further tryptic hydrolysis liberates a hexapeptide from the C-terminus of the B chain by splitting the arginyl–glycine (positions 22, 23) bond. The remaining structure is virtually inactive. The N-terminal portion of the molecule was degraded in stepwise fashion by leucine aminopeptidase, resulting in about 50% loss in activity in a 24-hour incubation. On the basis of the quantitative study, the first six residues of the B chain do not appear to be necessary for activity, although the N-terminus of the A chain or the sequence near the disulfide bridge of the B chain (positions 7, 8, 9) may be vital.

Glucagon is rapidly degraded by the various enzymes, pepsin, trypsin, leucine aminopeptidase, carboxypeptidase, chymotrypsin, or subtilisin, and in no instance has a smaller active molecule been detected. On the other hand, the action of N-bromosuccinimide results in loss of the C-terminal tetrapeptide with little decrease in activity.

Although small segments of the hormones may be removed without loss of activity, and certain of the functional groups of insulin do not appear to be vital, nevertheless it is clear that much of the known structures is necessary for activity. Particularly with insulin the evidence indicates that a short sequence of amino acids cannot be responsible for biologic function but rather that some specific three-dimensional configuration is required. Further knowledge of the tertiary structures of the hormones is obviously necessary and, in all probability, will be forthcoming from X-ray studies. How much light this may shed on the fundamental structure–function relationship is a moot point. Conceivably, a much greater knowledge on a molecular level of the sites of the hormonal action will be required before the subtle chemical interactions of the hormones in living systems will be understood.

References p. 151

ADDENDUM

The reader's attention is directed to a few of the pertinent publications that have appeared while this chapter was in press, and that would have appreciably changed the content of a particular section. K. MARCKER AND J. GRAAE, *Acta Chem. Scand.*, 16 (1962) 41; Sections 5(b)(i), 5(c), 6(b)(i). S. WILSON AND G. H. DIXON, *Nature*, 191 (1961) 877; Section 6(a)(i). C. T. O. FONG, L. SILVER, E. A. POPENOE AND A. F. DEBONS, *Biochim. Biophys. Acta*, 56 (1962) 190; Section 7. G. H. DIXON AND A. C. WARDLAW, *Nature*, 188 (1960) 721; Section 6(a)(ii). S. WILSON, G. H. DIXON AND A. C. WARDLAW, *Biochim. Biophys. Acta*, 62 (1962) 483; Section 7(a). P. G. KATSOYANNIS, *Eighth Natl. Med. Chem. Symp. Amer. Chem. Soc.*, Boulder, Colo., June 18, 1962, p. 1a; Section 6(a)(ii).

REFERENCES

[1] H. F. JENSEN, *Insulin*, Commonwealth Fund, New York, 1938, pp. 1–91.

[2] D. W. HILL AND F. O. HOWITT, *Insulin*, Chemical Publishing Co., New York, 1936, pp. 19–82.

[3] C. H. LI, in H. NEURATH AND K. BAILEY (Eds.), *The Proteins*, Vol. IIA, Academic Press, New York, 1953, p. 595.

[4] G. E. W. WOLSTENHOLME AND C. M. O'CONNOR (Eds.), *Ciba Foundation Colloquia on Endocrinology, Internal Secretion of the Pancreas*, Vol. 9, 1956, pp. 89–178.

[5] F. SANGER, *Brit. Med. Bull.*, 16 (1960) 183.

[6] O. K. BEHRENS AND W. W. BROMER, *Ann. Rev. Biochem.*, 27 (1958) 57.

[7] H. NEURATH AND G. H. DIXON, in R. H. WILLIAMS (Ed.), *Diabetes*, Paul B. Hoeber, New York, 1960, p. 14.

[8] R. ACHER, *Ann. Rev. Biochem.*, 29 (1960) 547.

[9] O. K. BEHRENS AND W. W. BROMER, *Vitamins and Hormones*, 16 (1958) 263.

[10] W. W. BROMER, in R. H. WILLIAMS (Ed.), *Diabetes*, Paul B. Hoeber, New York, 1960, p. 23.

[11] K. L. SMITH, in R. I. DORFMAN (Ed.), *Methods in Hormone Research*, Vol. II, Bioassay, Academic Press, New York, 1962, p. 413.

[12] E. L. FENTON, *Biochem. J.*, 71 (1959) 507.

[13] W. W. BROMER AND O. K. BEHRENS, in R. I. DORFMAN (Ed.). *Methods in Hormone Research*, Vol. II, Bioassay, Academic Press, New York, 1962, p. 459.

[14] R. G. ROMAN, D. A. SCOTT AND A. M. FISHER, *Ind. Eng. Chem.*, 32 (1940) 908.

[15] D. A. SCOTT AND A. M. FISHER, *Biochem. J.*, 29 (1935) 1048.

[16] C. W. PETTINGA, *Biochem. Preparations*, 6 (1958) 28.

[17] A. STAUB, L. G. SINN AND O. K. BEHRENS, *J. Biol. Chem.*, 214 (1955) 619.

[18] E. J. HARFENIST AND L. C. CRAIG, *J. Am. Chem. Soc.*, 74 (1952) 3083.

[19] B. W. Low, in H. NEURATH AND K. BAILEY (Eds.), *The Proteins*, Vol. IA, Academic Press, New York, 1953, p. 235.

[20] A. P. RYLE, F. SANGER, L. F. SMITH AND R. KITAI, *Biochem. J.*, 60 (1955) 541.

[21] H. LINDLEY AND J. S. ROLLETT, *Biochim. Biophys. Acta*, 18 (1955) 183.

[22] E. J. HARFENIST, *J. Am. Chem. Soc.*, 75 (1953) 5528.

[23] W. W. BROMER, A. STAUB, E. R. DILLER, H. L. BIRD, L. G. SINN AND O. K. BEHRENS, *J. Am. Chem. Soc.*, 79 (1957) 2794.

[24] F. SANGER, *Biochem. J.*, 39 (1945) 507.

[25] F. SANGER, *Biochem. J.*, 44 (1949) 126.

[26] F SANGER AND H. TUPPY, *Biochem. J.*, 49 (1951) 463, 481.

[27] F. SANGER AND E. O. P. THOMPSON, *Biochem. J.*, 53 (1953) 353, 366.

[28] F. SANGER, E. O. P. THOMPSON AND R. KITAI, *Biochem. J.*, 59 (1955) 509.

[29] D. S. H. W. NICOL AND L. F. SMITH, *Nature*, 187 (1960) 483.

[30] W. W. BROMER, L. G. SINN AND O. K. BEHRENS, *J. Am. Chem. Soc.*, 79 (1957) 2807.

[31] B. W. Low AND J. R. EINSTEIN, *Nature*, 186 (1960) 470.

[32] K. LINDERSTRØM-LANG, *Chem. Soc. (London)*, Spec. Publ. No. 2 (1955) 1.

[33] M. V. KING, *J. Mol. Biol.*, 1 (1959) 375.

[34] C. M. KAY AND M. M. MARSH, *Biochim. Biophys. Acta*, 33 (1959) 251.

[35] J. FRAENKEL-CONRAT AND H. FRAENKEL-CONRAT, *Biochim. Biophys. Acta*, 5 (1950) 89.

Volume 8

Part B

NUCLEIC ACIDS

Chapter III

Chemistry of the Nucleic Acids

Section a

Introduction

D. M. BROWN

University Chemical Laboratory, Cambridge (Great Britain)

AND

T. L. V. ULBRICHT

Twyford Laboratories Ltd., London (Great Britain)

It is generally considered that the discovery of the nucleic acids should be attributed to Miescher[1]. Almost one hundred years ago he observed the presence of an acid-insoluble, phosphorus-containing substance in pus cells and subsequently in salmon sperm heads to which the name of *nuclein* was applied. The evident importance of this material, recognised to be acidic and of high molecular weight led Hoppe-Seyler to repeat Miescher's work and to initiate many further studies. Altmann called the protein-free material nucleic acid, and chemical studies in the subsequent years led to the isolation and identification of the residues which were present in these complex substances. Foremost among early workers were Kossel, Neuman, Steudel, Hammarsten and Fischer who showed the presence of various heterocyclic bases. Following this phase, Levene and others identified D-ribose and 2-deoxy-D-ribose in hydrolysates and characterised the *nucleosides* as ribosides and deoxyribosides of the bases. The structures of these compounds were put on a firm basis by synthetic studies by Todd and his school. The *nucleotides*, or monophosphates of the nucleosides, were studied intensively by Levene and co-workers but due to difficulties in their separation from one another, progress was very slow until the application of ion-exchange analytical methods by Cohn in 1948 allowed chemical work to proceed. The structures of the isolated nucleotides were then rapidly clarified by degradation and synthesis, mainly by Todd and his co-workers. This led in 1952–54 to a clear understanding of the general chemistry of the nucleic acids, themselves, which had for some time been recognised, following work by Levene, Gulland and others to be *polynucleotides*. Indeed, although many views have been put forward on the matter it is now generally held that the nucleic acids are linear polymers in which the nucleoside residues are linked by phosphodiester bridges with the general structure

$$
\begin{array}{c}
| \\
\text{base—sugar—phosphate} \\
| \\
\text{base—sugar—phosphate} \\
| \\
\text{base—sugar—phosphate}
\end{array}
$$

The relationships outlined above can be summarised as follows:

$$
\begin{array}{c}
\text{nucleic acids (polynucleotides)} \\
\downarrow \\
\text{mononucleotides} \\
\downarrow \\
\text{nucleosides} + \text{orthophosphate} \\
\downarrow \\
\text{purine and pyrimidine bases} + \text{D-ribose or 2-deoxy-D-ribose}
\end{array}
$$

By 1930 it had become clear that the two types of nucleic acid, *ribonucleic* and *deoxyribonucleic* acid, were both present in all cellular organisms, and not, as had earlier been thought, that the former was characteristic of plant and the latter of animal cells. Subsequently it was shown that viruses, too, contained one or other of the nucleic acids and it seems clear, today, that these acids are quite essential for the continuance of life processes. The deoxyribonucleic acids (DNA) are recognised to be the primary genetic substances, while the ribonucleic acids (RNA) play a more functional role, essentially associated with protein synthesis. Recent work has shown that there are at least three different types of RNA, *all, however, having the same general primary structure*—the ribosomal RNA, the cytoplasmic or soluble RNA (s-RNA) and the transient messenger or informational RNA. Nuclear RNA has also been described; its relationship to or identification with any of the above classes has not been clearly established.

Early work had shown the presence of the heterocyclic bases adenine, guanine, cytosine and uracil (1–4) in RNA and the first three of these together with thymine (5) in DNA. The view was held for some time that the nucleic acids were tetranucleotides because of the base ratios in fortuitously chosen source materials and molecular weight studies on what are now recognised to have been highly degraded nucleic acids. The work of Chargaff and others demonstrated clearly that the four bases were not present in equimolar amounts, and indeed subsequent chromatographic studies showed that a variety of other bases related to (1–5) were to be found, generally, but not invariably, in trace amounts.

The observation by Chargaff and his co-workers, since amply confirmed, that in DNA the analytical ratios, adenine:thymine and guanine:cytosine are very close to unity, together with X-ray crystallographic studies on DNA fibres led to the proposal by Watson and Crick in 1953 that the macro-molecule is in fact a helical system composed of two chains, base pairing through hydrogen bonds between complementary bases conferring stability and considerable rigidity to the system as a whole. Following this, the past ten years have seen an enormous growth in interest in the physico-chemical properties of DNA and RNA and knowledge on the conformations of these molecules has found direct application to the study of their biological role.

This very brief résumé of the development of nucleic acid chemistry will be enlarged upon in succeeding pages. Reference to early studies can be made through the monographs of Jones[2], Feulgen[3], and Levene and Bass[4]. The three-volume treatise *The Nucleic Acids*[5], covers the subject as a whole, essentially exhaustively, while more concise treatments are by Jordan[6], and Steiner and Beers[7].

REFERENCES

[1] *Die histochemischen und physiologischen Arbeiten von Friedrich Miescher*, 2 Vols., Vogel, Leipzig, 1897.
[2] W. Jones, *Nucleic Acids – Their Chemical Properties and Physiological Conduct*, 2nd ed., Longmans, Green and Co., London, 1920.
[3] R. Feulgen, *Chemie und Physiologie der Nukleinstoffe*, Bornträger, Berlin, 1923.
[4] P. A. Levene and L. W. Bass, *Nucleic Acids*, Chemical Catalog Co., New York, 1931.
[5] E. Chargaff and J. N. Davidson (Eds.), *The Nucleic Acids, Chemistry and Biology*, 3 Vols., Academic Press, New York, 1955 and 1960. These volumes are referred to later as C. & D.
[6] D. O. Jordan, *The Chemistry of the Nucleic Acids*, Butterworth, London, 1960.
[7] R. F. Steiner and R. F. Beers, *Polynucleotides, Natural and Synthetic Nucleic Acids*, Elsevier, Amsterdam, 1961.

Chemistry of the Nucleic Acids

Nucleic Acid Bases and Nucleosides

T. L. V. ULBRICHT

Twyford Laboratories Ltd., London (Great Britain)

A. CHEMICAL CONSTITUTION OF THE NUCLEIC ACID BASES

1. General chemistry of purines and pyrimidines

(a) Introduction

m-Diazine, pyrimidine (1), and the fused imidazole derivative, purine (2), are numbered as shown.

Both ring systems show marked aromatic properties, including resistance to oxidation. The *meta*-position of the nitrogen atoms in the pyrimidine ring enhances their effect, and positions 2, 4 and 6 (and equally, positions 2, 6 and, to a lesser extent, 8 in purine) are markedly electron-deficient, position 5 (sometimes called the aromatic position) less so. There are therefore a wide variety of nucleophilic substitution reactions which occur in both systems, but examples of electrophilic substitution are virtually confined to position 5 in pyrimidine. (Electrophilic substitution of the 8-position in xanthine is possible, but such derivatives have not been of interest in nucleic acid chemistry.)

The physical properties of both purines and pyrimidines are strikingly dependent on the nature of the substituents: alkyl, aryl, alkoxyl, halogen and similar derivatives are liquids or relatively low-melting solids, and readily soluble in organic solvents, whereas compounds containing mercapto, hydroxyl and amino substituents are water-soluble and become increasingly insoluble in organic solvents and higher-melting with the number of such substituents. This is mainly due to strong intermolecular hydrogen-bonding. (Tautomerism is discussed in section B7a, p. 199.)

(b) Electrophilic substitution

Owing to the electron deficiency even at position 5 in pyrimidine, electrophilic substitution often requires the presence at other positions in the ring of electron-releasing (tautomeric) groups. The magnitude of their activating effect is in the order OH, NH_2 > SH, SR, OR > alkyl.

The reaction most sensitive to activation effects is a widely used one, namely, nitrosation. It appears to require the presence of two strongly activating groups. Thus it is possible to nitrosate 2,4-diamino-6-ethoxy-pyrimidine (3) but not 4-amino-6-methoxy-2-methylthiopyrimidine (4), which can, however, be brominated[1].

3   4

Chlorosulphonation[2] (e.g. of uracil, 5) and nitration[3] (4-methyluracil, 6) also require considerable activation. Both nitrosation and nitration are used to

5   6

introduce a 5-amino group, often required for conversion of pyrimidines to purines. Azocoupling[4] can also be used; it proceeds more readily than

References p. 204

nitrosation and under much milder conditions than nitration, which was why it was used with the ribose derivative (7):

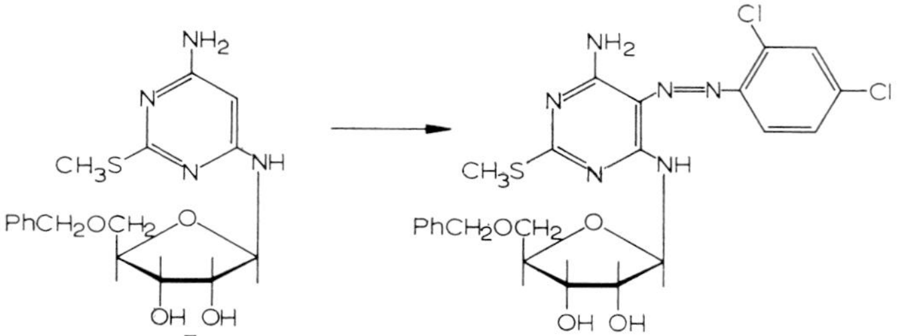

Certain uracil derivatives can be condensed with formaldehyde to give the 5-hydroxymethyl derivatives; in this way, uracil, uridine and 2'-deoxy-uridine all give the corresponding products[5]. The reactions are usually acid-catalysed. Uracil does not give a defined product with glucose, but 2,4-di-amino-6-hydroxypyrimidine reacts to give 60% of the 5-C-glycoside[6]. Condensation of aminopyrimidines is discussed in section A1d, iii (p. 164).

(c) Nucleophilic substitution

2-, 4- and 6-substituted pyrimidines and 2-, 4- and 8-substituted purines readily undergo a wide variety of nucleophilic displacement reactions. Particularly useful intermediates for such reactions are the chloro and mercapto compounds. Chloro compounds are usually synthesized by reaction of the corresponding hydroxy compound with phosphorus oxychloride; the yield is often improved by carrying out the reaction in the presence of di-methylaniline, first used in the synthesis[7] of 4-amino-6-chloro-2-methylthio-pyrimidine (8). However, in analogous syntheses of bromo compounds from

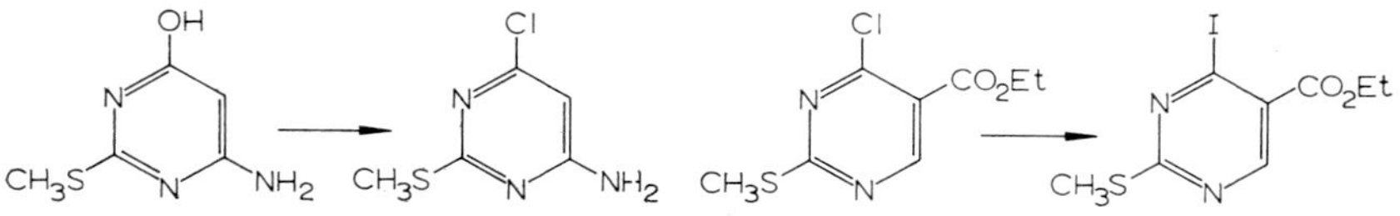

phosphorus oxybromide, it is best to omit dimethylaniline and use toluene as a solvent[8]. Iodides are prepared from chlorides by reaction with hydriodic acid, or, under milder conditions, as in the synthesis of 5-ethoxycarbonyl-6-iodo-2-methylthiopyrimidine (9), with sodium iodide in acetic acid[8].

Mercapto compounds (apart from the direct synthesis of 2-mercapto-pyrimidines from thiourea) are prepared either by reaction of hydroxy compounds with phosphorus pentasulphide in an inert solvent, as in the synthesis[9] of 6-mercaptopurine (11) from hypoxanthine (10), or by conversion of halogen compounds[10] with thiourea in boiling ethanol, e.g. 12 → 13.

Both chloro and mercapto compounds react with ammonia or amines to give amino or substituted amino derivatives, but the ease with which the reaction takes place varies greatly. In the pyrimidine (14) in which the chlorine is activated by the neighbouring cyano group, reaction[11] with

10	11	12	13

methanolic ammonia takes place in 96% yield at 0°, whereas it is necessary to heat the dichloropyrimidine (15) to 150° with ethanolic ammonia in a

14	15

sealed tube to replace even one chlorine[12]. The substituted adenine, kinetin (16), has been synthesized by heating 6-mercaptopurine with furfuryl-amine[13].

16	17	18

Alkaline hydrolysis (17) of halo and alkoxy compounds proceeds readily, but mercapto compounds do not react, as the sulphur atom is not sufficiently electronegative to activate the carbon atom to which it is attached. Acid hydrolysis (attack by water following protonation, 18) takes place with all

References p. 204

the above compounds. The principal hydrolytic reaction used in synthesis is the conversion of mercapto compounds (usually 2-mercaptopyrimidines synthesized from thiourea) to their oxygen analogues by refluxing with chloroacetic acid and hydrochloric acid. In this way, 2-thiocytosine (19) is converted[14] to cytosine (21) via the intermediate 2-thioglycollic acid (20), which is particularly susceptible to acid hydrolysis.

Alkoxy compounds are hydrolysed under mild conditions with sodium iodide in acetic acid (nucleophilic attack by iodide ion following protona-tion[15]). The alkoxy compounds are formed by reaction[16] of the halides with alkoxides in the corresponding alcohol (22).

In a dialkoxypyrimidine, O → N-alkyl rearrangement takes place readily with one group by reaction with alkyl iodide (24 → 25), but heating for many hours at over 200° is necessary to rearrange both groups[17]. This rearrange-ment is more easily carried out[15] by heating the pyrimidine with sodium iodide in acetonylacetone (23).

Finally there may be mentioned the reaction of amino compounds with

nitrous acid, leading to the formation of the corresponding hydroxy derivatives. In this way, adenine was long ago converted to hypoxanthine[18], and
cytosine similarly is converted to uracil.

The reactions with hydrazine and with hydroxylamine are discussed together with those of the nucleotides in Chapter IIIc (p. 260).

(d) Other reactions

(i) Reduction

Halo derivatives are readily reduced by catalytic hydrogenation, as in the
synthesis of the parent compounds purine (2) from 6-chloropurine (26)
(ref. 19), and of pyrimidine (1) (ref. 20). Even 5-halopyrimidines are readily
reduced at atmospheric pressure and room temperature in the presence of
palladium charcoal, e.g. 5-bromouracil to uracil[8].

26   2

Desulphurisation with Raney nickel has been used for converting 2-mercapto
compounds derived from thiourea into the 2-unsubstituted derivatives[10].

Reduction of the 4,5-double bond in pyrimidines is discussed in section
B1a (p. 178).

(ii) Alkylation

Hydroxy compounds react with diazomethane or dimethyl sulphate to
give N-alkyl compounds: uracil and thymine give 1- and 3-methyl and 1,3-
dimethyl derivatives[21,22], cytosine gives 1-methylcytosine (27) (ref. 23), and

27   28   29   30

xanthine (28) yields theobromine (29) and finally, caffeine (30) (refs. 24, 25).
With guanine (31), the initial reaction is at position 7, ethylene oxide[26] giving

References p. 204

7-hydroxyethylguanine (32), whereas adenine reacts with alkyl halides[27] in alkali to give 9-alkyladenines (33).

31   32   33

(iii) Condensation of aminopyrimidines

The condensation of 4,5-diaminopyrimidines with some derivative of formic acid is the final step of the Traube synthesis of purines (see p. 166), and a similar condensation with α-dicarbonyl compounds is a widely used pteridine synthesis[28]. In these syntheses, the first step is undoubtedly a reaction with the more basic 5-amino group. 4-(6)-Aminopyrimidines are very weakly basic and do not condense readily. Thus, 2,4-diamino-6-hydroxy-pyrimidine (34, R = H) will condense[29,30] with nitromalondialdehyde to give a product (35), but introduction of bromine at position 5 (34, R = Br) de-activates the pyrimidine sufficiently to prevent reaction with the amino group[29].

34   35

Similarly, in the original synthesis of adenosine[4], condensation of a 4-amino-pyrimidine with an aldehydosugar necessitated the presence of a 2-methyl-thio group (36).

36

Because of the weakly basic character of 4-(6)-aminopyrimidines, their acyl derivatives are very labile. Thus N^6-acetylcytosine (37, R = H) gives, on heating with 80% acetic acid for 1 h, a mixture of cytosine and uracil[31]; the

5-ethoxycarbonyl derivative (37, $R=CO_2Et$) is even more labile: it loses its acyl group on heating with absolute ethanol[8].

37

2. General methods of synthesis

(a) Pyrimidines

Although other methods of synthesis have been devised for special purposes[32,33], the most useful and versatile method of synthesis is that in which a three-carbon compound is condensed with a urea or amidine (38).

38   39

The order of reactivity of the latter components is guanidine > thiourea, alkylthiourea > amidines > urea. 2-Hydroxy compounds are often made from the 2-mercapto derivatives obtained from thiourea, since urea seldom reacts satisfactorily. The condensations are usually base-catalysed and carried out by refluxing with sodium ethoxide in ethanol, as in the preparation of 4,6-diamino-2-mercaptopyridimine (39) from thiourea and malononitrile[34]. Some substituted cytosines (41, $R=O$) can however be made by the

40   41   42

reaction of urea itself with ethyl cyanoacetate and ethyl orthoformate in the presence of acetic anhydride which gives the open-chain compound (40, $R=O$), which is cyclised by alkali[35]. Thiourea[8] reacts similarly ($R=S$).

Guanidine[36] condenses with ethyl cyanoacetate to give 2,4-diamino-6-hydroxypyrimidine (42), an important intermediate in the synthesis of pteridines as well as of purines. An example of an acid-catalysed reaction[37] is that of thiourea with acetylacetone to give the dimethylpyrimidine (43).

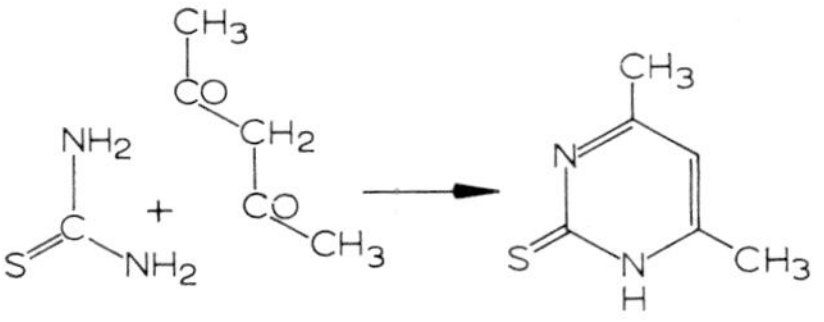

43    44

A number of pyrimidines may be prepared by a different route (44), particularly with formamide as the C_1-component, but the type of compound obtained is not of any direct interest in connection with nucleic acids. The method does, however, afford the first really practicable synthesis of pyrimidine (I) itself[38].

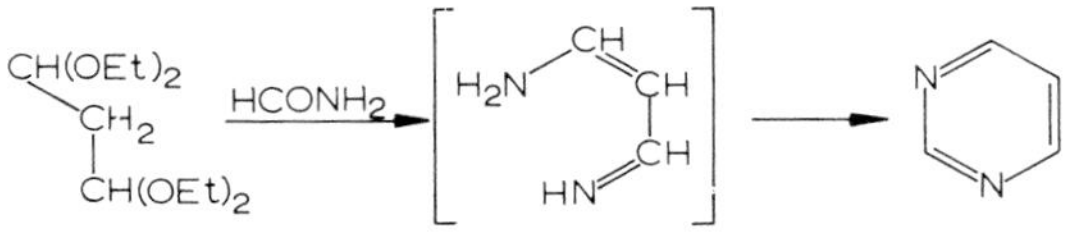

1

(b) Purines

The most useful synthesis of purines is that due to Traube[39]. Electrophilic substitution of a 4-aminopyrimidine (45) (nitrosation, nitration or azo-coupling) followed by reduction gives a 4,5-diaminopyrimidine (46) which, with a suitable source of C_1, cyclises to a purine (47).

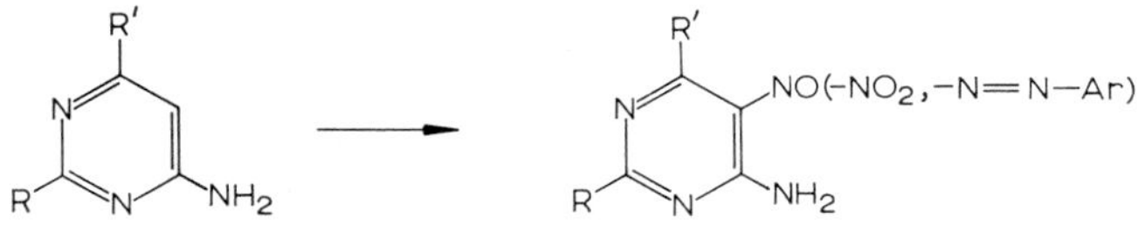

45

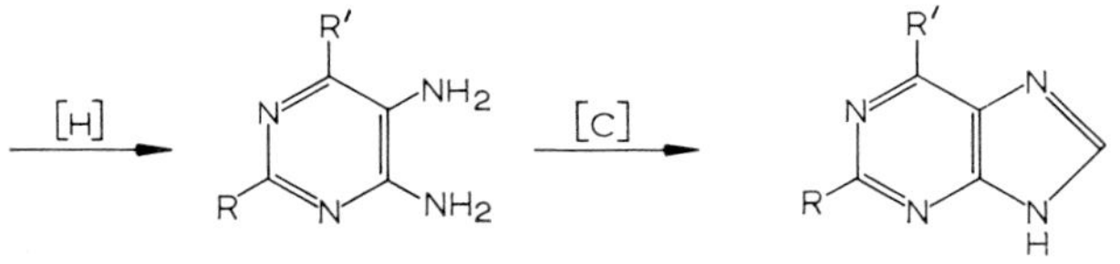

46   47

Traube reduced nitrosopyrimidines with ammonium sulphide; sodium hydro-sulphite[1] is often used (e.g. when $R = R' = NH_2$). Treatment of (46) with formic acid gives the 5-formyl derivative[34,39]. In some cases the cyclisation requires heating this derivative[40] or its salt to 150–300°, though with other derivatives, heating the pyrimidine with formic acid–sodium formate (for guanine, *vide infra*) or its sulphate with formic acid is sufficient.

Formamide has also been used, and Traube's synthesis of xanthine (47, $R = R' = OH$) has been simplified by nitrosating 4-aminouracil with sodium nitrite–formic acid in formamide, reducing with hydrosulphite and heating to effect ring-closure without isolation of intermediates, in 70% yield[38].

A method of ring-closure suitable for more sensitive compounds, such as 6-chloropurine, is to heat the diaminopyrimidine with ethyl orthoformate–acetic anhydride[41,42], or diethoxymethyl acetate[43]. Very weakly basic di-aminopyrimidines may be cyclised with a mixture of dimethylformamide and phosphorus oxychloride[44].

A quite different method of synthesizing purines has been developed[45], but without improving the yields obtained by Traube's method. Other methods have been reviewed[46].

3. Synthesis of the nucleic acid bases

(a) Uracil (5) (RNA)

Uracil was originally obtained from the acid hydrolysis of yeast nucleic acid[47] and first synthesized by E. Fischer[48]. It is best prepared, in a yield of 50–55% after recrystallisation, by heating a solution of malic acid and urea in fuming sulphuric acid[49,50].

(b) Thymine (49) (DNA)

Thymine was isolated from the acid hydrolysates of the nucleic acids from beef spleen and calf thymus[51,52]. Oxidation gave urea as one of the products[53], and the proposed structure was confirmed by synthesis[54]. In the best of numerous syntheses, methyl cyanoacetic acid is condensed with urea in the presence of acetic anhydride to methyl cyanoacetylurea (48), which on reduction with hydrogen in the presence of platinum black yields pure thymine (49) and ammonia[55].

48   49

(c) Cytosine (21) (RNA, DNA)

Cytosine was obtained from calf thymus nucleic acid[52] and the formation of uracil on deamination with nitrous acid led to the formulation of the correct structure[56], followed by synthesis[57]. However, no method for preparing cytosine in reasonable yield existed until quite recently[58]. Condensation of malondialdehyde acetal with hydroxylamine hydrochloride gives isoxazole (50), which is converted to β-ethoxyacrylonitrile (51) by treatment with diethyl sulphate and alkali.

50

51   21

The yield in the final condensation (43%) might be improved by using thiourea in place of urea, and then treating the product with chloroacetic acid.

(d) 5-Methylcytosine (54)

5-Methylcytosine is a minor component of DNA in various fish, insects and mammals, and an important component of wheat germ DNA[59,60]. It could not be found in bacterial nucleic acid[61], though T. B. Johnson had reported its isolation from tubercle bacilli[62] after synthesizing it many years earlier[63]. No satisfactory synthesis exists, and it is necessary to proceed from thymine[64]. Reaction with phosphorus pentasulphide in tetralin gives dithiothymine (52), which with ammonia yields 2-thio-5-methylcytosine (53), readily hydrolysed to 5-methylcytosine (54).

$$52 \qquad\qquad 53 \qquad\qquad 54$$

(e) 5-Hydroxymethylcytosine (57)

This base was obtained from the DNA of T-even bacteriophages of *Escherichia coli*[65], in which it occurs in place of cytosine. The base has not been found in any other source, including the host *E. coli*. It may readily be prepared as follows[1,66]:

$$55 \qquad\qquad 56$$

$$57$$

Ethoxymethylenecyanoacetic ester (55) can react in two ways, depending on whether the cyano or the ester group condenses, giving either (56) or the corresponding 6-hydroxy-5-cyanopyrimidine. With thiourea the two products are obtained in yields of 78 and 7% respectively[1,67], but if ethylisothiourea is used, the required 6-amino-5-ethoxycarbonyl compound is obtained in a maximum yield[68,69] of only 14%. Working on a moderately large scale[8], the overall yield of (57) is nearly 40%.

(f) Adenine (59) (RNA, DNA)

Adenine was discovered in acid hydrolysates of beef pancreas nucleic acid[18,70], and its structure proved by a partial synthesis by Fischer[71] (from uric acid). Of the numerous syntheses of adenine based on Traube's method, that of Todd[72] uses dithioformic acid in place of formic acid; the 5-thioformyl derivative (58) cyclises on boiling in water. The formamide method of cyclisation can also be used[38].

58   59

(g) Guanine (60) (RNA, DNA)

This purine was found in the faeces (guano) of birds, and later in nucleic acids[73], and its structure worked out by Fischer[71]. The original synthesis by Traube[39] has hardly been improved upon, though the final cyclisation has been carried out with formamide[74] and with ethylorthoformate–acetic anhydride[41].

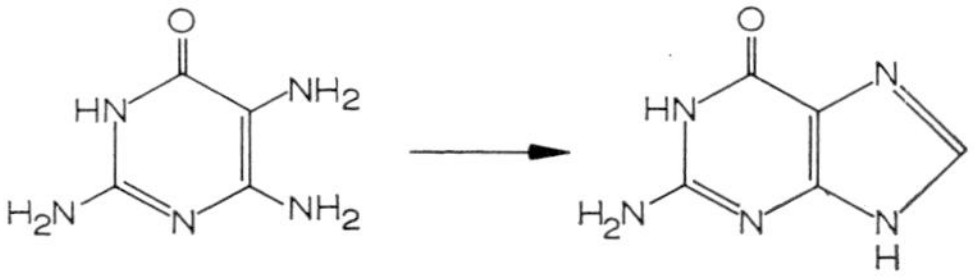

60

4. Synthesis of labelled bases and analogues

By using suitable derivatives of urea labelled with ^{14}C or ^{15}N it is obviously possible to synthesize both purines and pyrimidines labelled at C-2 or N-1 and N-3, and such syntheses will not be described unless unusual methods are used.

(a) $[2-^{14}C]4-(6)-Azauracil$

This widely studied analogue of uracil[75] is synthesized by converting $[^{14}C]$-urea to semicarbazide (61) by reaction with hydrazine hydrate; condensation with chloral hydrate is accompanied by simultaneous hydrolysis to give glyoxylic acid semicarbazone (62), which may be cyclised[76] to $[2-^{14}C]$-4-azauracil (63).

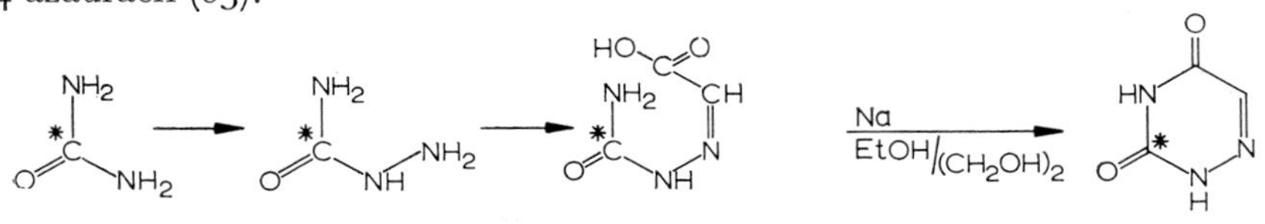

61   62   63

(b) [Me-^{14}C]Thymine

This is best prepared via the lithium intermediate (64), obtained by an exchange reaction from the bromo compound (22, see p. 162). Subsequent reaction with [^{14}C]-methyl iodide and hydrolysis gives [Me-^{14}C]thymine (65) in 40% yield[77].

22   64   65

(c) [1,3-^{15}N$_2$]Cytosine

This derivative (67) has been synthesized from labelled urea and the cyanoacetal (66), which is laborious to prepare and would not normally be used[78].

66   67

(d) [2,8-^{3}H$_2$]Adenine

This may be prepared by treating adenine with CH_3COO^3H in the presence of platinum oxide catalyst[79]. The simplicity of the method foreshadows the discovery that tritium labelling of organic compounds can be accomplished by exposure to tritium gas[80].

(e) [4,6-^{14}C$_{1/2}$]Adenine (68), [4-^{14}C]guanine (69), and [4-^{14}C]8-azaguanine (70)

This synthetic scheme[81], which illustrates many of the reactions previously discussed in this chapter, begins with sodium chloroacetate and labelled cyanide.

5. Action of ultraviolet light on nucleic acid bases

It was found that, on irradiation of dilute aqueous solutions with small doses of U.V. light, the U.V. absorption of uracil and cytosine rapidly decreased, whereas thymine, adenine and guanine were almost unaffected[82]. By heating or acidifying the solutions, the reaction was partially reversed, and in the case of uracil it has been rigorously shown that hydration of the 4,5-double bond to give (71) takes place. Cytosine also hydrates, but the structure of the product is not so clearly established (for a detailed review, see ref.[83]).

71

However, Beukers and Berends (they have ably reviewed their numerous papers[84]) found that the amount of uracil "irreversibly" converted, depended on the conditions: in the presence of oxygen and paramagnetic ions, the amount of "irreversible" conversion was reduced. Irradiation of thymine in frozen aqueous solution gives a dimer, with probable structure (72), which reverts to thymine after irradiation of the thawed solution. Uracil and uridine give mixtures of the water-addition product and dimer; a mixture of uracil and thymine gives three dimers, presumable U–U, U–T and T–T. Experiments with the dinucleotide GpU indicate that the uracil adds water, but no dimerisation takes place[85].

72

Irradiation of *Enterococcus Stei* cultures which had incorporated [2-^{14}C]-thymine led to the isolation of a labelled compound apparently identical[86] with the thymine dimer (72).

These experiments may explain the lethal and mutagenic effects of irradiation, but do not explain the phenomenon of photoreactivation (bacterial cultures become viable again after U.V.-irradiation if exposed to visible light) which has an action spectrum with a maximum[87] always above 300 mμ, whereas the action spectrum for the reversal of dimerisation of thymine is immeasurably small at 300 mμ, increasing as the wavelength decreases[88]. This has been confirmed by a study showing that the extent of dimerisation of thymine and thymine nucleotides varies with wavelength, the equilibrium[89] being on the side of the monomer at 235 mμ and on the side of the dimer at 285 mμ.

6. Base contents of the nucleic acids

(a) Minor components

(i) In DNA

5-Methylcytosine is present in small amounts in the DNA of higher animals and especially of plants (in wheat germ to the extent of 6%), but has not been found in the DNA of micro-organisms. As already mentioned, 5-hydroxymethylcytosine occurs uniquely in the T-even bacteriophages of *E. coli*, where it replaces *all* the cytosine.

A new base[90], 6-methylaminopurine, was found in *E. coli* DNA in 1955 and was subsequently shown to be a normal constituent of bacterial DNA, but not to occur in yeast, thymus etc.[91]. The amount of 6-methylaminopurine in different strains of *E. coli* was the same (1.7–1.8 mole% of adenine)[91], but varied as between different species. When a thymine-requiring mutant of *E. coli* (15 T⁻) is grown in the presence of thymine antagonists, the amount of 6-methylaminopurine found in the DNA increases, up to 15% of the adenine, and the proportion of thymine decreases. This seems to indicate that, in these circumstances, DNA of unusual structure is formed.

(ii) In RNA

6-Methylaminopurine has been reported to be present in RNA from a number of sources[92-94] but it was later shown that the 1-methyladenine[93] which is present (RNA of yeast, liver microsomes and s-RNA) is rearranged by alkali, used in the original isolation procedures, to give[95] the 6-methylamino compound (74), which is genuinely present[95a] only in the s-RNA from *E. coli*.

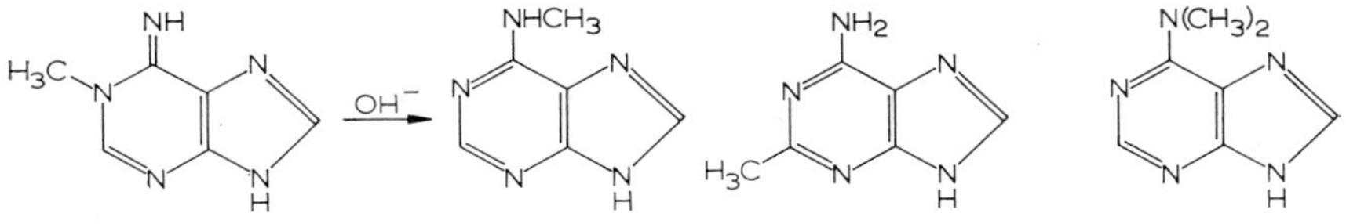

73   74   75   76

In addition, the following bases have been found to be present in small amounts: thymine, 2-methyladenine (75) and 6-dimethylaminopurine (76) (yeast[92]); the monomethylguanines (77 and 78) (yeast[96]) and together with the dimethyl compound (79) (several sources[97]); and 5-methylcytosine (*E. coli*[98]).

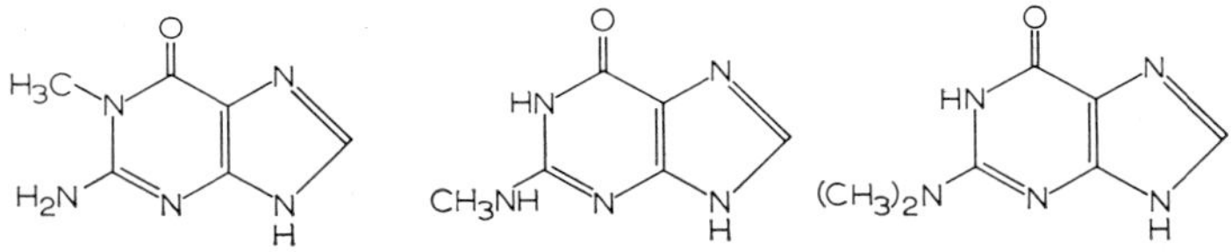

77   78   79

The finding of these small quantities of unusual bases (usually less than 0.5% of the uracil content) suggests that, since nucleic acids are not homogeneous, they may be concentrated in certain fractions in which they exercise a special function. This idea is supported by the finding that these bases are present in relatively much larger amounts in soluble RNA, as the figures of Table I indicate[93].

TABLE I

MINOR BASE COMPONENTS IN RAT LIVER

Component	Microsomal RNA*	s-RNA*
Pseudouridine	7.5	25
5-Methylcytosine	0.4	10
6-Methylaminopurine (1-Methyladenine)	0.5	8.1
6,6-Dimethylaminopurine	0.1	0.1
1-Methylguanine	0.1	3.3
2-Methylamino-6-hydroxypurine	0.1	2.3
2,2-Dimethylamino-6-hydroxypurine	0.1	3.0

* Moles% uracil.

(Pseudouridine is 5-ribosyluracil, see section B1a, p. 181).

Similarly, *E. coli* s-RNA contains relatively large amounts of pseudo-uridine and thymine (14 and 7 moles% U respectively[94]).

(b) Relative base composition of nucleic acids

(i) DNA

It was not until precise methods of analysis had been developed—in particular, chromatographic methods—that accurate, reproducible figures for the base contents (usually given as proportions in moles of base per 100 g atoms of phosphorus in hydrolysate, corrected to a 100% recovery) of nucleic acids became available. Not until 1949 was it clear that DNA from different sources showed significant differences in composition[99-102], as the figures for mammals in Table II indicate. However, it seems probable that the nucleic acids from different organs and tissues of the same host do not show significant differences[103].

Further results indicated that DNA was of three types: that in which adenine and thymine predominated (AT type, $(A+T)/(G+C)$ ratio > 1), a GC type ($(A+T)/(G+C)$ < 1) and an intermediate group in which the ratio is approximately one[103-105]. DNA from animal sources always appears to

TABLE II

BASE COMPOSITION OF DNA FROM DIFFERENT MAMMALS
(data from Chargaff[103])

Mammal	A	G	C	T	$(A + T)/(G + C)$
Ox	29.0	21.2	21.2	28.7	1.36
Pig	29.8	20.7	20.7	29.1	1.42
Man	30.4	19.9	19.9	30.1	1.53

TABLE III

BASE COMPOSITION OF DNA FROM VARIOUS MICRO-ORGANISMS
(data from Chargaff[103], and Belozersky and Spirin[106])

Species	A	G	C	T	$(A+T)/(G+C)$
Mycobacterium tuberculosis					
(Avian)	15.1	34.9	35.4	14.6	0.42
Aerobacter aerogenes	21.3	28.8	28.0	21.9	0.76
Escherichia coli (K-12)	26.0	24.9	25.2	23.9	1.00
Vaccinia virus	29.5	20.6	20.0	29.9	1.46
Yeast (*Saccharomyces cerevisiae*)	31.7	18.3	17.4	32.6	1.80
Clostridium perfringens					
(var. Fred)	36.9	14.0	12.8	36.3	2.70

TABLE IV

BASE RATIOS IN DNA
(from Chargaff[103])

No. of analyses of DNA	A/T	G/C	Purines/ Pyrimidines	6-Amino groups/ 6-Keto groups
101	1.009	1.001	1.000	1.008

be of the AT type, but in micro-organisms, in which the GC type and the intermediate group were found, further work has revealed an almost continuous spectrum of composition[106]. A few examples are given in Table III.

On the basis of the early analytical results, certain regularities were noted[101] which all later results have confirmed. These are that in DNA (*1*) the molar ratio of adenine to thymine, and (*2*) of guanine to cytosine, is equal to 1. It follows from this that the ratio of (*3*) purines to pyrimidines, and (*4*) 6-amino to 6-keto groups, is also 1. In Table IV are given the mean of 101 separate such ratios, calculated independently from different analyses[103]. (In analyses of higher animals and plants, 5-methylcytosine is included with the cytosine for purposes of calculation.)

One striking feature of the double helical structure[107] proposed for DNA is that an explanation is given for these results.

(*ii*) RNA

The earlier analytical work[108] on the base composition of RNA made it virtually impossible to draw any conclusions; different results were obtained in different laboratories; whether RNA was species-specific or not, was not at all clear; variation between organs of the same animal appeared possible; the base ratios did not obviously show any of the regularities found in DNA.

TABLE V

BASE COMPOSITION OF PLANT VIRUS RNA

(figures related to A = 10; from Magasanik[108])

Virus	Strain	A	G	C	U	Purines/Pyrimidines
TMV	TMV	10	8.5	6.2	8.8	1.24
TMV	M	10	8.9	6.5	8.8	1.23
TMV	J14D1	10	8.4	6.2	8.9	1.22
TMV	GA	10	8.9	6.6	8.9	1.22
TMV	YA	10	8.6	6.2	8.9	1.23
TMV	HR	10	8.8	6.2	9.2	1.22
Cucumber	CV3	10	9.9	7.1	11.9	1.05
Cucumber	CV4	10	10	7.5	11.5	1.05
Tomato bushy stunt	BS	10	10	7.4	8.9	1.23
Turnip yellow mosaic	TY	10	7.6	16.8	9.8	0.66

However, analyses of plant virus RNA preparations indicated that different viruses have a completely different RNA composition[109-112] (see Table V). A particularly important finding was that different strains of tobacco mosaic virus have the same composition. This clearly showed that in plant viruses RNA is species-specific.

Further work on RNA composition indicated the necessity of doing analyses directly on cells, rather than on purified isolated material, in order to avoid degradation by chemical agents and, in particular, by ribonuclease. Results of such analyses[113-116] gave consistent results, and showed that the ratio of 6-amino to 6-keto groups is equal to 1; but this is the only regularity found.

There had already been indications from the earlier work[108] that the composition of RNA from the particulate and supernatant fractions of cells differed; a striking confirmation of this kind of variation was the finding, previously mentioned (p. 175), that s-RNA contains much higher proportions of the rare bases than does microsomal RNA.

(c) Incorporation of base analogues

A number of synthetic analogues of nucleic acid purines and pyrimidines are incorporated into RNA and/or DNA in vivo. This is mainly of interest in connection with the biological effects, which include inhibition of growth, mutagenesis, death, and temporary anti-cancer action. Good evidence of incorporation exists for 8-azaguanine, 6-thioguanine, 4-(6)-azauracil, 5-fluorouracil[117,118], 5-chloro-, -bromo- and -iodouracil, 4-(6)-azathymine, 2-

thiouracil[118] and 2-aminopurine[119,120]. Purine and 2,6-diaminopurine are converted to some extent into adenine and guanine. The evidence about the incorporation of 6-mercaptopurine is not clear.

It was thought at one time that the biological activity of these analogues was necessarily related to their incorporation, particularly into DNA; this may be true to some extent of mutagenesis, but not of the other biological effects. Thus it may be mentioned that incorporation is essentially irrelevant to the activity of 6-mercaptopurine (inhibition of the inter-conversion of purines at the ribotide lével), 4-(6)-azauracil (its ribotide inhibits the decarboxylation of orotidylic acid) and 5-fluorouracil (whose deoxyriboside inhibits the synthesis of thymidine[117,118]) and that it is possible to find analogues with biological activity which proves to be unrelated to nucleic acid metabolism; an example is methioprim, the 2-methylthio analogue of hydroxymethylcytosine[1,66] which is an antagonist of pyridoxine and of the pyrimidine portion of thiamine[121].

B. CHEMICAL CONSTITUTION OF THE NUCLEOSIDES

1. Ribonucleosides

(a) Structure

(i) The sugar

Hydrolysis of the purine nucleosides liberated a new sugar (80) which was obtained crystalline[122-124], and oxidised to D-ribonic acid (81) and optically inactive trihydroxyglutaric acid (82). The identity of D-ribose (80) was confirmed by synthesis[125].

Pyrimidine nucleosides are stable to dilute acids; strong acids liberate the bases but convert the sugar to furfural. The best procedure for liberating the sugar is reduction of the 4,5-double bond, which labilises the glycosidic linkage (see p. 163), followed by dilute acid hydrolysis. In this way, uridine (83) was converted to dihydrouridine (84) and so to dihydrouracil (85) and D-ribose[126].

The methods now used for accomplishing the reduction of the 4,5-double bond are catalytic hydrogenation with a rhodium catalyst[127], or reduction with sodium in ethanol[128] or sodium amalgam and water[129]. The latter method permits quantitative estimation of the sugar in pyrimidine nucleosides and nucleotides.

(ii) Position of the glycosidic linkage

The readiness with which purine nucleosides are hydrolysed suggests that they are N- and not C-glycosides. The primary amino groups in adenosine and guanosine cannot be involved, since deamination yields inosine (86) and xanthosine (87, R = H) respectively, in which the sugar is unchanged. Moreover, methylation of xanthosine gives theophylline riboside (87, R = CH$_3$)[130], showing that the sugar can only be attached to N-7 or N-9. The similarity of the U.V. spectra of adenosine and 9-methyladenine[131] and of guanosine and 9-methylguanine[132] was strong evidence that the natural purine ribosides

were 9-glycosides, and this was eventually confirmed by synthesis (see p. 182).

In the pyrimidine nucleosides, position 6 cannot be involved since cytidine (88) can be deaminated to uridine (83). Comparison of the U.V. spectra of uracil and uridine shows a considerable difference at alkaline pH values, indicating that either the N-1 or N-3 hydrogen must be replaced by the sugar in the nucleoside[133]. Methylation of uridine gives a mono-N-methyluridine (89) (whereas methylation of uracil gives a dimethyl derivative, 1,3-dimethyl-uracil), which hydrolyses to 1-methyluracil (90), showing that uridine (and hence also cytidine) are 3-glycosides[134].

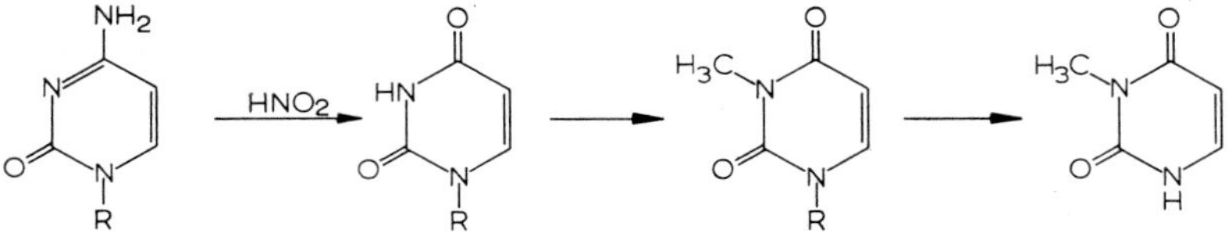

(iii) The ring structure of the sugar

A good deal of work has been done to establish the structure of nucleosides as ribofuranosides[135]. Conclusive evidence comes from the action of periodate on these compounds[136]; one mole of periodate is consumed per mole of nucleoside, giving a dialdehyde but no formic acid:

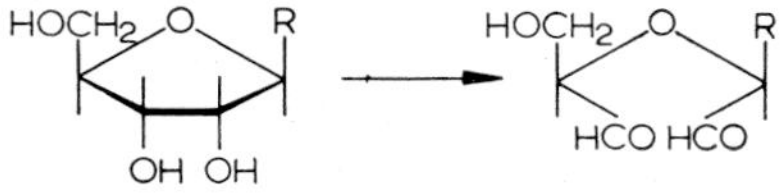

(iv) Configuration of the glycosidic linkage

The β-configuration of the glycosidic linkage in adenosine and in cytidine was shown by the conversion of the 5'-tosyl-2,3-isopropylidene derivatives of these nucleosides to the cyclonucleosides (91) and (92) respectively[137], with elimination of tosylate ion. Had the configuration at C-1 of the sugar

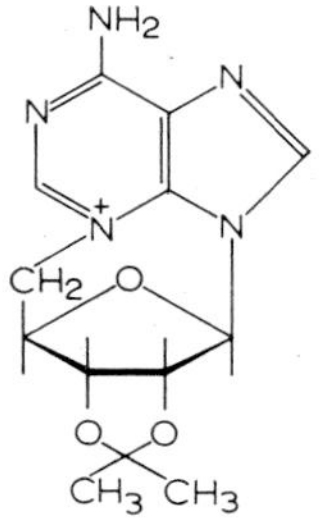

been α, the base and the $-CH_2OTs$ group would have been on opposite sides of the sugar ring, and no intramolecular cyclisation could have occurred.

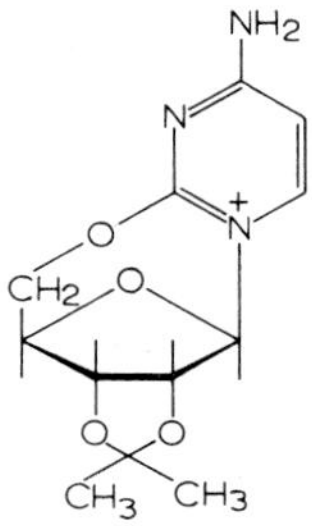

An X-ray examination of crystalline cytidine confirmed its structure as the 3-β-D-ribofuranoside of cytosine, with the plane of the pyrimidine ring at right angles to that of the sugar[138].

(v) The structure of pseudouridine

A new nucleoside has been isolated from ribonucleic acid and its structure was determined in 1959. This compound, called pseudouridine (93) is an isomer of uridine. The U.V. spectra at pH 7 and 12 closely resemble those of 5-hydroxymethyluracil[139,140]; the characteristic shift of the maximum in alkali indicates that the ribose cannot be attached to nitrogen or, indeed, to oxygen, since O-alkyl compounds have different spectra. That the sugar was attached at C-5 and not C-4 was shown by the nuclear magnetic resonance spectrum and by the degradative sequence shown, which led to the isolation[140] of 5-hydroxymethyluracil (94).

As it did not prove possible to liberate ribose from pseudouridine, some doubt about its structure remained; also, there was at that time no evidence relating to the glycosidic configuration. Since then, both syntheses (see p. 185) and conversion of pseudouridine to $O^6,5'$-cyclopseudouridine[141] have shown that it is the 5-β-D-ribofuranosyl derivative of uracil as shown.

(b) Synthesis

Of historical importance is an unambiguous method of synthesizing purine 9-glycosides, by which 9-β-D-mannopyranosyladenine (99) was synthesized as shown[142]. Condensation of the diaminopyrimidine (95) with glucose gave (96), which was converted to the purine (98) by the modification of the Traube procedure, using the thioformyl derivative (97). Final desulphurisation with Raney nickel gave the adenine-9-glycoside (99).

References p. 204

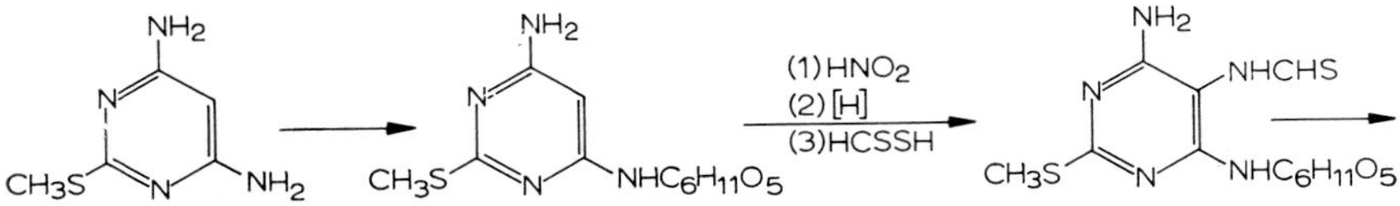

95 96 97

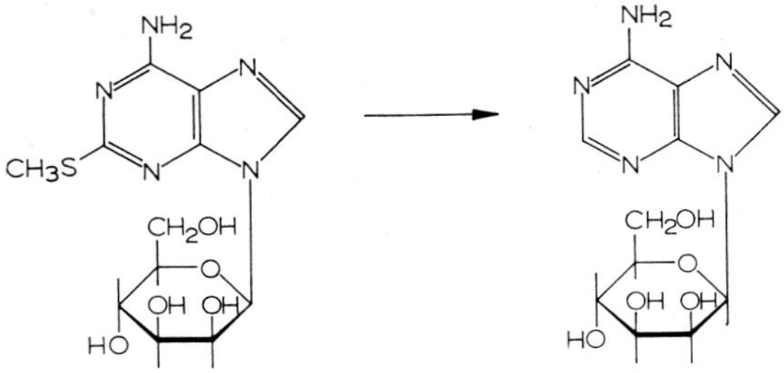

98 99

A modification of this method, using 5-*O*-benzyl-2,3,4-tri-*O*-acetyl-D-ribose (see p. 164) was used in a synthesis of adenosine[4]. A benzyl group in position 5 ensures the formation of a furanoside ring; since acyl groups can migrate under alkaline conditions, mixtures of furanose and pyranose derivatives may be formed if one simply uses a 5-*O*-acetyl- or -benzoylriboside.

The importance of the mannoside was due to the fact that this glycoside (99), natural adenosine (100) and the long-known D-glucosyladenine (101) (ref. 143) all gave the same dialdehyde on oxidation with periodate[142,144]:

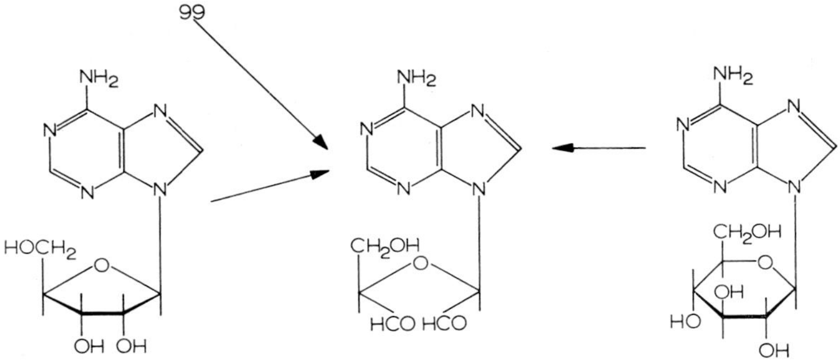

100 102 101

This showed not only that adenosine and the glucoside were 9-substituted adenines, but since the glucoside had been synthesized by the reaction of the silver salt of a purine with an α-bromoacetosugar (Fischer–Helferich method), that they probably had the β-configuration, since an inversion was to be expected in this reaction. The modification of this type of synthesis in which chloromercuri derivatives are used has become the best general method of preparing purine nucleosides. An example is the following synthesis[145] of guanosine (103), which used triacetylribofuranosyl chloride:

103

Attempts to apply the Fischer–Helferich method[143] to pyrimidines were unsuccessful. In these experiments, carried out on silver salts of compounds containing the tautomeric group

$$-NH-CO- \rightleftharpoons -N=C\diagdown^{OH}$$

O-glycosides were produced[146,147].

Pyrimidine N-glycosides are obtained by the action of glycosyl halides on 2,6-dialkoxypyrimidines. This method was developed by analogy with the reaction of such compounds with alkyl iodides, when O→N-alkyl rearrangement occurs to give (25) (see p. 162). Treatment of this product with ethanolic hydrogen chloride gave 3-methyluracil (104), whereas alcoholic ammonia gave the corresponding cytosine (105).

In a similar manner, using acetobromoglucose and 2,6-diethoxypyrimidine (106), 3-glucosyluracil and 3-glucosylcytosine were prepared[148,149], and the

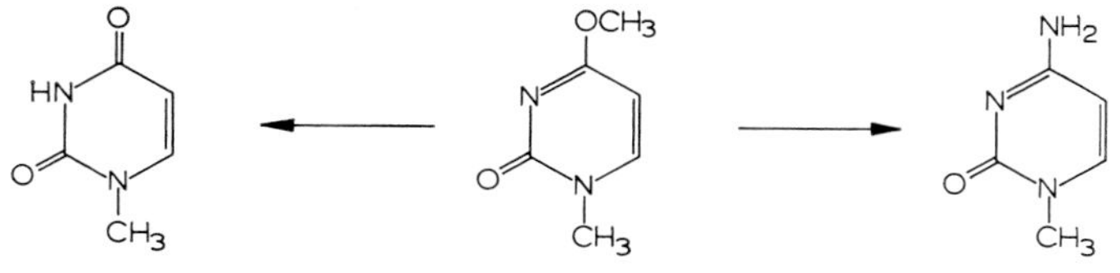

104   25   105

natural nucleosides uridine and cytidine were synthesized by using triacetyl-ribofuranosyl bromide[150].

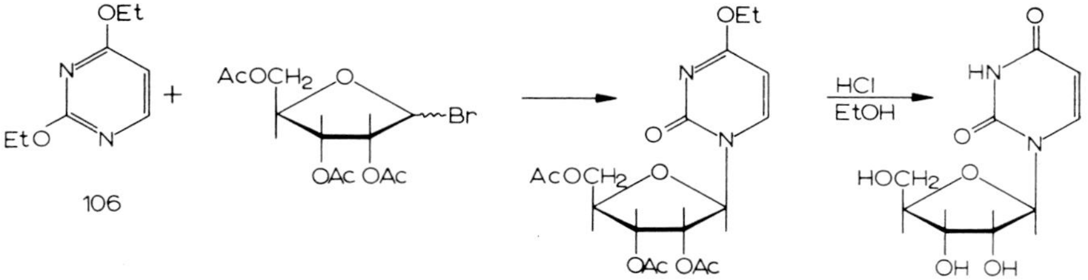

106

The Fischer–Helferich procedure with pyrimidines has been reinvestigated, and it was found that when mercuri derivatives were employed, N-glycosides were obtained[151]. Thus, dithyminylmercury and tri-O-benzoyl-D-ribofuranosyl chloride yielded, after deacetylation, 5-methyluridine[152]. The β-configuration in the product was established by conversion of the product to spongothymidine (see p. 198). 3-β-D-Xylofuranosylthymine was prepared similarly, and cytidine (108) has been synthesized from N-acetylcytosine-mercury[153], and also by employing the phosphorus pentasulphide reaction (see p. 161) on tribenzoyluridine (107) (ref. 154).

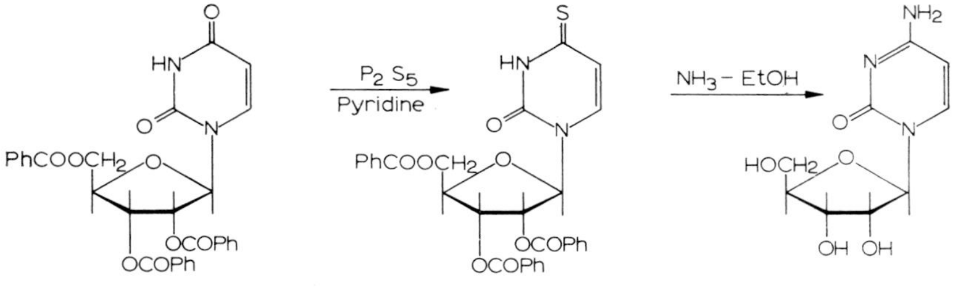

107   108

The mercuri procedure for the synthesis of pyrimidine nucleosides is an un-doubted and important improvement on the Hilbert–Johnson procedure. It is, however, necessary to investigate the possible mercury derivatives of each base and to see which is suitable. It has not proved possible to synthesize uridine from a mercury-uracily. The mechanism of the reaction has been discussed in a review of nucleoside synthesis[151]; it probably involves O→N-glycosyl rearrangement in many cases, catalysed by mercuric salts.

A different approach to nucleoside synthesis[155] involves the use of a ribofuranosylamine (109) which was condensed with β-ethoxy-N-ethoxy-carbonylacrylamide (110); debenzoylation of the product gave uridine[156].

The synthesis of pseudouridine constitutes a special problem. It had been suggested that pyrimidine C-glycosides could be made by a reaction between a pyrimidine-lithium compound and a glycosyl halide[77]. Pseudouridine (111) has been synthesized[157], albeit in small yield, by condensing 5-lithio-2,6-dimethoxypyrimidine with tribenzoylribofuranosyl bromide. Some reorganisation of the lactol ring system resulted from the use of strong acid to remove protecting groups, so that other nucleosides isomeric with (111) were also obtained. These have already been studied[140] and are formed by acid-catalysed $\beta \rightarrow \alpha$ and furanose $\rightarrow$ pyranose changes. An alternative synthesis involves the condensation of the above-mentioned lithiopyrimidine and dibenzylidene *aldehydo*ribose followed by acid-catalysed removal of protecting groups and ring-closure[158].

2. Deoxyribonucleosides

(a) Structure

Evidence for the structure of ribonucleosides having been presented in some detail, the corresponding evidence for the deoxyribonucleosides can be indicated more briefly. Purine deoxyribosides are readily hydrolysed by dilute acids, liberating 2-deoxy-D-ribose, which was obtained crystalline from deoxyguanosine[159,160] and identified by comparison with synthetic 2-deoxy-L-ribose[161].

The pyrimidine deoxyribosides, thymidine and deoxycytidine, have been reduced with sodium in ethanol, and the dihydro compounds yielded 2-deoxy-D-ribose on hydrolysis[128,162]. It had been found previously that the pyrimidine deoxyribonucleosides do not react with sodium periodate, and the purine compounds only react very slowly (probably due to glycolytic cleavage), indicating a deoxypentofuranoside structure[163].

Spectroscopic evidence[132,164] suggested that the purine compounds were 9-glycosides. Treatment of 3′-O-acetyl-2′-deoxyadenosine with p-toluene-sulphonyl chloride gave a covalent product (112) which, on heating in acetone, rearranged[165] to give the cyclonucleoside (113), analogous to the adenosine derivative (p. 180). This is consistent only with a 9-β-glycosidic structure.

112   113

Confirmation of the pyrimidine structure is provided by the analogous reaction of 3′-O-acetyl-2′-deoxycytidine, which also gives a cyclonucleoside salt[165]. Treatment of 3′-iodo-3′-deoxythymidine (114) with silver acetate in acetonitrile containing a little base gave a cyclothymidine (115), which on acid hydrolysis gave thymine and 2-deoxy-D-xylose, showing that thymidine is 3-β-2'-deoxy-D-ribofuranosylthymine[166]. X-ray analysis of 5'-bromo-5'-deoxythymidine also confirmed the 3-β-glycosidic structure[167].

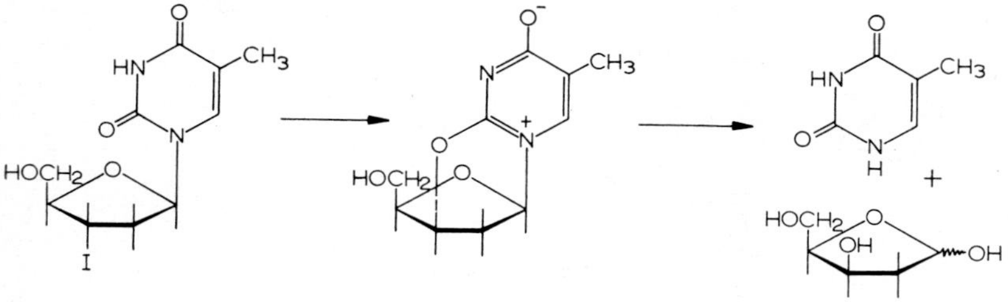

114   115

Following the isolation of 5-hydroxymethylcytosine (HMC)[65,168] and of its deoxyriboside[169] from the T-even bacteriophages of *E. coli*, it was found that the DNA of these phages also contained glucose, apparently attached to the hydroxymethyl group of HMC[170-173]. Investigations by Lehman[174,175] with an enzyme from *E. coli* which can quantitatively degrade the DNA of these bacteriophages to 5'-mononucleotides showed that three distinct HMC nucleotides could be obtained, containing 0, 1 or 2 moles of glucose per mole of nucleotide. The proportions vary in the different phages, as shown in Table VI.

TABLE VI

PROPORTIONS OF GLUCOSE IN HMC NUCLEOTIDES IN DNA OF
T-EVEN BACTERIOPHAGES

(data from ref. 175)

Phage	Diglucosylated	Monoglucosylated % of total nucleotide	Non-glucosylated
T2	6	69	25
T4	< 0.5	100	< 0.5
T6	72	3	25

By studying the susceptibility of the different compounds to α- and β-glucosidases, it was found that in T2 and T6 glucose is bound to the hydroxymethyl group of HMC in an α-glycosidic linkage. In the diglucosylated form, the second glucose is bound to the first by a β-linkage. In T4, in which all the HMC is monoglucosylated, 70% has the glucose attached in the α-configuration and 30% has a β-linkage[175]. Structure (115a) has been proposed for the monoglucosyl nucleoside from T2. The sugar in T6 has been identified as gentiobiose; hence the nucleoside[176] has structure (115b).

References p. 204

115a   115b

(b) Synthesis

In the earliest attempts to synthesize a deoxynucleoside[177], silver theophylline was condensed with crude 3',4'-di-O-acetyl-2'-deoxyribopyranosyl chloride and a small yield of a mixture of α- and β-glycosides was obtained. The glycosyl halides used were obviously impure and unstable, and in view of the poor yield and the mixture of stereoisomers obtained, no further work along these lines was done.

Treatment of anhydrosugars with thiomethoxide followed by Raney nickel had been developed as a method of synthesis for deoxysugars; for example, when the epoxide ring in a 2,3-anhydro derivative of D-allose was opened with thiomethoxide, the desulphurisation product was 2-deoxy-D-allose[178]. However, a similar reaction with 2,3-anhydro-β-methyl-L-ribopyranoside gave 3-deoxy-β-methyl-L-xylopyranoside containing at most only traces of a 2-deoxypentoside[179]. A similar change in the ratio of isomers obtained respectively from hexoses and pentoses was observed in the reaction of epoxides with hydrobromic acid: a 2,3-anhydroalloside gave a mixture of 2-bromoaltrose and 3-bromoglucose derivatives[180], mainly the former, whereas 2,3-anhydro-β-methyl-D-ribopyranoside gave the corresponding 3- and 2-bromo-substituted products in a ratio[181] of 9:1. These results were not hopeful as regards a possible synthesis of 2-deoxyribosides, but they were carried out with pyranosides, and a corresponding investigation with ribofuranosides was obviously worthwhile.

116   117   118

Treatment of 2',3'-anhydro-7-α-D-lyxofuranosyltheophylline (116) with thioethoxide gave as the major product (∼ 90%) the 3'-deoxy-3'-ethylthioarabofuranoside (117) and less than 1% of the 2'-deoxy-2'-ethylthioxylofuranoside (118), and similar yields of 3'- and 2'-derivatives were obtained from a 2,3-anhydroribofuranoside[182]. Experiments in which the anhydrocompounds were treated with lithium aluminium hydride were also unpromising.

A direct synthesis of 2'-deoxyribonucleoside from 2-deoxy-D-ribose appeared unattractive for several reasons: (1) 2-deoxy-D-ribose was itself difficult to prepare; (2) it was to be expected that a compound such as 2,5-di-O-acetyl-2-deoxyribofuranosyl chloride would be unstable and easily dehydrohalogenated, as indeed proved to be the case in early unsuccessful experiments with this derivative[183]; and (3) such a synthesis would not be stereospecific—the formation of both α- and β-derivatives would occur (see section B3, p. 193.) Consequently a good deal of work was devoted to the conversion of suitable derivatives of ribonucleosides to 2'-deoxyribonucleosides.

The reactions of 2'-O-tosyladenosine with lithium aluminium hydride, and with thiocyanate followed by Raney nickel, were difficult to interpret and unpromising[184]. The reaction of the same nucleoside derivative with excess sodium borohydride in ethanol, followed by acetylation of the product, led to the isolation of 6-acetamidopurine[8]; adenosine and 2'-deoxyadenosine were unaffected by treatment with borohydride. Similar reactions with O,2'-cyclouridine and 2'-O-tosyluridine led to hydrolysis with formation of spongouridine[8].

Other experiments also concentrated on the use of secondary sulphonyl esters. These compounds used to have a reputation for unreactivity which was the basis of Oldham and Rutherford's rule[185] that isolated sugar secondary sulphonyloxy groups would not react with sodium iodide in acetone at 100°. However, in the very first experiment in which the 2'-O-tosyluridine (119, R=H) was allowed to react with sodium iodide in acetonylacetone at 100°, a high yield of a crystalline deoxyiodo derivative (120, R=H) was obtained, which on reduction[186] gave 2'-deoxyuridine (121, R=H). In a similar manner, the corresponding derivative of thymine (119, R=CH$_3$) was converted[187] to thymidine (121, R=CH$_3$).

Normally, one would expect the iodo derivative to have been formed by a single S$_{N}$2 reaction, and consequently to have the arabo configuration, but elucidation of the mechanism of the reaction[188] showed it to have the ribo configuration as shown (120). Treatment of the tosyl compound (119, R=H) with sodium azide in acetonitrile or with sodium acetate in acetonylacetone gave the O,2'-cyclouridine (122, R=H), which with sodium iodide in acetic acid yielded the *same* iodo derivative as had previously been obtained from the direct reaction of (119) (the mechanism of this reaction with iodide ion in the presence of acid is strictly analogous to the dealkylation of alkoxypyrimidines under the same conditions[15]). Reaction of the iodo compound with azide ion reforms the cyclonucleoside. The only reasonable explanation is that the reaction of (119) with iodide must have involved (122) as an intermediate, yielding a product (120) of the ribo configuration; cyclonucleoside formation also explains the readiness with which the whole reaction proceeds.

Work had begun earlier on the action of thioethoxide on $O^2,2'$-cylouridine (123), the product of which could be desulphurised to a new deoxynucleoside. Reduction and acid hydrolysis yielded 3-deoxyribose, showing that the

nucleoside was 3'-deoxyuridine (126). The authors suggested[189] that, under the alkaline conditions of the reaction, the anion (124) is formed and yields

the anhydroriboside (125) which would be expected to react predominantly at the 3'-position with thioethoxide (see p. 188).

126

An alternative synthesis of thymidine has been described; 5-methyl-2-thiouridine (128), which may be prepared from the $O,5'$-cyclouridine (127) as shown, should give a thiocyclonucleoside (130) and after hydrolysis (131) and desulphurisation, thymidine (132).

127   128   129

130   131   132

The synthesis was carried out, using a trityl protecting group (129, 130, R = CPh₃) and a small yield of thymidine obtained[190].

Although the reactivity of 2'-O-tosyluridine derivatives is obviously due to cyclonucleoside formation, other secondary sulphonyloxy groups might undergo nucleophilic displacement if appropriate conditions could be found. As 2'-O-tosyladenosine did not react with sodium iodide below temperatures at which decomposition occurred[191], an intermediate more susceptible to nucleophilic displacement was sought. Reaction of p-nitrobenzenesulphonyl chloride with 5′-O-acetyladenosine gave, after deacetylation, two isomeric mono-p-nitrobenzene-sulphonyladenosines. One of these reacted with sodium iodide to yield a crystalline deoxyiodo derivative which was reduced in

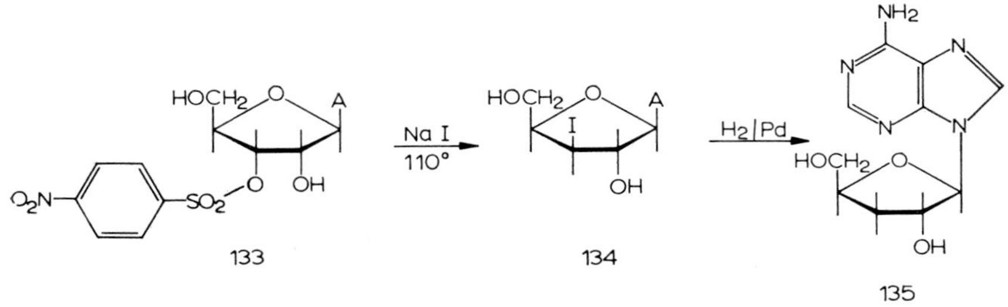

133   134   135

quantitative yield to a new deoxynucleoside, 3′-deoxyadenosine (135), and the reaction sequence must be as shown[191]. The 2′-isomer of (133) did not react with sodium iodide or with lithium bromide at temperatures below which decomposition supervenes; this may be due to the steric inaccessibility of the 2′-carbon atom in such compounds.

An alternative preparation of 3′-deoxyadenosine has been reported[192], and the same group carried out an ingenious synthesis of the 2′-isomer[193]. The key steps are probably as shown:

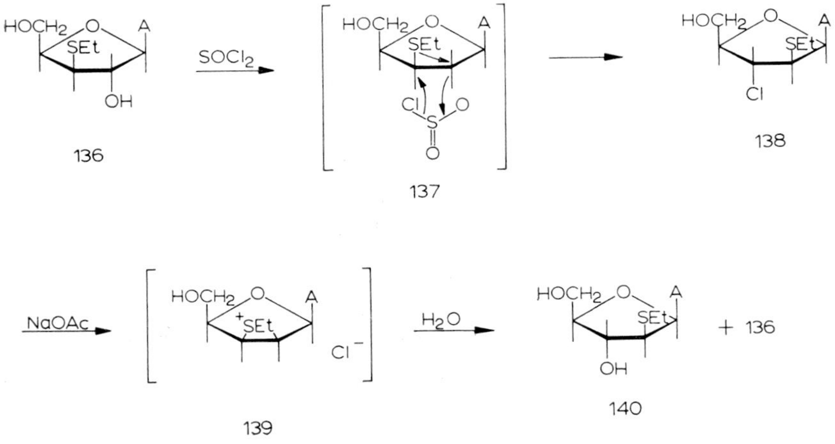

136   137   138

139   140

Compounds (140) and (136) were obtained in a ratio of 6:1 and separated by selective extraction; treatment of (140) with Raney nickel gave 2′-deoxy-adenosine in an overall yield of 0.5% from a xylose derivative which itself is made in five steps from D-xylose.

The development of a practicable method for preparing 2-deoxy-D-ribose[194] led to syntheses using deoxyribofuranosyl halides. Reaction of chloromercuri-6-benzamidopurine with crude 3,5-di-*p*-nitrobenzoyl-2'-deoxyribofuranosyl chloride (later obtained crystalline[195]) in dimethyl sulphoxide gave, after deacetylation and chromatography on cellulose, 10% 2'-deoxyadenosine and 19% of the α-anomer[196]. It is curious that in a slightly different synthesis[197] in which the silver salt of 2,8-dichloroadenine was condensed with 3,5-di-*O*-acetyldeoxyribofuranosyl chloride, only the natural β-anomer of 2'-deoxyadenosine was isolated. By appropriate manipulation of the purine substituents, the latter method was also used to synthesize 2'-deoxyguanosine and 2'-deoxyinosine.

A mixture of pyrimidine α- and β-2'-deoxynucleosides was obtained by the mercuri method using crystalline 3,5-di-*O*-*p*-chloro- (or *p*-methyl)-benzoyl-2-deoxyribofuranosyl chlorides[198-200]. The ratios of the isomers (β:α) obtained were: thymidine (10:1), 2'-deoxycytidine (3:2), and the analogue 5-fluoro-2'-deoxyuridine (3:2). The synthesis of relatively stable, crystalline deoxyribofuranosyl halides represents a discovery of great importance, since it permits the direct synthesis of many purine and pyrimidine deoxyribonucleosides by the versatile mercuri procedure.

The thiation–amination procedure for converting uracil into cytosine derivatives (see p. 184) has been used to prepare 5-methyl-2'-deoxycytidine from thymidine[201]. No synthesis has yet been reported of 5-hydroxymethyl-2'-deoxycytidine or of its glucosides.

Schramm *et al.*[202-204] have described the use of ethyl polymetaphosphate in effecting the direct condensation of sugars and bases.

3. Stereochemistry of nucleoside synthesis

It was suggested by Baker[205,206] that condensation of a heavy metal salt of a purine with an acylated glycosyl halide will form a nucleoside with a C-1—C-2 *trans*-configuration in the sugar, regardless of the original configuration at C-1—C-2. If the halosugar has the 1,2-*cis*-configuration, the purine base will enter by a single S_N2 reaction with inversion at C-1, giving a nucleoside with the 1,2-*trans*-configuration, which may be α or β (arabinose gives an α-nucleoside, ribose a β-nucleoside) (see formulae on p. 193).

Sugars with a 1,2-*trans*-configuration undergo two S$_N$2 reactions, the first of which is intramolecular, with participation of the acyloxy group:

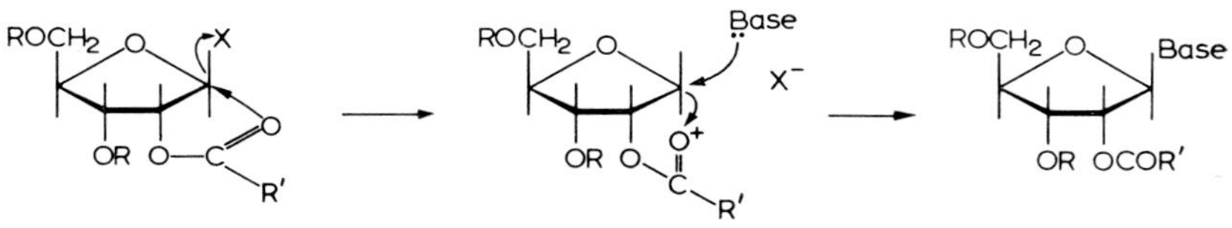

According to this argument, formation of ribosides of the β-configuration from ribose derivatives depends on the neighbouring group effect of the acyloxy group, and in the absence of this (as in 2-deoxyribose) a mixture of products is to be expected. Numerous experiments confirm this view, which must be extended to include both the Hilbert–Johnson synthesis and the mercury salt procedure for pyrimidine nucleosides.

The successful synthesis of the natural ribonucleosides from acylated ribose derivatives all yielded exclusively the β-compounds (see p. 183). On the other hand, mixtures were obtained in the synthesis of theophylline-2′-deoxyribopyranosides from a deoxyribopyranosyl halide (p. 188) and in the synthesis of 2′-deoxynucleosides from 2′-deoxyribose compounds. Crystalline 2,5-di-*O*-benzoyl-3-phthalimido-3-deoxy-β-D-ribofuranosyl chloride, *known to have the C-1—C-2 trans-configuration*, reacts with purine derivatives to give β-nucleosides (C-1—C-2 *trans*)[207,208]. 2,3,5-Tri-*O*-benzoyl-β-D-ribofuranosyl bromide (141) reacts with triethylammonium phosphate to give the pure β-phosphate[209], whereas the halide with a cyclic carbonate protecting group

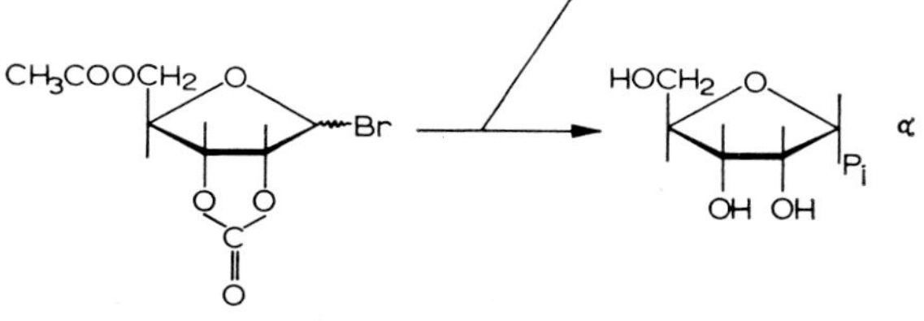

141

142

(142) (which cannot participate) gives a mixture[210] (see formulae on p. 194). Similarly, condensation of 5-O-benzoyl-D-ribofuranosyl bromide-2,3-cyclic carbonate with chloromercuri-6-benzamidopurine yielded, after removal of protecting groups, both natural adenosine and its α-anomer[211].

4. Synthesis of nucleoside analogues and labelled compounds

Nucleoside analogues which have biological activity have proved to be those in which the base has been altered, and such compounds are usually made by orthodox routes that do not call for comment. An exception is 4-(6)-aza-uridine (143), the nucleoside of 4-(6)-azauracil[76]. Synthesis by the mercuri procedure gave a 14% yield of (143), the major product being an isomer presumed to be the 1-riboside[212]. This is apparently due to the fact that in 4-(6)-azauracil it is the hydrogen attached to N-1 which is most acidic. A logical and unambiguous synthesis using a derivative blocked at N-1 has been devised[213], giving 4-(6)-azauridine in an overall yield of 25%, but as it involves six steps in place of two, it is of doubtful practical advantage.

Many analogues containing other sugars have been synthesized, but as they are not biologically active, only one example will be given here.

References p. 204

The synthesis of the ribo- and xylo-furanosides of thymine by Fox and co-workers has already been mentioned (see p. 184) and the same workers have synthesized the arabinoside (see p. 198). Obviously a lyxofuranosyl halide would give an α-nucleoside, and so the lyxoside (146) was prepared from the xyloside (144) via a cyclonucleoside intermediate (145) as shown[214]. Descriptions of the numerous syntheses of nucleoside analogues, mainly by Fox and by B. R. Baker and their respective co-workers, will be found in reviews[215,216].

Labelled nucleosides are usually prepared from labelled bases by standard methods. By an extension of the method developed for [Me-^{14}C]methyl-thymine (see p. 171), 5-bromodeoxyuridine (147) (and hence deoxyuridine) may be converted to thymidine, permitting specific labelling of the methyl group[69].

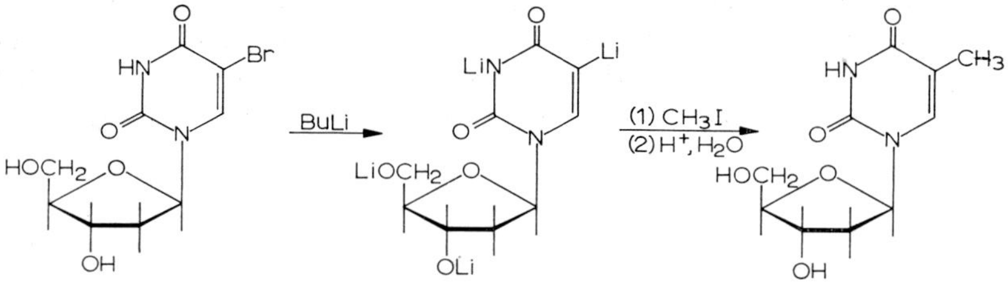

147

5. The hydrolysis of nucleosides

It was pointed out by Kenner[217] that trimethylammonium glycoside (148) is stable to acid, whereas dimethylamine glucoside (149) is very labile, and nucleosides are intermediate. How is this to be explained? Kenner rejected a mechanism of hydrolysis in which the proton is attached to the glycosidic nitrogen because of the stability of the trialkylammonium com-

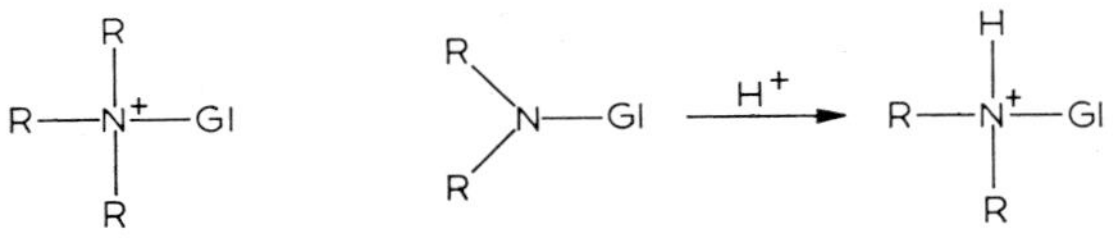

148   149   150

pounds (148) in which the positive charge prevents the approach of a proton. Hence an entirely analogous structure like (150), derived by protonation at the glycosidic nitrogen atom from a dialkylamine glycoside, or nucleoside, should be equally stable. The ready hydrolysis of (150) must be therefore due to the transfer of a proton to another atom, which Kenner suggests must be the ring oxygen atom (151). In fact there is ample evidence that the initial site of protonation in nucleosides is not at the glycosidic linkage but at N-1 in adenine, at N-7 in guanine, and at N-1 in cytosine derivatives[218-220].

Hydrolysis by this mechanism will occur if protonation at the ring oxygen takes place, either by transfer from the heterocyclic base, or by addition of a second proton, if the charge on the first is sufficiently widely distributed. Examples will make these points clear.

(*1*) The positive charge in protonated cytidine is distributed by resonance (152 a, b, c) but the glycosidic nitrogen still carries appreciable positive charge; hydrolysis occurs, but slowly.

(*2*) When the 4,5-double bond is hydrogenated, a structure equivalent to (152c) can no longer be written, and the approach of a second proton is greatly facilitated; 4,5-dihydropyrimidine nucleosides are much more susceptible to hydrolysis.

(*3*) Resonance structures also distribute the positive charge in a purine nucleoside cation between three nitrogen atoms, but here the tautomeric contribution from the cation with hydrogen at N-3 (153) facilitates proton *transfer*, and hence purine nucleosides are more readily hydrolysed than pyrimidine nucleosides. The particularly rapid hydrolysis of 5-amino-imidazole riboside (154) and of isocytidine (155) (ref. 188) may be similarly explained[218].

(4) There has been striking reluctance to offer an explanation of the much greater stability of ribosides as compared to deoxyribosides. It is clear from the examples given that the rate of hydrolysis is very sensitive to structural

changes. Introduction of an electron-attracting group like OH at C-2 in the sugar will reduce the availability of electrons at the ring oxygen and make the acceptance of a proton more difficult. Consistent with this is the fact that ribosides have slightly lower pK values than the corresponding 2'-deoxyribosides (see Table VII). Substitution of a more strongly electronegative group at C-2 should further increase the stability to hydrolysis; in fact, 2-p-nitrobenzenesulphonyladenosine is completely stable under conditions in which adenosine is hydrolysed[220].

6. Sponge nucleosides

Two nucleosides, spongothymidine and spongouridine, which have been isolated from *Cryptotethia* sponges have been shown to be the arabinosides of thymine and uracil respectively[221-223]. Spongouridine (157) has been syn-

thesized by the acid hydrolysis of $O^2,2'$-cyclouridine (156) (ref. 224) and spongothymidine in an analogous manner[225]. Another nucleoside from the same source, spongosine, has been identified[226] as the riboside of 2-methoxyadenine (158).

7. Physical properties

(a) U.V. spectra, pK values and tautomerism

Pyrimidines with OH, NH_2 and SH substituents in the 2-, 4- or 6-positions can exist in tautomeric forms.

159   160

The best evidence concerning this much discussed problem has come from a comparison of the U.V. and I.R. spectra of such compounds with those of their unambiguously synthesized O- and N-alkyl derivatives. Such work has shown quite clearly that hydroxypyrimidines exist[227] in the lactam form (159), and mercaptopyrimidines similarly in the thione form, whereas aminopyrimidines exist[228] as the amino compounds (160). Similar conclusions apply to 2- and 6-substituted purines[229].

Additional evidence regarding the structure of uracil came from an X-ray crystallographic analysis in which the positions of the hydrogen atoms were determined directly[230].

In the scheme for the transmission of genetic information by replication of DNA it was proposed by Watson and Crick[107] that mutation might occur if a base were in its less likely tautomeric form, causing it to pair with an anomalous base. This has been used to explain the mutagenic activity of 5-bromouracil[231,232] by assuming that it would be more likely than thymine, which it replaces, to occur in the tautomeric form capable of pairing with

161   162

guanine, instead of the normal partner, adenine. In the equilibrium (161, 162) the tautomeric ratio $K_T = 10^{3.3}$ when R=H and $10^{1.7}$ when R=Br, showing that structure (159) is relatively more likely to occur in derivatives of 5-bromouracil than in thymine[233].

Alternatively, the increase in acidity from thymidine ($pK_a' = 9.8$) to 5-bromodeoxyuridine ($pK_a' = 8.1$) suggests that mutagenesis may be due to ionisation. At neutral pH, about 8% of 5-bromodeoxyuridine would exist as the anion, compared with 0.16% of thymidine. The anomalous base pairing of ionised bromouracil with guanine (163) would result in the conversion of a T–A into a C–G pair[234].

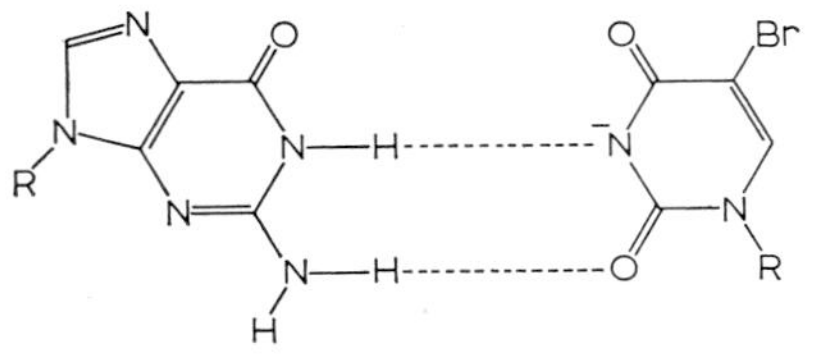

163

The pK_a' values of some bases and nucleosides are given in Table VII. The values are discussed by Jordan[235] and appear to require little comment. The

TABLE VII

pK_a' VALUES OF BASES AND NUCLEOSIDES

	Amino —NH₃+	—N¹H—C⁶O—	—N³H—C²O—	Imidazole —NH—	Sugar hydroxyl
Adenine[a]	4.15			9.8	
Adenosine[a]	3.45				12.5
Cytosine[b]	4.45		12.2		
Cytidine[b]	4.11				>13
Deoxycytidine[b]	4.25				>13
5-Methylcytosine[b]	4.6		12.4		
5-Methylcytidine[b]	4.28				>13
5-Methyldeoxycytidine[b]	4.40				>13
Guanine[a]	3.3	9.6		12.3	
Guanosine[a]	1.6	9.2			12.3
Thymine[a]		9.82			
Thymine riboside[c]		9.68			
Thymidine[a]		9.8			
Uracil[a]		9.45			
Uridine[a]		9.17, 9.25[e]			12.5
Deoxyuridine		9.3[e]			
Pseudouridine[d]		9.6			

a Ref. 235.   b Ref. 155.   c Ref. 239.   d Ref. 140.   e Ref. 240.

TABLE VIII

U.V. SPECTRA OF BASES AND NUCLEOSIDES

	pH	Max. mµ	$\varepsilon \cdot 10^{-3}$
Adenine[a]	I	262.5	13.1
	7	260.5	13.35
	13	269	12.3
Adenosine[b]	2	257	15.1
	7	259	15.4
	11	259	15.4
Cytosine[c]	1–2	276	10.0
	7	267	6.13
	13	281.5	7.06
Cytidine[d]	1–2	280	13.4
	7	271	9.1
	13	272.5	9.15
Deoxycytidine[d]	1–2	280	13.2
	7	271	9.0
	13	271.5	9.06
5-Methylcytosine[c]	1–2	283.5	9.79
	7	273.5	6.23
	13	288	6.95
5-Methyldeoxycytidine[e]	I	286	11.61
	7	277	8.81
5-Hydroxymethylcytosine[b]	I	279	9.7
	7.4	269.5	—
	13	283.5	—
5-Hydroxymethyldeoxycytidine[g]	I	282	—
	7	272	—
	13	272	—
Guanine[a]	I	248.5	11.4
		275.5	7.35
	7	246	10.7
		275.5	8.15
	11	246	6.3
		273.5	8.0
Guanosine[b]	I	256	12.3
	7	252	13.7
	11	258	11.3
Thymine[c]	2–7	264.5	7.89
	13	291	5.44

(continued on p. 202)

TABLE VIII (*continued*)

	pH	Max. mμ	ε·10^{-3}
Thymidine[d]	1–7	267	9.65
	13	267	7.38
Uracil[c]	2–7	259.5	8.2
	13	284	6.15
Uridine[d]	1–7	262	10.1
	13	263	7.41
Pseudouridine[h]	7	262	—
	12	286	—

[a] Ref. 237. [b] Ref. 241. [c] Ref. 236. [d] Ref. 240. [e] Ref. 242. [f] Ref. 65.
[g] Ref. 243. [h] Ref. 140.

values for the nucleosides are somewhat lower than those for the free bases, that is, the acidity has increased. This is the effect one would expect from the introduction of a mildly electronegative group. It is noteworthy that the pK's of the ribosides are lower than those of the corresponding deoxyribosides, *i.e.* the 2′-hydroxyl group exerts a definite effect, consistent with its effect on the rate of acid hydrolysis (see section 5, p. 196).

At one time changes in the U.V. spectra of nucleic acid components with pH were interpreted in terms of keto–enol tautomerism, but it is now realised that the changes are due to ionisation[236]. U.V. spectra are of enormous value in identifying these compounds, and have also been used in establishing the structure of glycosides. Complete spectra and absorbance ratios of different wavelengths etc., are given in *The Nucleic Acids*[237]. Table VIII gives the maxima of bases and their nucleosides at different pH values.

(b) I.R. and N.M.R. spectra

The main applications of I.R. spectra so far have been (*1*) to check the identity of natural and synthetic products, and (*2*) in helping to settle the question of keto–enol tautomerism (preceding section). It has hardly yet been used to determine the structure of new substances, though the I.R. spectrum of 5-hydroxymethyluracil[238] confirmed the structure of this reaction product of uracil and formaldehyde[5], which was in doubt because earlier workers had reported it to be unstable. Compounds like uracil, thymine, cytosine, 5-methyl- and 5-hydroxymethylcytosine give characteristically different I.R. spectra (ref. 238, and references therein). Applications of N.M.R. spectra are just beginning. The spectra of a number of purines, pyrimidines and nucleosides and nucleotides have been reported[244], and the conformation of the sugar ring in thymidine has been discussed in relation to the N.M.R. spectrum of this nucleoside[245]. In this chapter the use of N.M.R. spectra in determining the structure of pseudouridine (p. 181) and of the reaction product of cytosine derivatives with hydroxylamine (section c, p. 261) have been noted.

REFERENCES

[1] T. L. V. Ulbricht and C. C. Price, *J. Org. Chem.*, 21 (1956) 567.
[2] R. R. Herr, T. Enkoji and T. J. Bardos, *J. Am. Chem. Soc.*, 78 (1956) 401.
[3] H. L. Wheeler and H. S. Bristol, *Am. Chem. J.*, 33 (1905) 441.
[4] G. W. Kenner, C. W. Taylor and A. R. Todd, *J. Chem. Soc.*, (1949) 1620.
[5] R. E. Cline, R. M. Fink and K. Fink, *J. Am. Chem. Soc.*, 81 (1959) 2521.
[6] H. Rembold and H. J. Schramm, *Angew. Chem.*, 72 (1960) 578.
[7] J. Baddiley and A. Topham, *J. Chem. Soc.*, (1944) 678.
[8] T. L. V. Ulbricht, unpublished.
[9] G. B. Elion, E. Burgi and G. H. Hitchings, *J. Am. Chem. Soc.*, 74 (1952) 411.
[10] M. P. V. Boarland and J. F. W. McOmie, *J. Chem. Soc.*, (1951) 1218.
[11] A. Dornow and G. Petsch, *Ann. Chem.*, 588 (1954) 45.
[12] R. Hull, B. J. Lovell, H. T. Openshaw and A. R. Todd, *J. Chem. Soc.*, (1947) 41.
[13] C. O. Miller, F. Skoog, F. S. Okumura, M. H. von Saltza and F. M. Strong, *J. Am. Chem. Soc.*, 77 (1955) 2662.
[14] D. J. Brown, *J. Soc. Chem. Ind.*, 69 (1950) 353.
[15] T. L. V. Ulbricht, *J. Chem. Soc.*, (1961) 3345.
[16] G. E. Hilbert and E. F. Jansen, *J. Am. Chem. Soc.*, 56 (1934) 134.
[17] G. E. Hilbert and T. B. Johnson, *J. Am. Chem. Soc.*, 52 (1930) 4489.
[18] W. Kossel, *Z. physiol. Chem.*, 10 (1886) 248.
[19] A. Bendich, P. J. Russell and J. J. Fox, *J. Am. Chem. Soc.*, 76 (1954) 6073.
[20] N. Whittaker, *J. Chem. Soc.*, (1953) 1646.
[21] F. H. Case and A. J. Hill, *J. Am. Chem. Soc.*, 52 (1930) 1536.
[22] T. B. Johnson and S. H. Clapp, *J. Biol. Chem.*, 5 (1908) 59.
[23] P. Brookes and P. D. Lawley, *J. Chem. Soc.*, (1962) 1348.
[24] H. Bietz and A. Beck, *J. prakt. Chem.*, 118, ii (1928) 198.
[25] P. A. W. Self and W. R. Rankin, *Quart. J. Pharm.*, 4 (1931) 346.
[26] P. Brookes and P. D. Lawley, *J. Chem. Soc.*, (1961) 3923.
[27] M. Kruger, *Z. physiol. Chem.*, 18 (1894) 434.
[28] G. R. Ramage and T. S. Stevens, in E. H. Rodd (Ed.), *Chemistry of Carbon Compounds*, Vol. IVC, Elsevier, Amsterdam, 1960, p. 1760.
[29] T. L. V. Ulbricht and C. C. Price, *J. Org. Chem.*, 22 (1957) 235.
[30] R. Bernetti, F. Mancini and C. C. Price, in the press.
[31] D. M. Brown, A. R. Todd and S. Varadarajan, *J. Chem. Soc.*, (1956) 2384.
[32] G. W. Kenner and A. R. Todd, in R. C. Elderfield (Ed.), *Heterocyclic Compounds*, Vol. VI, Wiley, New York, 1957.
[33] G. R. Ramage, in E. H. Rodd (Ed.), *Chemistry of Carbon Compounds*, Vol. IVB, Elsevier, Amsterdam, 1959, p. 1259.
[34] W. Traube, *Ann. Chem.*, 331 (1904) 64.
[35] C. W. Whitehead, *J. Am. Chem. Soc.*, 74 (1952) 4267.
[36] W. Traube, *German Patent* 134,984; *Friedl.*, 6, 119.
[37] P. N. Evans, *J. prakt. Chem.*, 48 (1893) 493.
[38] H. Bredereck, R. Gompper, H. G. v. Schuh and G. Theilig, *Angew. Chem.*, 71 (1959) 753.
[39] W. Traube, *Ber.*, 33 (1900) 1371, 3035.
[40] See A. Bendich, in E. Chargaff and J. N. Davidson (Eds.), *The Nucleic Acids*, Vol. 1, Academic Press, New York, 1955, p. 81.
[41] L. Goldman, J. W. Marsico and A. L. Gazzola, *J. Org. Chem.*, 21 (1956) 599.
[42] J. A. Montgomery, *J. Am. Chem. Soc.*, 78 (1956) 1928.
[43] J. A. Montgomery and L. B. Holum, *J. Am. Chem. Soc.*, 80 (1958) 404.
[44] J. Clark and J. H. Lister, *J. Chem. Soc.*, (1960) 5048.
[45] E. Richter, J. E. Loeffler and E. C. Taylor, *J. Am. Chem. Soc.*, 82 (1960) 3144.
[46] G. A. Howard, in E. H. Rodd (Ed.), *Chemistry of Carbon Compounds*, Vol. IVC, Elsevier, Amsterdam, 1960, p. 1635.
[47] A. Ascoli, *Z. physiol. Chem.*, 31 (1900–01) 161.
[48] E. Fischer and G. Roeder, *Ber.*, 34 (1901) 3751.

⁴⁹ D. DAVIDSON AND O. BAUDISCH, *J. Am. Chem. Soc.*, 48 (1926) 2382.
⁵⁰ D. A. SHIRLEY, *Preparation of Organic Intermediates*, Chapman and Hall, London, 1951, p. 297.
⁵¹ A. KOSSEL AND A. NEUMANN, *Ber.*, 26 (1893) 2753.
⁵² A. KOSSEL AND A. NEUMANN, *Ber.*, 27 (1894) 2215.
⁵³ H. STEUDEL, *Z. physiol. Chem.*, 30 (1900) 539.
⁵⁴ H. STEUDEL, *Z. physiol. Chem.*, 32 (1901) 241.
⁵⁵ W. BERGMANN AND T. B. JOHNSON, *J. Am. Chem. Soc.*, 55 (1933) 1733.
⁵⁶ A. KOSSEL AND H. STEUDEL, *Z. physiol. Chem.*, 38 (1903) 49.
⁵⁷ W. L. WHEELER AND T. B. JOHNSON, *Am. Chem. J.*, 29 (1903) 492.
⁵⁸ P. J. TARSIO AND L. NICHOLL, *J. Org. Chem.*, 22 (1957) 192.
⁵⁹ G. R. WYATT, *Nature*, 166 (1950) 237.
⁶⁰ G. R. WYATT, *Biochem. J.*, 48 (1951) 581, 584.
⁶¹ G. R. WYATT, *J. Gen. Physiol.*, 36 (1952) 201.
⁶² T. B. JOHNSON AND R. D. COGHILL, *J. Am. Chem. Soc.*, 47 (1925) 2838.
⁶³ H. L. WHEELER AND T. B. JOHNSON, *Am. Chem. J.*, 31 (1904) 591.
⁶⁴ G. H. HITCHINGS, G. B. ELION, E. A. FALCO AND P. B. RUSSELL, *J. Biol. Chem.*, 177 (1949) 357.
⁶⁵ G. R. WYATT AND S. S. COHEN, *Nature*, 170 (1952) 1072.
⁶⁶ T. L. V. ULBRICHT AND C. C. PRICE, *Chem. Ind. (London)*, (1955) 1221.
⁶⁷ T. L. V. ULBRICHT, T. OKUDA AND C. C. PRICE, *Org. Syn.*, 39 (1959) 34.
⁶⁸ A. DORNOW AND G. PETSCH, *Ann. Chem.*, 588 (1954) 45.
⁶⁹ C. S. MILLER, *J. Am. Chem. Soc.*, 77 (1955) 752.
⁷⁰ A. KOSSEL, *Ber.*, 18 (1885) 79.
⁷¹ E. FISCHER, *Ber.*, 30 (1897) 2226.
⁷² J. BADDILEY, B. LYTHGOE AND A. R. TODD, *J. Chem. Soc.*, (1943) 386.
⁷³ A. KOSSEL, *Z. physiol. Chem.*, 8 (1883–1884) 404.
⁷⁴ L. F. CAVALIERI AND G. B. BROWN, *J. Am. Chem. Soc.*, 71 (1949) 2246.
⁷⁵ R. E. HANDSCHUMACHER AND A. D. WELCH, in E. CHARGAFF AND J. N. DAVIDSON (Eds.), *The Nucleic Acids*, Vol. 3, Academic Press, New York, 1960, p. 453.
⁷⁶ P. K. CHANG AND T. L. V. ULBRICHT, *J. Am. Chem. Soc.*, 80 (1958) 976.
⁷⁷ T. L. V. ULBRICHT, *Tetrahedron*, 6 (1959) 225.
⁷⁸ A. BENDICH, H. GETLER AND G. B. BROWN, *J. Biol. Chem.*, 177 (1949) 565.
⁷⁹ M. L. EIDINOFF AND J. E. KNOLL, *J. Am. Chem. Soc.*, 75 (1953) 1992.
⁸⁰ K. E. WILZBACH, *J. Am. Chem. Soc.*, 79 (1957) 1013.
⁸¹ E. L. BENNETT, *J. Am. Chem. Soc.*, 74 (1952) 2420.
⁸² R. L. SINSHEIMER AND R. HASTINGS, *Science*, 110 (1949) 505.
⁸³ D. SHUGAR, in E. CHARGAFF AND J. N. DAVIDSON (Eds.), *The Nucleic Acids*, Vol. 3, Academic Press, New York, 1960, p. 39.
⁸⁴ R. BEUKERS AND W. BERENDS, *Biochim. Biophys. Acta*, 49 (1961) 181.
⁸⁵ A. WACKER, D. WEINBLUM, L. TRÄGER AND Z. H. MOUSTAFA, *J. Mol. Biol.*, 3 (1961) 790.
⁸⁶ A. WACKER, H. DELLWEG AND D. WEINBLUM, *Naturwiss.*, 47 (1960) 477.
⁸⁷ J. JAGGER, *Bacteriol. Rev.*, 22 (1958) 99.
⁸⁸ R. SETLOW, *Biochim. Biophys. Acta*, 49 (1961) 237.
⁸⁹ H. E. JOHNS, S. A. RAPOPORT AND M. DELBRÜCK, *J. Mol. Biol.*, 4 (1962) 104.
⁹⁰ D. B. DUNN AND J. D. SMITH, *Nature*, 175 (1955) 336.
⁹¹ D. B. DUNN AND J. D. SMITH, *Biochem. J.*, 68 (1958) 627.
⁹² J. W. LITTLEFIELD AND D. B. DUNN, *Nature*, 181 (1958) 254.
⁹³ D. B. DUNN, *Biochim. Biophys. Acta*, 34 (1959) 286.
⁹⁴ D. B. DUNN, J. D. SMITH AND P. F. SPAHR, *J. Mol. Biol.*, 2 (1960) 113.
⁹⁵ D. B. DUNN, *Biochim. Biophys. Acta*, 46 (1961) 198.
⁹⁵ᵃ References to similar re-arrangements are given in ref. 23.
⁹⁶ M. ADLER, B. WEISSMAN AND A. B. GUTMAN, *J. Biol. Chem.*, 230 (1958) 717.
⁹⁷ J. D. SMITH AND D. B. DUNN, *Biochem. J.*, 72 (1959) 294.
⁹⁸ H. AMOS AND M. KORN, *Biochim. Biophys. Acta*, 29 (1958) 444.
⁹⁹ E. CHARGAFF, E. VISCHER, R. DONIGER, C. GREEN AND F. MISANI, *J. Biol. Chem.*, 177 (1949) 405.

[100] E. Vischer, S. Zamenhof and E. Chargaff, *J. Biol. Chem.*, 177 (1949) 429.
[101] E. Chargaff, *Experientia*, 6 (1950) 201.
[102] E. Chargaff, S. Zamenhof and C. Green, *Nature*, 165 (1950) 756.
[103] E. Chargaff, in E. Chargaff and J. N. Davidson (Eds.), *The Nucleic Acids*, Vol. 1, Academic Press, New York, 1955, p. 307.
[104] E. Chargaff, S. Zamenhof, G. Brawerman and L. Kerin, *J. Am. Chem. Soc.*, 72 (1950) 3825.
[105] E. Chargaff, *Federation Proc.*, 10 (1951) 654.
[106] A. N. Belozersky and A. S. Spirin, in E. Chargaff and J. N. Davidson (Eds.), *The Nucleic Acids*, Vol. 3, Academic Press, New York, 1960, p. 147.
[107] J. D. Watson and F. H. C. Crick, *Nature*, 171 (1953) 737.
[108] B. Magasanik, in E. Chargaff and J. N. Davidson (Eds.), *The Nucleic Acids*, Vol. 1, Academic Press, New York, 1955, p. 373.
[109] R. Markham and J. D. Smith, *Biochem. J.*, 49 (1951) 401.
[110] C. A. Knight, *J. Biol. Chem.*, 197 (1952) 241.
[111] F. L. Black and C. A. Knight, *J. Biol. Chem.*, 202 (1953) 51.
[112] R. W. Donner and C. A. Knight, *J. Biol. Chem.*, 205 (1953) 959.
[113] R. Thomas, *Biochim. Biophys. Acta*, 8 (1952) 71.
[114] D. Elson, I. Gustafson and E. Chargaff, *J. Biol. Chem.*, 209 (1954) 235.
[115] D. Elson and E. Chargaff, *Nature*, 173 (1954) 1073.
[116] D. Elson and E. Chargaff, *Biochim. Biophys. Acta*, 17 (1955) 367.
[117] H. G. Mandel, *Pharmacol. Rev.*, 11 (1959) 743.
[118] R. E. Handschumacher and A. D. Welch, in E. Chargaff and J. N. Davidson (Eds.), *The Nucleic Acids*, Vol. 3, Academic Press, New York, 1960, p. 453.
[119] A. Wacker, S. Kirschfeld and L. Träger, *J. Mol. Biol.*, 2 (1960) 241.
[120] H. Gottschling and E. Freese, *Z. Naturforsch.*, 166 (1961) 515.
[121] T. L. V. Ulbricht and J. S. Gots, *Nature*, 178 (1956) 913.
[122] P. A. Levene and L. A. Jacobs, *Ber.*, 41 (1908) 2703.
[123] P. A. Levene and L. A. Jacobs, *Ber.*, 42 (1909) 1198.
[124] P. A. Levene and L. A. Jacobs, *Ber.*, 44 (1911) 746.
[125] W. A. van Ekenstein and J. J. Blanksma, *Chem. Weekblad*, 10 (1913) 664
[126] P. A. Levene and F. B. La Forge, *Ber.*, 45 (1912) 608.
[127] W. E. Cohn and D. G. Doherty, *J. Am. Chem. Soc.*, 78 (1956) 2863.
[128] D. C. Burke, *Chem. Ind. (London)*, (1954) 1393.
[129] L. Haavaldsen, S. Laland, J. M. McKee and E. Roth, *Biochim. Biophys. Acta*, 33 (1959) 201.
[130] P. A. Levene, *J. Biol. Chem.*, 55 (1923) 437.
[131] J. M. Gulland and E. R. Holiday, *J. Chem. Soc.*, (1936) 765.
[132] J. M. Gulland and L. F. Story, *J. Chem. Soc.*, (1938) 692.
[133] J. M. Ploeser and H. S. Loring, *J. Biol. Chem.*, 178 (1949) 431.
[134] P. A. Levene and R. S. Tipson, *J. Biol. Chem.*, 104 (1935) 385.
[135] Earlier work is summarised by J. Baddiley, in E. Chargaff and J. N. Davidson (Eds.), *The Nucleic Acids*, Vol. 1, Academic Press, New York, 1955, p. 138.
[136] B. Lythgoe and A. R. Todd, *J. Chem. Soc.*, (1944) 592.
[137] V. M. Clark, A. R. Todd and J. Zussman, *J. Chem. Soc.*, (1951) 2952.
[138] S. Furberg, *Acta Chem. Scand.*, 4 (1950) 751; *Acta Cryst.*, 3 (1950) 325.
[139] C.-T. Yu and F. W. Allen, *Biochim. Biophys. Acta*, 32 (1959) 393.
[140] W. E. Cohn, *J. Biol. Chem.*, 235 (1959) 1488.
[141] W. E. Cohn and A. M. Michelson, *Biochemistry*, 1 (1962) 490.
[142] B. Lythgoe, H. Smith and A. R. Todd, *J. Chem. Soc.*, (1947) 355.
[143] E. Fischer and B. Helferich, *Ber.*, 47 (1914) 210.
[144] J. Davoll, B. Lythgoe and A. R. Todd, *J. Chem. Soc.*, (1944) 833.
[145] J. Davoll and B. A. Lowy, *J. Am. Chem. Soc.*, 73 (1951) 1650.
[146] E. Fischer, *Ber.*, 47 (1914) 1377.
[147] P. A. Levene and H. Slobotka, *J. Biol. Chem.*, 65 (1925) 469.
[148] G. E. Hilbert and T. B. Johnson, *J. Am. Chem. Soc.*, 52 (1930) 4489.
[149] G. E. Hilbert and E. F. Jansen, *J. Am. Chem. Soc.*, 58 (1936) 60.
[150] G. A. Howard, B. Lythgoe and A. R. Todd, *J. Chem. Soc.*, (1947) 1052.

[151] T. L. V. ULBRICHT, *Angew. Chem. (Intern. Ed. Engl.)*, 1 (1962) 476.
[152] J. J. FOX, N. YUNG, J. DAVOLL AND G. B. BROWN, *J. Am. Chem. Soc.*, 78 (1956) 2117.
[153] J. J. FOX, N. YUNG, I. WEMPEN AND I. L. DOERR, *J. Am. Chem. Soc.*, 79 (1957) 5060.
[154] J. J. FOX, D. VAN PRAAG, I. WEMPEN, I. L. DOERR, L. CHANG, J. E. KNOLL, M. L. EIDINOFF, A. BENDICH AND G. B. BROWN, *J. Am. Chem. Soc.*, 81 (1959) 178.
[154a] T. L. V. ULBRICHT, *Proc. Chem. Soc.*, (1962) 298.
[155] J. BADDILEY, J. G. BUCHANAN, R. HODGES AND J. F. PRESCOTT, *J. Chem. Soc.*, (1957) 4769.
[156] G. SHAW, R. N. WARRENER, M. H. MAGUIRE AND R. K. RALPH, *J. Chem. Soc.*, (1959) 1648.
[157] R. SHAPIRO AND R. W. CHAMBERS, *J. Am. Chem. Soc.*, 83 (1961) 3920.
[158] D. M. BROWN, N. B. BARDON AND P. SLATCHER, unpublished.
[159] P. A. LEVENE AND E. S. LONDON, *J. Biol. Chem.*, 81 (1929) 711; 83 (1929) 793.
[160] P. A. LEVENE AND T. MORI, *J. Biol. Chem.*, 83 (1929) 803.
[161] P. A. LEVENE, L. A. MIKESTA AND T. MORI, *J. Biol. Chem.*, 85 (1930) 785.
[162] D. C. BURKE, *J. Org. Chem.*, 20 (1955) 643.
[163] D. M. BROWN AND B. LYTHGOE, *J. Chem. Soc.*, (1950) 1990.
[164] J. M. GULLAND AND L. F. STORY, *J. Chem. Soc.*, (1938) 259.
[165] W. ANDERSON, D. H. HAYES, A. M. MICHELSON AND A. R. TODD, *J. Chem. Soc.*, (1954) 1882.
[166] A. M. MICHELSON AND A. R. TODD, *J. Chem. Soc.*, (1955) 816.
[167] M. HUBER, *Acta Cryst.*, 10 (1957) 129.
[168] G. R. WYATT AND S. S. COHEN, *Biochem. J.*, 55 (1953) 774.
[169] S. S. COHEN, *Cold Spring Harbor Symposia Quant. Biol.*, (1953) 221.
[170] R. L. SINSHEIMER, *Science*, 120 (1954) 551.
[171] E. VOLKIN, *J. Am. Chem. Soc.*, 76 (1954) 5892.
[172] M. A. JESAITIS, *J. Exptl. Med.*, 106 (1957) 233.
[173] J. LICHTENSTEIN AND S. S. COHEN, *J. Biol. Chem.*, 235 (1960) 1134.
[174] I. R. LEHMAN, *J. Biol. Chem.*, 235 (1960) 1479.
[175] I. R. LEHMAN AND E. A. PRATT, *J. Biol. Chem.*, 235 (1960) 3254.
[176] S. KUNO AND I. R. LEHMAN, *J. Biol. Chem.*, 237 (1962) 1266.
[177] J. DAVOLL AND B. LYTHGOE, *J. Chem. Soc.*, (1949) 2527.
[178] R. JEANLOZ, D. A. PRINS AND T. REICHSTEIN, *Helv. Chim. Acta*, 29 (1946) 371.
[179] S. MUKHERJEE AND A. R. TODD, *J. Chem. Soc.*, (1947) 969.
[180] F. H. NEWTH, W. G. OVEREND AND L. F. WIGGINS, *J. Chem. Soc.*, (1949) 10.
[181] P. W. KENT, M. STACEY AND L. F. WIGGINS, *J. Chem. Soc.*, (1949) 1232.
[182] J. DAVOLL, B. LYTHGOE AND S. TRIPPETT, *J. Chem. Soc.*, (1951) 2230.
[183] B. R. BAKER, in G. E. W. WOLSTENHOLME AND C. M. O'CONNOR (Eds.), *The Ciba Foundation Symposium on the Chemistry and Biology of Purines*, J. and A. Churchill, London, 1957, p. 128.
[184] A. M. MICHELSON, unpublished.
[185] J. W. H. OLDHAM AND J. K. RUTHERFORD, *J. Am. Chem. Soc.*, 54 (1932) 366.
[186] D. M. BROWN, D. B. PARIHAR, C. B. REESE AND A. R. TODD, *Proc. Chem. Soc.*, (1957) 321.
[187] D. M. BROWN, D. B. PARIHAR, C. B. REESE AND A. R. TODD, *J. Chem. Soc.*, (1958) 3055.
[188] D. M. BROWN, D. B. PARIHAR AND A. R. TODD, *J. Chem. Soc.*, (1958) 4242.
[189] D. M. BROWN, D. B. PARIHAR, A. R. TODD AND S. VARADARAJAN, *J. Chem. Soc.*, (1958) 3028.
[190] G. SHAW AND R. N. WARRENER, *J. Chem. Soc.*, (1959) 50.
[191] A. R. TODD AND T. L. V. ULBRICHT, *J. Chem. Soc.*, (1960) 3275.
[192] W. W. LEE, A. BENITEZ, C. D. ANDERSON, L. GOODMAN AND B. R. BAKER, *J. Am. Chem. Soc.*, 83 (1961) 1906.
[193] C. D. ANDERSON, L. GOODMAN AND B. R. BAKER, *J. Am. Chem. Soc.*, 81 (1959) 3967.
[194] H. W. DIEHL AND H. G. FLETCHER, JR., *Arch. Biochem. Biophys.*, 78 (1958) 386.
[195] R. K. NESS, D. L. MACDONALD AND H. G. FLETCHER, JR., *J. Org. Chem.*, 26 (1961) 2895.
[196] R. K. NESS AND H. G. FLETCHER, JR., *J. Am. Chem. Soc.*, 81 (1959) 4752; 82 (1960) 3434.
[197] H. VENNER, *Ber.*, 93 (1960) 140.

[198] M. Hoffer, R. Duschinsky, J. J. Fox and N. Yung, *J. Am. Chem. Soc.*, 81 (1959) 4112.
[199] M. Hoffer, *Ber.* 93 (1960) 2777.
[200] J. J. Fox, N. Yung, I. Wempen and M. Hoffer, *J. Am. Chem. Soc.*, 83 (1961) 4066.
[201] J. J. Fox, D. V. Praag, I. Wempen, I. L. Doerr, L. Cheong, J. E. Knoll, M. L. Eidinoff, A. Bendich and G. B. Brown, *J. Am. Chem. Soc.*, 81 (1959) 178.
[202] G. Schramm, *Colloquium on Ribonucleic Acids and Polyphosphates, Strasbourg, July 1961*, Editions C.N.R.S. Paris, 1962.
[203] G. Schramm, H. Grötsch and W. Pollmann, *Angew. Chem.*, 73 (1961) 619.
[204] G. Schramm, H. Grötsch and W. Pollmann, *Angew. Chem.* (*Intern. Ed. Engl.*), 1 (1962) 1.
[205] B. R. Baker, J. P. Joseph, R. E. Schaub and J. H. Williams, *J. Org. Chem.*, 19 (1954) 1786.
[206] B. R. Baker, ref. 183, p. 120.
[207] B. R. Baker, J. P. Joseph and R. E. Schaub, *J. Am. Chem. Soc.*, 77 (1955) 5905.
[208] B. R. Baker, R. E. Schaub and H. M. Kissman, *J. Am. Chem. Soc.*, 77 (1955) 5911.
[209] R. S. Wright and H. G. Khorana, *J. Am. Chem. Soc.*, 78 (1956) 811.
[210] G. M Tener, R. S. Wright and H. G. Khorana, *J. Am. Chem. Soc.*, 79 (1957) 441.
[211] R. S. Wright, G. M. Tener and H. G. Khorana, *J. Am. Chem. Soc.*, 80 (1958) 2004.
[212] R. E. Handschumacher, *J. Biol. Chem.*, 235 (1960) 764.
[213] M. Prystas, J. Gut and F. Sorm, *Chem. Ind.* (*London*), 947 (1961).
[214] J. J. Fox, J. F. Codington, N. Yung, L. Kaplan and J. O. Lampen, *J. Am. Chem. Soc.*, 80 (1958) 5155.
[215] J. J. Fox and I. Wempen, *Advan. Carbohydrate Chem.*, 14 (1959) 283.
[216] A. M. Michelson, *Ann. Rev. Biochem.*, 30 (1961) 133.
[217] G. W. Kenner, in G. E. W. Wolstenholme and C. M. O'Connor (Eds.), *The Ciba Foundation Symposium on the Chemistry and Biology of Purines*, J. and A. Churchill, London, 1957, p. 312.
[218] C. A. Dekker, *Ann. Rev. Biochem.*, 29 (1960) 463.
[219] R. F. Bryan and K. Tomita, *Nature*, 192 (1961) 812.
[220] T. L. V. Ulbricht, in preparation.
[221] W. Bergmann and J. R. Feeney, *J. Org. Chem.*, 16 (1951) 981.
[222] W. Bergmann and D. F. Burke, *J. Org. Chem.*, 20 (1955) 201.
[223] W. Bergmann and D. F. Burke, *Angew. Chem.*, 67 (1955) 127.
[224] D. M. Brown, A. R. Todd and S. Varadarajan, *J. Chem. Soc.*, (1956) 2388.
[225] J. J. Fox, N. Yung and A. Bendich, *J. Am. Chem. Soc.*, 79 (1957) 2775.
[226] W. Bergmann and D. F. Burke, *J. Org. Chem.*, 21 (1956) 226.
[227] D. J. Brown, E. Hoerger and S. F. Mason, *J. Chem. Soc.*, (1955) 211.
[228] D. J. Brown, E. Hoerger and S. F. Mason, *J. Chem. Soc.*, (1955) 4035.
[229] D. J. Brown and S. F. Mason, *J. Chem. Soc.*, (1957) 682.
[230] G. F. Parry, *Acta Cryst.*, 7 (1954) 313.
[231] E. Freese, *J. Mol. Biol.*, 1 (1959) 87.
[232] R. M. Litman and A. B. Pardu, *Biochim. Biophys. Acta*, 42 (1960) 131.
[233] A. R. Katritzky and A. J. Waring, *J. Chem. Soc.*, in the press.
[234] P. D. Lawley and P. Brookes, *J. Mol. Biol.*, 4 (1962) 216.
[235] D. O. Jordan, *The Chemistry of the Nucleic Acids*, Butterworth, London, 1960, p. 134.
[236] D. Shugar and J. J. Fox, *Biochim. Biophys. Acta*, 9 (1952) 199.
[237] G. H. Beaven, E. R. Holiday and E. A. Johnson, in E. Chargaff and J. N. Davidson (Eds.), *The Nucleic Acids*, Vol. 1, Academic Press, New York, 1955, p. 493.
[238] T. L. V. Ulbricht, *Naturwiss.*, 45 (1958) 416.
[239] J. J. Fox, J. F. Codington, N. Yung, L. Kaplan and J. O. Lampen, *J. Am. Chem. Soc.*, 80 (1958) 5155.
[240] D. Shugar and J. J. Fox, *Biochim. Biophys. Acta*, 9 (1952) 369.
[241] R. M. Bock, N. Ling, S. A. Morell and S. H. Lipton, *Arch. Biochem. Biophys.*, 62 (1956) 253.
[242] C. A. Dekker and D. T. Elmore, *J. Chem. Soc.*, (1951) 2864.
[243] S. S. Cohen, *Cold Spring Harbor Symposia Quant. Biol.*, 18 (1953) 221.
[244] C. D. Jardetzky and O. Jardetzky, *J. Am. Chem. Soc.*, 82 (1960) 222.
[245] R. V. Lemieux, *Can. J. Chem.*, 39 (1961) 116.

Chapter III

Chemistry of the Nucleic Acids

Section c

Nucleotides and Polynucleotides

D. M. BROWN

University Chemical Laboratory, Cambridge (Great Britain)

1. Isolation of nucleic acids

(a) General considerations

The earliest preparative methods were evolved on the assumption that the nucleic acids were labile substances, but later workers were less careful in this matter. It is true to say that most of the conclusions regarding the primary structure of the nucleic acids are based on work done on extensively degraded materials. More recently it has become clear that extraordinary care is necessary in order to obtain materials approximating to the native state. For most nucleic acid preparations no measurable biological activity can be discerned. In such cases a variety of physico-chemical methods may be brought to bear on the preparation[1]. A study of hydrodynamic properties, leading to estimates of molecular weight, is very valuable, due care being taken that partial aggregation is avoided (p. 283). Ultraviolet absorption spectra have been much used in view of the ease of measurement and because of the observation that nucleic acids in general have a considerably lower absorbance than the equivalent solution of mononucleotides. This hypochromism is particularly characteristic of carefully prepared DNA, and is related to the interactions of the oriented base residues in the helical system[2,3]. A useful criterion, developed by Chargaff[4], is the $\varepsilon(P)$ value of the preparation, *i.e.* the extinction coefficient at 260 mμ per mole of phosphorus in dilute salt solution at pH 7. A more detailed discussion of the physical chemistry of nucleic acids is given on p. 280 *et seq.*, and in its light the modern isolation methods can be better understood. In one or two cases,

References p. 262

e.g. the pneumococcal and other transforming principles (DNA) and certain virus nucleic acids (RNA), biological activity provides a useful criterion for the intactness of the material[5,6] but it is by no means definitive as recent studies show[7]. Meanwhile we should note that recorded molecular weights of DNA may range[8] from $1 \cdot 10^6$ to $15 \cdot 10^6$ and a recent measurement[9] of the DNA from T2 bacteriophage gives a value of $62 \cdot 10^6$. RNA lies in the range $1-2 \cdot 10^6$, although soluble RNA is clearly much smaller, having a molecular weight of about 25,000, equal to about 80 nucleotide residues[10]. Essentially the isolation of good specimens of nucleic acids requires that the following considerations be kept in mind. Nuclease activities should be inhibited as far as possible; to this end, arsenate, citrate and complexing agents such as EDTA have been added. Phenol and detergents, both used in nucleic acid extraction, are also good inhibitors. The very stable and ubiquitous enzyme, ribonuclease, is a major offender. Adsorption on bentonite is a valuable method for its quantitative removal from solutions[11]. Rapid working is clearly advantageous in any procedure. Extremes of temperature and pH must be avoided in order to prevent hydrolysis of labile linkages and breakdown or reorganisation of secondary, hydrogen-bonded, structure. For the same reason a relatively low but finite concentration of electrolyte should be maintained; the secondary structure of DNA is disrupted in distilled water at room temperature[12]. The thread-like nature of DNA, in particular, requires that high speed blending be kept to a minimum since mechanical cleavage of the molecule occurs. Ultrasonic vibrations[13], or even ejection of solutions from a narrow orifice[14] are sufficient to cause a large reduction in molecular weight. We should distinguish between molecular weights as derived from careful physico-chemical studies on purified nucleic acids and those adduced from other types of study. In the latter category we have the evidence of Hershey and colleagues[15] that the T2 bacteriophage DNA is present as one piece in the particle and hence has a calculated molecular weight of about $130 \cdot 10^6$. Simple stirring is enough to cause chain scission.

(b) *Isolation of DNA*

The isolation of DNA has been the subject of an enormous number of studies[16,17]. The nucleic acids in cells exist in more or less close association with protein. It is not the intention here, to discuss these complexes, which may contain protamines or histones or other less basic proteins, but it has been found advantageous in many cases first to isolate the nucleoprotein and then, in a second step, to dissociate the two components of the complex. Separation of ribo- from deoxyribonucleic acids can be effected, although not readily, but the corresponding nucleoproteins have very different solubilities in sodium chloride solutions, as noted by Mirsky and Pollister[18], and carefully studied by Frick[19]. Thus RNA-protein is much more soluble than DNA-protein in 0.14 N sodium chloride solution and utilising this their separation can be effected.

The removal of protein from a DNA-protein can be carried out by a variety of methods. Repeated emulsifying of a salt solution of the nucleoprotein with chloroform–octanol causes separation of the protein at the interface and the sodium nucleate can then be precipitated by alcohol[20]. Another much used method involves anionic detergents such as sodium dodecyl sulphate[21, 22]. These not only dissociate the nucleoprotein but also precipitate the protein, which can then be removed. The detergent method is probably the most generally useful. Other methods involve the use of phenol extraction in the presence of certain salts[23]. Bacteriophages are excellent sources of DNA since they are, in general, simply nucleoproteins. The protein coat may be removed mildly by osmotic shock[24] and then the solution deproteinised by one or other of the usual methods[25, 26]. Small amounts of contaminating RNA in a DNA preparation can be removed by treatment with alkali. The RNA is hydrolysed to mononucleotides; the DNA although denatured is still macromolecular and is suitable for such purposes as base analysis[27].

(c) Isolation of RNA

The earlier isolation methods have been reviewed in detail by Magasanik[28]. Recent practice has been to use either a detergent or a phenol extraction method. So many variants have been used that it is not possible here to discuss the subject in detail, but a monograph has recently been published[28a].

The detergent method is exemplified by the isolation of RNA from yeast[29]. The latter is added to a warm buffered solution of sodium dodecyl sulphate. The RNA remains in the supernatant solution, after centrifugation, from which it can be recovered by ethanol. The high molecular weight RNA is insoluble in 1 M sodium chloride and this allows its isolation free from soluble RNA. The s-RNA can then be isolated from the salt solution, by precipitation with a base such as salmine[30] or streptomycin[31]. The detergent method can be effectively applied to s-RNA isolation from microorganisms[32].

The phenol method was perfected by Kirby[33, 34] and by Gierer and Schramm[35, 36] and has very wide application. Essentially the fragmented cells are shaken in a two-phase aqueous buffer–phenol system. The aqueous phase contains the RNA. A further purification from polysaccharide and other contaminants is effected by extraction of the nucleic acid into 2-methoxyethanol. The RNA may then be retransferred to an aqueous phase and precipitated by one of a number of methods. The phenol method is very mild and for example yields infective RNA from tobacco mosaic virus[11, 37].

The method may be extended to the isolation of soluble RNA. The s-RNA is extracted from intact yeast cells by aqueous phenol uncontaminated by higher molecular weight RNA, and the ribosomal RNA can then be isolated independently[38].

It should, of course, be realised that these and other procedures can be applied to isolated cell fractions, *e.g.* microsomes (or ribosomes) and nuclei[39,40].

(d) Heterogeneity and fractionation of nucleic acids

There seems little doubt that, generally speaking, isolated nucleic acids are more or less degraded. This must mean that such preparations are heterogeneous. An additional source of heterogeneity lies in the fact that cellular organisms must contain one or more molecular species of DNA; presumably the minimal number of DNA species would correspond to the number of chromosomes, and the figure could be very much greater. Certainly mammalian (*e.g.* thymus) DNA is much more heterogeneous than a range of bacterial DNA's, judged by density gradient ultracentrifugation[41,42]. Heterogeneity in this sense implies that there are a range of molecular species differing in their $(C + G)/(A + T)$ ratio, and hence differing in their density per unit length. The method tells nothing about degradations by double-chain scission to give lower molecular weight products which retain the double helical conformation[42].

Isolation procedures are normally designed to give maximum yield and thus little fractionation is to be expected. Physical methods (*vide supra*) show marked heterogeneity in most isolated nucleic acid samples and with this knowledge many fractionation studies have been made. In the case of DNA, fractionation, assessed by changes in the $(C + G)/(A + T)$ ratio, was obtained by progressive dissociation of DNA-protein gel by increasing concentrations of sodium chloride[43]. Column procedures have been studied. Thus discontinuous elution from histone-coated kieselguhr was observed with increasing salt in the eluant[44]. A much studied method is that due to Bendich and co-workers in which the cellulose-based anion-exchange Ecteola is used[45,46]. Complex but reproducible elution patterns have been obtained with quantitative recovery. It is concluded that molecular size and shape are important factors in the fractionation, but there is no reason to suppose that any one fraction represents a simple molecular species. Hershey and Burgi[47] use a column of methyl esterified albumin for the separation of T2 phage DNA from fragments, derived by double chain scission. A number of studies, too, have been directed to the fractionation[48] of RNA. Elution from Ecteola-cellulose with phosphate buffer gives different patterns for RNA's from different sources, or RNA's isolated from the same source by different methods. All fractions are found to be heterogeneous[49].

A very interesting quantitative separation has been achieved by Bautz and Hall[50] of T4 specific RNA from *E. coli* RNA by chromatography on a T4DNA-cellulose column. Other methods include countercurrent distribution[51]. The separation of ribosomal from soluble RNA has already been mentioned and the further fractionation of s-RNA is dealt with on p. 249. Of the high molecular weight RNA's probably the purest yet isolated is that from tobacco mosaic virus, following the extremely careful purification study of Fraenkel-Conrat and Singer[52]. It seems quite clear that the RNA in the intact virus consists of only one molecular species.

2. Mononucleotides

(a) Monoalkyl phosphates

Before entering on a discussion of the mononucleotides some points relating to the general chemistry of monoesters of phosphoric acid may be of value. Monoalkyl phosphates (1) have pK_a values in the region of 1.5 and 6. The dianion (3), as would be expected, is exceptionally stable, so that, for example mononucleotides are very stable to alkali. Alkyl phosphates undergo acid hydrolysis which becomes rapid in strong mineral acid (conditions which of course also cause fission of the glycosidic linkage in nucleosides).

Of considerable interest is the general observation that an additional maximum is to be found in the pH rate profile for hydrolysis[53]. The curve for methyl phosphate shows that the rate of hydrolysis in the intermediate range is accurately proportional to the concentration[54] of the monoanion (2). The view has been hazarded that the breakdown leads to metaphosphate ion which is then rapidly hydrated[54, 55]. The practical value of this, in nucleotide chemistry, is that removal of phosphate can be effected under conditions in which acid-labile groupings need not be affected. The so-called "neutral" hydrolysis—boiling aqueous pyridine or ammonia—much used by Levene and co-workers for the conversion of nucleotides to nucleosides is presumably a manifestation of this aspect of phosphate ester chemistry[56].

When a vicinal hydroxyl group suitably oriented is present, phosphate migration occurs at low pH values The process is reversible, as shown by the equilibration of glycerol 1- and 2-phosphates, under acid conditions, where hydrolysis is hardly appreciable[57]. This neighbouring group reaction has been shown to be intramolecular, and presumed to proceed via the cyclic di-ester[58]; $P-O$ bond formation and cleavage is observed so that no inversion of asymmetric centres occurs[59]. Its importance to nucleotide chemistry is considerable and is discussed in that context below. The lability of phos-

phates of free sugars as compared with alkyl phosphates and indeed, of some phosphates of glycosides, is dependent on phosphate migration along the sugar chain to form, ultimately, the glycosyl 1-phosphates; these, as is well known, hydrolyse rapidly, in common with glycosyl-halides, and -esters.

Certain heavy metal ions catalyse the hydrolysis of phosphate esters to an impressive degree at pH values near or slightly above neutrality[60-62]. Thus, the hydroxides of Ce^{3+} and La^{3+} are active and, for example, a suspension of PbO in water effects the hydrolysis of mononucleotides to nucleosides[63].

As noted above, alkyl phosphates are stable to alkali. However, a carbonyl (or related activating group) in the β-position causes extreme instability; elimination, and not hydrolysis, occurs as is shown by the rapid conversion of triose phosphate to lactic acid[64]

$$^{2-}O_3PO \cdot CH_2 \cdot CH(OH) \cdot CHO \rightarrow HPO_4^{2-} + CH_3CO \cdot CHO \rightarrow CH_3CH(OH) \cdot CO_2H$$

and of glucose 3-phosphate to metasaccharinic acid[65]. Important extensions of this reaction to nucleotide chemistry are discussed later (see p. 244).

(b) Ribonucleotides

(i) 5′-Ribonucleotides

The first nucleotide isolation was performed by Liebig in 1847, who obtained inosinic acid from muscle extracts, but it was many years before its structure was completely known. Suffice it to say that neutral hydrolysis afforded inosine and orthophosphate while mild acid led to a ribose phosphate. Levene showed the latter to be D-ribose 5-phosphate which was fully confirmed by a synthesis[56,66] from methyl 2,3-O-isopropylidene ribofuranoside (4; R = Me).

Much later, in 1927, Embden and Zimmermann isolated an adenine nucleotide from muscle which was evidently the precursor of inosinic acid, since it was converted to the latter by enzymic or chemical deamination. The clarification of the lactol ring structure and glycosidic linkage position of the purine nucleosides (see previous section) then allowed muscle inosinic and adenylic acid to be formulated as (5) and (6) respectively.

An excellent synthesis of the latter, using 2',3'-O-isopropylideneadenosine (4; R = adenine residue), completed the structural proof[67]. In accord with the structure (6) the substance on oxidation with periodate rapidly consumes one molecule of oxidant and liberates neither formic acid nor formaldehyde[68]. The *cis*-glycol structure may also be demonstrated by borate complexing, which can be conveniently detected by differences in migration rate on paper chromatograms or electrophoretograms and in anion-exchange systems in presence and absence of borate[69,70].

The definitive synthesis of adenosine 5'-phosphate, in good yield, was followed by the preparation of the 5'-phosphates of the other three ribonucleosides, essentially by the same means. Thus treating the 2,3-O-isopropylidene (or benzylidene) derivatives of cytidine and uridine with dibenzylphosphorochloridate and removing protecting groups[71] yielded uridine 5'-phosphate (7; R=OH) and cytidine 5'-phosphate (7; R=NH$_2$). Isopropylideneguanosine was phosphorylated more conveniently with tetra-*p*-nitrophenyl pyrophosphate whence guanosine 5'-phosphate (8) was obtained by hydrolysis of the protecting groups[72]. Probably the most useful reagent for mononucleotide synthesis is the combination of β-cyanoethyl-phosphate and dicyclohexylcarbodiimide (DCC), developed recently by Tener[73]. The phosphate couples readily with suitably protected nucleosides to give a cyanoethyl ester; base catalysed elimination of acrylonitrile then liberates the nucleotide

$$ROH + CN \cdot CH_2CH_2OPO_3H_2 \xrightarrow{\text{DCC}} ROPO(OH) \cdot OCH_2 \cdot CH_2 \cdot CN \xrightarrow{\text{OH}^-} ROPO(OH)_2 + CH_2{=}CH{-}CN$$

The many other phosphorylation methods that have been developed in recent years, mainly in association with nucleotide chemistry, cannot be discussed here, but detailed reviews are available[74,75]. The above three mononucleotides have since been found to be present in cellular organisms, either as such or in combined form in coenzymes, although quantitatively less important than the adenine nucleotides. Their relationship to RNA will be developed later.

(ii) 2'- and 3'-Ribonucleotides

It had long ago been known that ribonucleic acids gave mononucleotides on alkaline hydrolysis[76]. Up to 1949 only four such nucleotides had been isolated, viz., monophosphates of adenosine, guanosine, uridine and cytidine[56]. Acid hydrolysis provided a convenient means of obtaining the two pyrimidine nucleotides, since the acid-lability of the purine glycosidic linkage led to the destruction of the two purine nucleotides[77]. Mainly as a result of degradation studies by Levene and his co-workers it had been concluded that these were the 3'-phosphates (10; R = purine or pyrimidine residue)[78,79]. Thus the adenylic acid (from yeast RNA) was converted to the corresponding inosinic acid by deamination, mild acid hydrolysis of which gave a ribose phosphate. It was clearly different from ribose 5-phosphate and on reduction gave a ribitol phosphate which was optically inactive and therefore taken to be the symmetrical 3-phosphate (11). The sugar phosphate from which it was derived was therefore D-ribose 3-phosphate. Yeast guanylic acid was considered to yield the same ribose phosphate. Thus the nucleotides were formulated as 10 (R = adenine and guanine, respectively). The two pyrimidine nucleotides, too, were formulated as 10 (R = uracil or cytosine residue), mainly on grounds of analogy[80].

Isolation of only these four nucleotides made it very difficult to rationalise the hydrolytic process or to define the internucleotidic linkage points in RNA[81,82]. However the situation was radically changed when Carter and Cohn[83] showed that the four nucleotides in fact consisted of four pairs of closely similar isomers. Cohn was able to separate these in substance by ion-exchange chromatography and he termed them the a and b isomers, corresponding to their order of elution[84-86]. The adenylic acids were initially

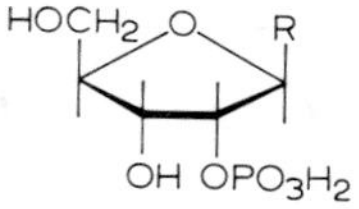

9

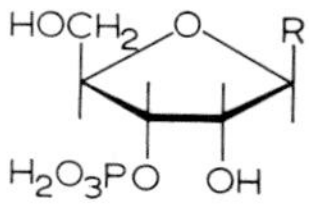

10

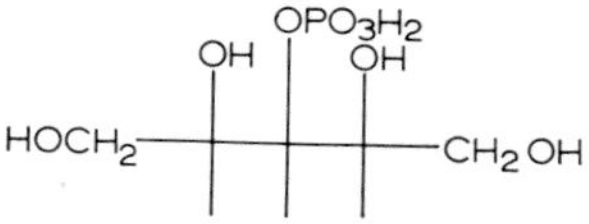

11

most extensively studied and the evidence showed that they were the 2'- and 3'-phosphates of adenosines (9 and 10; R=adenine residue) although not necessarily respectively[87]. They were stable to periodate. They could, too, be synthesized from adenosine, via the 5'-trityl derivative (12); phosphorylation with dibenzylphosphorochloridate and then removal of protecting groups by mild acid hydrolysis followed by hydrogenolysis gave a separable mixture of the two acids. In addition, they were interconvertible in acid to give an equilibrium mixture, under conditions which did not affect adenosine 5'-phosphate. Finally, they were both converted to the same cyclic phosphate (13; R=adenine residue) by treatment with trifluoroacetic anhydride[88].

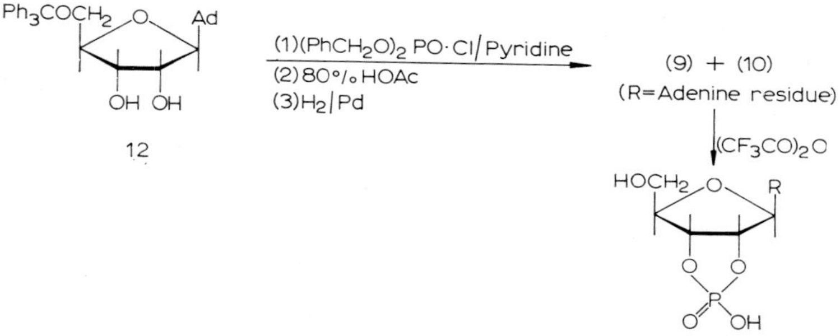

12

(1)(PhCH$_2$O)$_2$ PO·Cl/Pyridine
(2) 80% HOAc
(3) H$_2$/Pd

(9) + (10)
(R=Adenine residue)

(CF$_3$CO)$_2$O

13

Further work then defined completely the orientation of the phosphoryl group in the isomeric acids. Cavalieri[89] made accurate measurements of their pK values and densities of their aqueous solutions. The greater density and lower pK value of the amino group in the b isomer was taken to indicate greater charge separation in the zwitterion and hence it was concluded that the a and b isomers were the 2'- and 3'-nucleotides (9 and 10 respectively). Khym and Cohn drew the same conclusion[90]. They showed that the acid form of the sulphonic acid resin, Dowex-50, hydrolysed the isomeric acids giving rise to ribose phosphates, predominantly the 2- and 3-isomers. Fission of the glycosidic linkage and acid-catalysed phosphate migration proceeded at comparable rates, but by using short hydrolysis times they were able to relate each ribose phosphate to its parent nucleotide. Thus the a and b isomers were related as the 2'- and 3'-adenylic acids. Orientation of the ribose phosphates was effected by reduction to the ribitol phosphate: the 2-phosphate above was optically active. This work confirmed experimentally the earlier proposal that Levene's original orientation of yeast adenylic acid as the 3'-phosphate mentioned above, was invalid, since the optical inactivity of the ribitol phosphate could arise from acid-catalysed phosphate migrations and hence racemisation[87].

The orientation question was put beyond doubt by a synthesis of adenylic acid *a* by a procedure which precluded phosphate migration[91]. 5'-*O*-Acetyl-adenosine (15) was mono-acetylated and gave a crystalline *x*,5'-di-*O*-acetyl-adenosine. Phosphorylation of this gave adenylic acid *a* and none of the *b* isomer. Tosylation of the original diacetyladenosine and methylation of the

deacetylated tosyladenosine led to 3,5-di-*O*-methylribose. The tosyl group was therefore in the 2'-position, the diacetate was 3',5'-di-*O*-acetyladenosine (16) and hence adenylic acid *a* was adenosine 2'-phosphate. At the same time the *b* isomer was shown to be adenosine 3'-phosphate by an X-ray crystallographic structure determination[92].

Turning to the other three nucleotide pairs, it was evident that these were also the 2'- and 3'-isomers. The conversion of each pair to a single cyclic 2',3'-phosphate by trifluoroacetic anhydride sufficiently demonstrated this point[88]. A number of reagents have been used since for this cyclisation, including dicyclohexylcarbodiimide[93,94] and ethyl chloroformate[95], the latter being particularly effective since it effects the conversion quantitatively in aqueous solution.

Guanylic acids *a* and *b* were shown by Khym and Cohn to be the 2'- and 3'-nucleotides (9 and 10; R=guanine residue) respectively, using the method they had applied to the adenylic acids[90].

The pyrimidine nucleotides appeared to present a more difficult problem, by virtue of the much greater stability of the glycosidic linkage compared with that in the purine nucleotides. But the relationship $a(2')$ and $b(3')$ was again established. Several workers on the basis of physical measurements took the view that cytidylic acids a and b were cytidine 2'- and 3'-phosphate respectively[96-98]. The connection between the cytidylic and uridylic acids was established by showing that the cytidylic acid b underwent slow deamination in alkali and that the sole product was uridylic acid b, no phosphate migration being possible under these conditions[99]. The orientation problem was solved by the use of a reaction applied first to uracil and later to uridine by Levene and Bass[100]. They showed that hydrazine under rather mild conditions effects the cleavage of the pyrimidine ring to give pyrazolone and urea, or, probably, ribosylurea in the case of uridine. Baron and Brown[101] then showed that uridylic and cytidylic acids b (17 and 18) gave pyrazolone and aminopyrazole respectively together with ribose 3-phosphate (19). Cytidylic acid a gave ribose 2-phosphate. There was no cross-contamination of the sugar phosphates, since they had been formed under basic conditions. More recently Cohn and Doherty[102] have utilised the fact that hydrogenation of the 4,5-double bond in pyrimidine nucleotides greatly increases the ease of fission of the glycosidic linkages. Using rhodium on alumina as catalyst they hydrogenated uridylic acid b, converted the product by dilute alkali to the β-ureidopropionic acid glycoside (20; R = ribosyl residue) which under mild acid conditions gave predominantly ribose 3-phosphate.

A structurally definitive synthesis of uridylic acid a has been described by Brown, Todd and Varadarajan[103], while a complete X-ray crystallographic structure determination on cytidylic acid b has been made by Alver and Furberg[104]. Both confirm the conclusions drawn above.

The evidence as a whole shows, beyond doubt, that the a and b ribonucleotides are the 2'- and 3'-phosphates. This result was foreshadowed by the enzymic experiments of Shuster and Kaplan[105] who isolated a nucleotidase which specifically dephosphorylated all of the b-isomers; the a-isomers were not attacked.

In addition to the nucleotides based on adenine, guanine, cytosine and uracil, a number of others have been found in hydrolysates of RNA. Where a and b isomers have been observed no orientation experiments have been performed. They must be the 2'- and 3'-phosphates but not necessarily respectively. The nucleotides corresponding to the minor bases may be confined to the soluble fractions of RNA, where analytical methods at present show that they predominate. The most completely studied are the nucleotides based on 5-ribosyluracil, a and b isomers being obtained by alkaline hydrolysis and the 5'-phosphate resulting from venom diesterase fission of s-RNA[106−108]. The others are essentially methylated derivatives of the common nucleotides and have been mentioned in the previous section.

(c) Deoxyribonucleotides

Progress in the deoxynucleotide series was much retarded because of the relative unavailability of deoxynucleosides and because chemical hydrolysis of DNA did not lead to the simple monomeric units as it did in the case of RNA. Klein and Thannhauser[109] in 1935 had succeeded, by enzymic hydrolysis using an arsenate-inhibited intestinal phosphatase preparation, in isolating, in crystalline state, four nucleotides (deoxyadenylic, deoxyguanylic, deoxycytidylic and thymidylic acids). The later separation of these by ion-exchange methods made them readily available for structural study[110]. It was noted that their ion-exchange behaviour emulated that of the ribonucleoside 5'-phosphates and dephosphorylation[111] by a specific 5'-nucleotidase provided good circumstantial evidence that they were nucleoside 5'-phosphates and not nucleoside 3'-phosphates as had been commonly assumed. Much further enzymic and chemical hydrolytic work has been done in recent years and will be discussed later, but our knowledge of the structures of the monodeoxyribonucleotides rests essentially on chemical syntheses carried out by Todd, Michelson and co-workers[112-114].

Monotritylation of deoxynucleosides proceeds exclusively on the 5'-hydroxyl groups and this allows the differentiation of the 3'- and 5'-positions on which unambiguous synthesis of the two series of mononucleotides rests. 5'-Tritylthymidine (21) was phosphorylated with dibenzyl phosphorochloridate to yield (22; R=thymine) whence mild acid hydrolysis to remove the trityl group and then hydrogenolysis afforded thymidine 3'-phosphate (23; R=thymine residue).

Acetylation of the original trityl derivative and then detritylation gave 3'-O-acetylthymidine (24), phosphorylation of which yielded (25), readily converted to thymidine 5'-phosphate (26; R=thymine residue)[112]. A complete X-ray crystallographic structure analysis on calcium thymidine 5'-phosphate has been carried out[113].

In an exactly analogous way 5'-trityldeoxycytidine was converted to deoxycytidine 3'-phosphate (23; R=cytosine residue). The amino group in the cytidine and deoxycytidine series has considerable reactivity and by-products were obtained corresponding to N⁶-phosphorylated compounds. Acetylation of trityldeoxycytidine gave the O³,N⁶-diacetyl derivative from which, on removal of the trityl group and phosphorylation, deoxycytidine 5'-phosphate (26) was obtained[114].

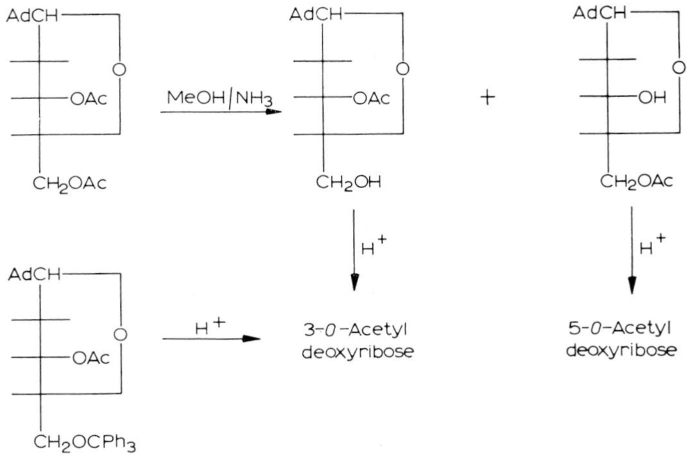

AdCH⎯

⎯OAc →(MeOH/NH₃) AdCH⎯ ⎯OAc + AdCH⎯ ⎯OH

CH₂OAc   CH₂OH   CH₂OAc

AdCH⎯ ⎯OAc →(H⁺)

CH₂OCPh₃

$\downarrow$ H⁺

3-O-Acetyl deoxyribose

$\downarrow$ H⁺

5-O-Acetyl deoxyribose

The purine deoxynucleotides presented a greater problem, due to lower reactivity of the hydroxyl groups and much greater lability of the glycosidic bonds; direct use of the trityl protecting group was therefore precluded since its removal necessitated acid hydrolysis, hydrogenolysis apparently being ineffective in this series. In the deoxyadenosine series the 3'-O-acetyl and 5'-O-acetyl derivatives were made by partial deacetylation of the diacetate, and separated by countercurrent distribution[115]. The monoacetyl nucleosides were oriented by gentle acid hydrolysis to the acetyldeoxyriboses and comparison of these with authentic 3-O-acetyldeoxyribose derived from 3'-O-acetyl-5'-O-trityldeoxyadenosine. The two monoacetyl deoxyguanosines were, likewise, prepared and oriented. An alternative phosphorylating agent to dibenzyl phosphorochloridate was used since the latter gave very low yields in these instances. The mixed anhydride O-benzylphosphorous O,O-diphenylphosphoric anhydride, $Ph \cdot CH_2OPO(H) \cdot OPO(OPh)_2$, proved successful, leading, in the case of 3'-O-acetyldeoxyadenosine to the 3'-O-acetyl-5'-benzylphosphite, convertible to the benzyl phosphate by N-

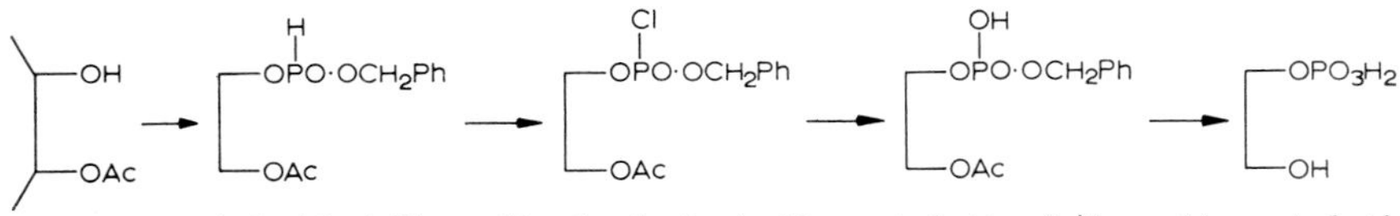

⎯OH → ⎯OPO·OCH₂Ph (H) → ⎯OPO·OCH₂Ph (Cl) → ⎯OPO·OCH₂Ph (OH) → ⎯OPO₃H₂

⎯OAc   ⎯OAc   ⎯OAc   ⎯OAc   ⎯OH

chlorosuccinimide followed by hydrolysis. Deacetylation followed by catalytic debenzylation gave deoxyadenosine 5'-phosphate. Virtually identical procedures starting with the appropriate acetyldeoxynucleoside gave deoxyadenosine 3'-phosphate and deoxyguanosine 3'- and 5'-phosphate[116]. The cyanoethyl phosphate method of Tener has since been used very successfully for deoxyribonucleotide synthesis[73,74].

The synthetic deoxynucleoside 5'-phosphates were shown to be identical to the natural nucleotides obtained by Klein and Thannhauser and Volkin *et al.* More recently Cunningham[117] discovered a micrococcal nuclease which catalysed the hydrolysis of DNA in part to deoxynucleoside 3'-phosphates, the structures being ultimately defined by comparison with the corresponding synthetic compounds since both natural and synthetic compounds were unaffected by 5'-nucleotidase.

Cohn[118] has given convincing evidence for the presence of 5-methyl-deoxycytidine 5'-phosphate as a minor component in diesterase hydrolysates of thymus DNA.

The T bacteriophages contain no cytosine. Although earlier reports indicated only three bases, less drastic hydrolytic procedures showed that the more labile 5-hydroxymethylcytosine was present, replacing cytosine quantitatively (see p. 169). 5-Hydroxymethyldeoxycytidine 3',5'-diphosphate was isolated from acid hydrolysates[119]. Another early observation was that these nucleic acids contained a higher proportion of sugar than normal. It transpired that glucose was present and linked glycosidically to the hydroxymethyl group. A recent study of Lehman and Pratt[120] of the 5'-nucleotides derived enzymically from these bacteriophage DNA's reveals a complex and intriguing picture in which it is seen that the hydroxymethyl radical may be unglucosylated, monoglucosylated (α- or β-linked) or carry a diglucosyl residue. The glucosylation pattern is discussed on p. 187; it is quite clear that the degree and pattern of glucosylation are genetically determined[121,122]. Kuno and Lehman have recently shown that the diglucoside is in fact an α-gentibioside[123].

3. The general structure of the nucleic acids

Many attempts have been made in the past to formulate general structures for the nucleic acids since it became evident that they were polynucleotides. The earlier discussions have been adequately reviewed and will not be dealt with here. During the last ten years the nature of the internucleotide linkage has been settled for both RNA and DNA and only the evidence on which these developments have been based will be considered.

Electrometric titration of monoribonucleotides and of RNA and DNA led Levene and Simms[124] to the concept of nucleic acids as polynucleotides in which nucleoside residues were linked by phosphodiester bridges. This was consequent on the ratio of primary to secondary phosphoryl dissociations being unity for the mononucleotides and greater than unity for RNA and DNA. A great deal of further and more refined titration work[17,125] on much better samples of nucleic acids than Levene and Simms could command has shown that the amount of secondary dissociation is vanishingly small, a result consistent with an extended polynucleotide.

The question of chain branching has been seriously considered, and will be discussed, but the evidence now appears to be satisfied by linear structures. Types of internucleotide linkage present to a minor extent, *e.g.* those involving C-1 of the deoxyribose residues or the base residues have been invoked, but have not been substantiated by later work (see ref. 126 p. 411 for references). They are probably to be accounted for, in retrospect, by the strong hydrogen bonding which is now recognised to exist between bases in the native nucleic acids and the fission of these bonds on denaturation, with consequent liberation of titrable groups.

(a) Aspects of phosphodiester chemistry

At an early time it had been noted that RNA broke down to mononucleotides with alkali at room temperature while DNA remained unhydrolysed. A method of analysis of RNA and DNA in tissues originated by Schmidt and Thannhauser[127] utilised this fact—hydrolysis by base, then acidification, led to precipitation of the DNA while the ribonucleotides remained in solution. The explanation of this very clear difference between the two acids led in turn to a precise definition of the internucleotide linkage points.

There were in the chemical literature on phosphate esters examples of compounds which emulated RNA and DNA, as first pointed out by Fonó[128] in 1947. First of all it was clear that if DNA was a poly-phosphodiester its behaviour was quite normal. Dialkyl phosphates are extremely stable to alkali[129] as might be expected, since, as with mono-esters, they carry a negative charge. The observation is general although only dimethyl phosphate[130] and dibenzyl phosphate[131] have been studied in any detail, rate constants having been recorded. We should note here that RNA and DNA are considered to undergo hydrolysis at pH 7 at very similar rates which are also close to those for the simple diesters. Thus for instance the molecular weights of RNA and denatured (single-stranded) DNA are halved[132] in aqueous solution at 20° in 90 h and 116 days respectively; at 100° the times are 5 and 15 min. Clearly no special mechanism pertains with RNA at neutrality.

Examples of alkali-labile diesters were known through the work of Bailly and Gaumé[133]. They had shown that although glycerol 1-phosphate was stable to alkali, glycerol 1-methylphosphate (27; R = Me) gave methanol and glycerol 1- and 2-phosphate; no methyl phosphate was formed. Baer and Kates[134], too, showed that the choline ester (27; R = choline) with alkali gave choline together with glycerol 1- and 2-phosphate. 2-Hydroxyethyl-dimethyl phosphate (28) with dilute alkali gave 2-hydroxyethyl phosphate (29) but 2-methoxyethyl dimethyl phosphate (30) gave 2-methoxyethyl methyl phosphate (31) which was stable to further hydrolysis[133]. These

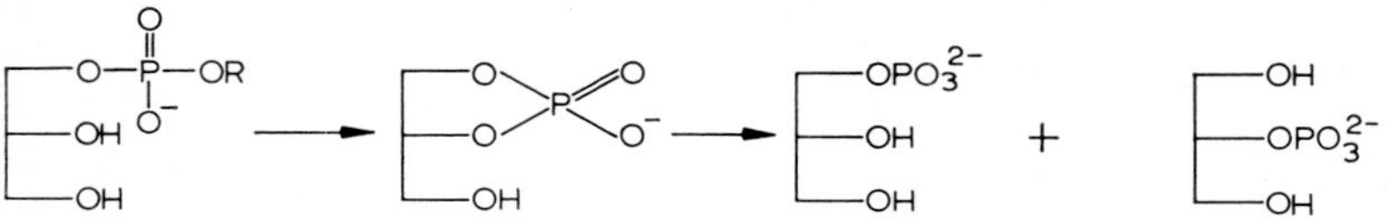

27

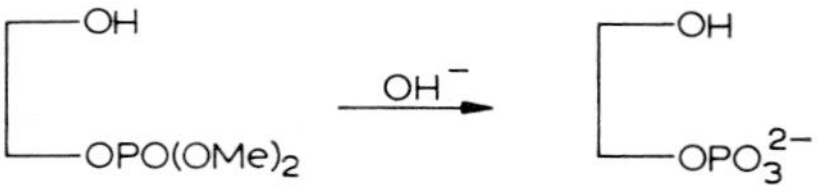

28 $\xrightarrow{\text{OH}^-}$ 29

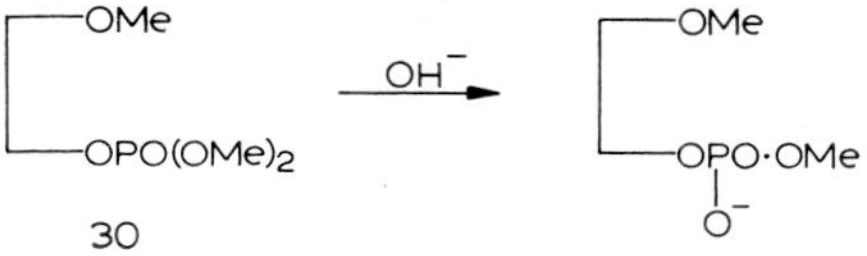

30 $\xrightarrow{\text{OH}^-}$ 31

observations showed that alkali-lability was associated with the presence of a neighbouring hydroxyl group. The lability of RNA and the stability of DNA to base, it was pointed out[135], were to be ascribed, in principle, to the presence respectively of an hydroxyl group on C-2' in the case of RNA and its absence in DNA. The validity of this was established[87] by showing that esters of adenosine 2'- and 3'-phosphate underwent hydrolysis in a fashion exactly analogous to those of glycerol 1-phosphate. Adenosine 3'-benzyl phosphate (referred to as the *b* isomer since the orientation studies had not then been completed) (32) with base or acid gave adenosine 2'- and 3'-phosphate; the 2'-ester gave the same mixture of products. Adenosine 5'-benzyl phosphate was completely stable under the same conditions.

It will be recalled that adenosine 2'- and 3'-phosphate are stable to and not interconvertible by base. Clearly then the 2'- and 3'-nucleotides were derived from a common intermediate. The hydrolytic process was discussed first by postulating a cyclic triester (33) or related entity, which underwent hydrolysis to the cyclic diester (34), this, in turn giving the two isomeric nucleotides. This view of the mechanism was later modified when it was suggested that the process involved a base-catalysed attack of the neighbouring hydroxyl group on phosphorus with simultaneous displacement[136] of the R group as an alkoxide ion, as in (35).

This mechanism, in which the first step is essentially a transesterification involving an S$_{N}$2 displacement on phosphorus has been verified. In the first

References p. 262

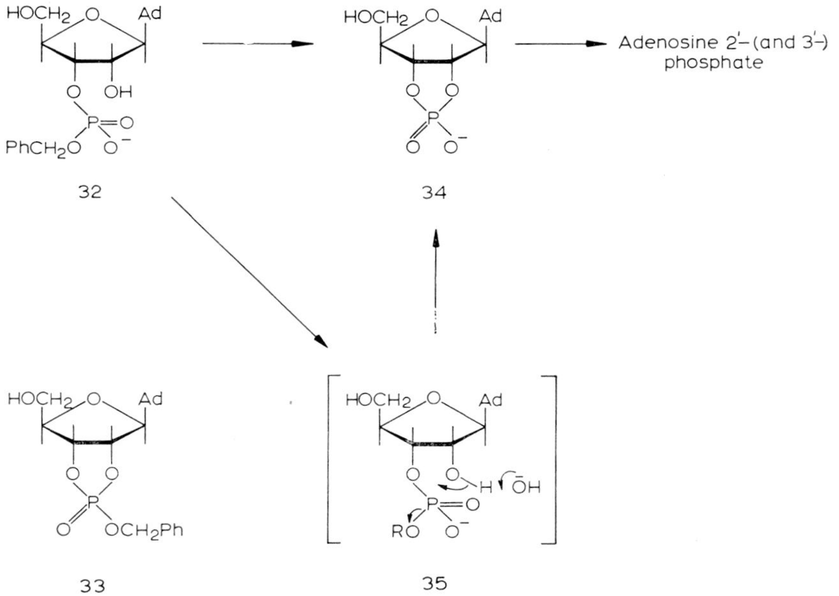

HOCH₂ O Ad ⟶ HOCH₂ O Ad ⟶ Adenosine 2′-(and 3′-) phosphate

PhCH₂O ... P=O ... OH

32   **34**

HOCH₂ O Ad   [HOCH₂ O Ad]

33   **35**

place the cyclic nucleoside 2′,3′-phosphates (34) were synthezised, as mentioned on p. 218, and were shown to undergo hydrolysis with extreme ease in base or acid, so that they had the desired characteristics. It may be noted that in the glycerol series, glycerol 1,2-phosphate has been shown to be an obligatory intermediate in the hydrolysis of esters of glycerol 1-phosphate since they and the 1,2-cyclic phosphate both gave glycerol 1- and 2-phosphate in exactly the same ratio[137] of 45:55.

Markham and Smith[138] showed that small amounts of cyclic nucleoside 2′,3′-phosphate could be observed when RNA was hydrolysed by barium carbonate in hot water or by hot aqueous ammonia. High yields of the cyclic phosphates were formed when RNA was treated with potassium *tert.*-butoxide in dimethylformamide; the alkoxide catalysed the trans-esterification step (35) to give the cyclic phosphate (34) but due, no doubt, to large steric hindrance in the attack of *tert.*-butoxide on the cyclic ester no subsequent displacement to form a *tert.*-butyl ester occurred[139].

The decision as to whether or not the triester (33) was involved in hydrolysis was reached by Lipkin and coworkers[140] who hydrolysed RNA in ¹⁸O-enriched water. Approximately one ¹⁸O was incorporated in a phosphate residue for every diester linkage hydrolysed. Formation and fission of the triester would have necessitated the incorporation of two ¹⁸O atoms. Although this eliminated (33) from consideration it clearly did not preclude structures of type (36), related to those involved in the hydrolysis of carboxylic esters. The intermediate depicted in (36) would imply the possibility of rearrangement without hydrolysis necessarily occurring; that depicted in (37), in which the displaced group is on the rear-side with respect to the attacking hydroxyl group, should allow of no migration of the phosphoryl group without concomitant hydrolysis. Brown *et al.*[141] showed that (37) provided the best representation of the process. When the hydrolysis of cytidine 3'-benzyl phosphate was carried to half-completion and un-

36   37

changed ester then recovered it was shown that the latter contained no detectable amount of cytidine 2'-benzyl ester. The reaction is therefore more nearly analogous to an S_N2 displacement at a saturated carbon atom and presumably passes through a trigonal bipyramidal transition state.

Acid hydrolysis of esters of nucleoside 2'- and 3'-phosphates (and of RNA) undoubtedly proceeds via cyclic intermediates. The products are the same as those formed in the base-catalysed hydrolysis, although the 2'- and 3'-nucleotides undergo subsequent equilibration. The hydrolysis is very much faster than would be considered normal for a simple dialkyl phosphate. It is probable that a protonated species derived from the free acid is involved, but it is difficult to discuss in any detail the intermediates involved. However after half hydrolysis of cytidine 3'-benzyl phosphate, it could be shown that 25% of the recovered ester was cytidine 2'-benzyl phosphate, *i.e.* rearrangement without hydrolysis occurred[141]. Partial acid hydrolysis of RNA, too, has been shown to lead to dinucleotides with partially rearranged internucleotide linkages[142, 143]. The point is important since it means that no reliance can be put on evidence from acid hydrolysis on the question of the orientation of the internucleotide linkage.

The hydrolytic chemistry of RNA is closely associated with the peculiar reactivity of the cyclic nucleoside 2',3'-phosphates. As noted above, their very easy hydrolysis by base and acid accords with and allows an explanation of the production of nucleoside 2'- and 3'-phosphates from RNA. The high reactivity is a feature of the 5-membered cyclic phosphates so far studied, the 6-membered ring compounds, on the contrary, having a stability comparable to open-chain dialkyl phosphates[74]. Ethylene 1,2-phosphate is hydrolysed by base with P–O fission about 10^7 times as fast as its open-chain analogue dimethyl phosphate[144]. The reason for this high reactivity is still open to dispute.

39   40   38

The heat of hydrolysis of methyl ethylene phosphate (39) is considerably greater than that of the related[145] open-chain hydroxyethyl dimethyl phosphate (38). It may be that O–O repulsion can account for the effect, since bond-angle strain itself would not provide a sufficient explanation. While alkaline hydrolysis of a nucleoside 2′,3′-phosphate is of course irreversible, reaction with alkoxides is reversible. Lithium methoxide in dimethyl formamide converts RNA to nucleoside 2′-(and 3′-)methyl phosphates; undoubtedly the latter are formed by the methanolysis of an

intermediate cyclic phosphate[146]. Such a process has, in fact, been studied as a method of preparation of nucleotide 2′-(and 3′-)esters while an acid-catalysed alcoholysis is also observed under anhydrous conditions[147-149].

The cis-diol system in the ribofuranosyl residue of the ribonucleosides is exceptionally favourable for the neighbouring hydroxyl group participation in the hydrolysis of nucleotide 2′-(3′-)esters. The trans-disposition of the $C^{5'}$-OH effectively prevents formation of nucleoside 3′,5′-phosphates so that alkyl esters of ribonucleoside 5′-phosphates and deoxyribonucleoside 3′-phosphates are stable to base. Thymidine 3′-p-nitrophenyl phosphate does, however, give the stable 3′,5′-cyclic phosphate with base under forcing conditions due to the fact that the nitrophenolate ion is an excellent leaving group, but this is essentially irrelevant to nucleic acid chemistry[150].

These considerations can now be applied directly to the question of structure of RNA.

(b) The structure of RNA

The early observations that RNA is hydrolysed completely by base to 2′- and 3′-nucleotides have been confirmed by many more recent studies using chromatographic and electrophoretic separation methods. This statement must be qualified by the fact that very small amounts of alkali-stable dinucleotides, of which twelve have been recognised, can be isolated from the hydrolysates of several RNA's. They appear to contain modified nucleosides, carrying, probably, a 2-O-methyl group which prevents hydrolysis occurring *i.e.* renders that part of the polynucleotide DNA-like[151]. These observations do not affect the essential validity of the following arguments. General structures[135] for RNA can be written with this knowledge, in the light of the discussion in the previous section. First of all it is clear that the 2'- or the 3'-position of the individual ribonucleoside residues is involved. Moreover C-5'—C-5' internucleotide linkages* as in (51) are not permissible since no neighbouring hydroxyl group would then be available to allow easy hy-

50　　　　　　　　　51　　　　　　　　　　52

53　　　　　　　　　54　　　　　　　　　　2'— and 3'— nucleotides

drolysis; the alkali-stability of nucleoside 5'-alkyl phosphates has already been discussed and the compound adenosine 5'-uridine 5'-phosphate has been synthesized and likewise shown to be stable to base[152]. Structures for linear polynucleotides based on structures (52–54) do satisfy the hydrolytic requirements, (52) involves the 5'-position, while (53) and (54) do not. The two latter structures require that hydrolysis should proceed in a stepwise fashion, by removal of mononucleotide units from the end of the chain carrying a free 2'- or 3'-hydroxyl group. Not a great deal of chemical evidence is available to test this point but the isolation of small oligonucleotides from acid[143], alkaline[153], and heavy metal hydroxide[63] hydrolysates favours a simultaneous rather than stepwise hydrolysis of the chain. Formation of small oligonucleotides shows that C-3'—C-5' (or C-2'—C-5') internucleotide linkages must be present (as in 52). Enzymic and other evidence, to be discussed later, establishes C-5' as a major linkage point. A 2',5'-internucleotide linkage on the evidence so far presented is equally as acceptable as (52). Hydrolytic studies provide no means of distinction. Indeed, the dinucleoside phosphate adenosine 2'-uridine 5'-phosphate has been synthesized; it is hydrolysed by alkali to uridine and adenosine 2'- and 3'-phosphate[154]. Justification for the

---

* The symbol (50) represents a nucleotide, the numbers referring to the positions of the OH groups. A, G, U, C, T refer to the common bases and P indicates the phosphate residue.

structure (52) containing a 3',5'-linkage came mainly from enzymic evidence which is now considered.

(i) *Evidence for nucleoside 5'-linkages*

Acceptance of the 5'-position as a linkage point in RNA came only after it was realised that failure to isolate nucleoside 5'-phosphates from chemical hydrolysates was a necessary consequence of the mechanism of the reaction. The formation of oligonucleotides from RNA by a variety of hydrolytic methods (see p. 229) is itself strong circumstantial evidence for a recurrent 5'-linkage. Some evidence had been forthcoming at an early date from enzymic studies, particularly those of Gulland and Jackson[155] using Russell's viper venom, which contains a 5'-nucleotidase, a phosphodiesterase and a weak non-specific phosphatase. The observed production of orthophosphate from yeast RNA by the action of the venom was an indication of the intermediate liberation of nucleoside 5'-phosphates. Cohn and Volkin[156] confirmed the presence of 5'-phosphoester linkages by treating RNA first with ribonuclease and then with intestinal phosphatase, in presence of arsenate to inhibit monoesterase activity. They were able to identify the four ribonucleoside 5'-phosphates, among the products, by ion-exchange chromatography. Later these authors[157], using a purified venom diesterase, were able to increase the yield of 5'-nucleotides to about 60%. Nucleoside 2'(3'),5'-diphosphates were also observed. The probable source of the diphosphates will be mentioned later but it is evident that the products of venom diesterase on RNA largely carry a 5'-phosphate residue. Consistently, the diesterase splits adenosine 5'-benzyl phosphate, but not the 3'-esters[158].

Further very strong evidence comes from a study of the products of pancreatic ribonuclease action (discussed in the next section and on p. 242).

Since clarification of the structural point relating to the 5'-linkage point much equivalent evidence has accrued which would be difficult to understand on other terms. Of this, probably the most convincing is the demonstration that ribonucleic acids can undergo phosphorolysis under catalysis by enzymes from a variety of sources, the end products being nucleoside 5'-pyrophosphates[1, 159].

$$\text{RNA} + n\text{P}_i \rightleftharpoons n \text{ nucleoside 5'-PP}$$

(ii) *Evidence for nucleoside 3'-linkages*

In 1940, Kunitz isolated in crystalline form the enzyme ribonuclease from pancreas and made some simple and telling experiments relating to its action[160] on RNA. Since then numerous studies have been made[161] some of which have a direct bearing on the structure of RNA.

The enzyme was found to break only a proportion of the internucleotide

linkages, as judged by titration, and the products were only in part dialysable[162]. The smaller fragments were richer in pyrimidine nucleoside
derivatives, the larger showed a high purine–pyrimidine ratio. This led to the
suggestion, afterwards confirmed, that the enzyme had a specificity for
pyrimidine nucleoside sites in the RNA molecule[163, 164]. Indeed substantial
amounts of cytidylic and uridylic acids were found to be present in ribonuclease digests[165,166]. From the point of view of RNA structure the work
of Schmidt, Thannhauser and their co-workers[167,168] was very enlighten-
ing. When exhaustive ribonuclease digestion of RNA was followed by
treatment with prostatic phosphomonoesterase, inorganic phosphate was
liberated, equivalent to 93% of the pyrimidine nucleoside content of the
RNA. The remaining bound phosphate was present almost entirely as purine
nucleotide phosphorus, that is, subsequent hydrolysis with base gave
pyrimidine nucleosides and purine nucleotides. They also showed that RNA
and the products of its digestion with ribonuclease were not oxidised by
periodate: after phosphomonoesterase treatment periodate oxidation showed
an uptake of oxidant equivalent to the orthophosphate liberated by the
monoesterase. All the oligonucleotide fragments must therefore terminate in
a pyrimidine nucleotide residue. Since periodate oxidation in the nucleotide
series is dependent on a free 2′,3′-diol system, Brown and Todd[135] pointed
out that the monoesterified phosphate in all the ribonuclease digest fragments must have been attached to the terminal 2′- or 3′-position. Schmidt
et al.[168] took the view therefore that in the oligonucleotide fragments the
remainder of the chain was attached to a position other than C-2′, or C-3′, of
the terminal pyrimidine nucleotide residue. It was a simple matter[135] to
equate that position with C-5′, after the hydrolytic mechanism had been
formulated.

Further experiments, mainly by Markham and Smith[169-172], provided the
essential details on which present views of the action of RNAase on RNA are
founded. They noted two products, present in partial digests which, by
further ribonuclease action, were converted to uridylic and cytidylic acids
respectively. These were identified as uridine and cytidine 2′,3′-phosphates
by comparison with the synthetic cyclic phosphates. Brown, Dekker and
Todd[99] showed that ribonuclease action on the cyclic phosphates gave, in
fact, the 3′-mononucleotides exclusively and this correlated with the observation that the pyrimidine mononucleotides in digests of RNA were also
exclusively the nucleoside 3′-phosphates. Thus the precursors of the mononucleotides were nucleoside 2′,3′-phosphates and Markham and Smith were
able to show that oligonucleotides carrying a terminal cyclic phosphate
grouping were also precursors of the oligonucleotides proper[172]. Brown,
Dekker and Todd pointed out that, on this evidence, the oligonucleotides
should also terminate in a 3′-phosphate residue. This was substantiated by

Volkin and Cohn[173] who hydrolysed a ribonuclease digest of RNA with alkali, and showed that the products were purine nucleoside 2'- and 3'-phosphates and pyrimidine nucleoside 3'-phosphates. The intermediate formation of cyclic phosphates was also consistent with the observations of Chantrenne, Linderstrøm-Lang and Vandendriessche[174, 175] who noted that, initially, depolymerisation occurred without liberation of acidic functions. A consistent scheme incorporating the above evidence can be set out as follows (Py=uracil or cytosine residue, Pu=adenine or guanine residue):

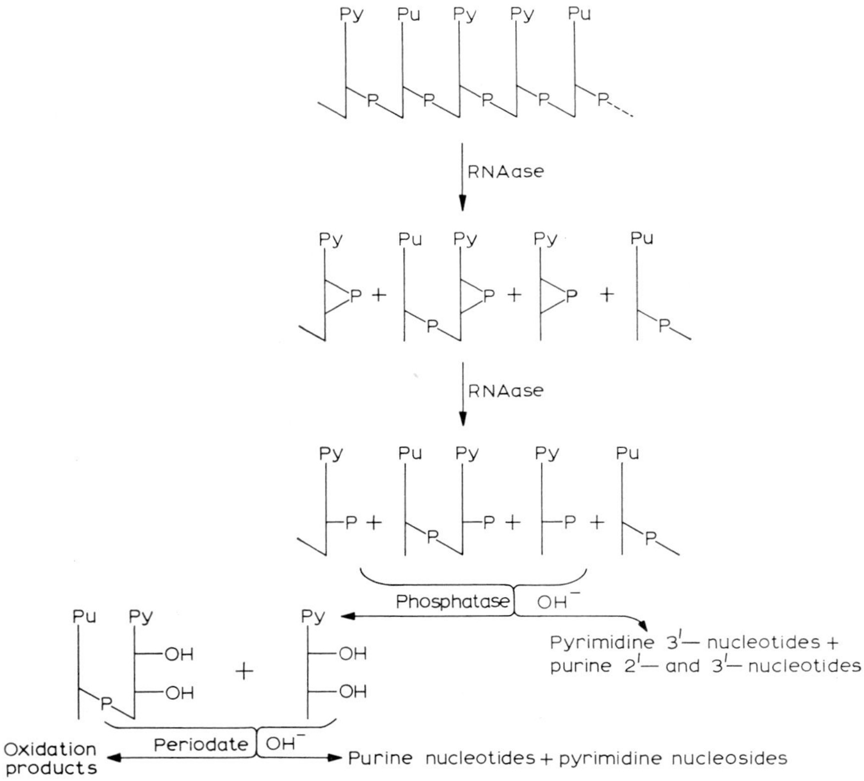

We shall discuss the oligonucleotides in more detail later, but it is evident from the foregoing evidence that they are purine oligonucleotides terminated by a pyrimidine nucleotide residue[172]. The production of pyrimidine nucleoside 3'-phosphates or oligonucleotides terminating in a 3'-phosphate does not of itself indicate the internucleotide linkage point other than C-5', since pseudo symmetrical cyclic phosphates intervened, apparently as obligatory intermediates. Brown and Todd observed[136] that the action of ribonuclease appeared to be quite analogous to that of alkali with the added specificity for pyrimidine sites; more detailed discussions have been given recently[176]. If this were the case then simple esters of the pyrimidine nucleotides should equally be hydrolysed by the enzyme. Accordingly, it was found[136] that cytidine 3'-benzyl phosphate (55; Py=cytosine residue) was hydrolysed via the cyclic phosphate to cytidine 3'-phosphate. The 2'- and 5'-esters were inert. Analogous observations were made in the uridine series, while corresponding purine nucleotide derivatives were unaffected by the enzyme. The 2'- and 3'-esters were oriented by hydrogenation to the parent nucleotide, a process which avoided phosphate migration. (It should be noted that many of the papers quoted in this section refer to the 2'- and 3'-nucleotides as the *a* and *b* isomers, since the orientation question had not been completely solved). These experiments establish unequivocally that the 3'-position of the pyrimidine nucleoside residues is involved in the internucleotide linkage. They say nothing of the corresponding linkage to the purine nucleoside residues. Fortunately there are a number of enzymes with nuclease activity which provide the necessary evidence[176,177]. Enzyme fractions from spleen degrade RNA and oligonucleotides derived from RNA by ribonuclease action to give high yields of mononucleotides, the adenylic and the guanylic acid being the 3'-isomers. The same fractions converted

cytidine and adenosine 3'-benzyl phosphates to the corresponding nucleotides; the 2'-isomers were unaffected[178,179]. Several other enzymes hydrolyse RNA. Where studied, these enzymes hydrolyse the 3'-esters but in no case the 2'-esters[180-183]. Taken together these studies show clearly that both the purine and pyrimidine nucleoside residues in RNA are linked at the 3'-position. A strictly chemical method has also been devised and applied to several oligonucleotides derived from RNA. The process is discussed in detail later (p. 244) in relation to the structure of oligonucleotides and nucleotide sequence; it confirms the conclusions derived from enzymic studies.

56

The general structure (56) is therefore established for RNA. There remains the question of chain branching but we may note that no studies on oligonucleotides have given any evidence that they are other than linear.

(iii) Chain branching in RNA

If we take, again, as a criterion, the ability of RNA to be hydrolysed by base to mononucleotides, it is possible to limit the number of possible types of branching. Brown and Todd[135] analysed this question in some detail and reduced the probable types to: (a) branching by means of a phosphodiester bridge from C-2′ on a sugar residue in the main chain to C-3′ in the first residue in the chain as in (57) and (b) branching through phosphotriester linkage as in (58).

57   58

Branching on sugar was proposed by Anderson et al.[184] on the basis of methylation studies on yeast ribonucleic acid. Isolation of ribose and mono- and dimethylriboses after acid hydrolysis were taken to indicate branching of type (57), these sugars being derived from residues D, B and A (terminal) respectively. Brown, Magrath and Todd[185] studied the methylation of uridine 3'-phosphate and showed clearly that the process was slow and therefore difficult to bring to completion and that phosphoryl migration occurred. The method, they concluded, was unlikely to afford reliable evidence when applied to polynucleotides as internucleotidic bond fission must be expected to accompany methylation. The products of methylation of RNA could therefore be accounted for without recourse to a branching hypothesis. Evidence for branching was also forthcoming from enzymic studies, in which it was shown that venom diesterase hydrolysis of RNA gave, in addition to nucleoside 5'-phosphates, some nucleosides (mainly purine) and pyrimidine 3'-nucleotides, considerable quantities of pyrimidine nucleoside 2',5'- and 3',5'-diphosphates[157]. It seemed possible that the latter came from the branch points in the main chain by C-3'–O–P fission and that the nucleosides represented end groups (i.e. residue A in 57). A satisfactory explanation of these results on the basis of a linear structure for RNA involves (a) the known ubiquity of ribonuclease and (b) the specificity of venom diesterase which rapidly attacks polynucleotides which carry either a cyclic 2',3'-phosphate group, or lack a 3'-phosphate group[186]. Thus a very small quantity of ribonuclease would liberate oligonucleotides with a 2',3'-cyclic phosphate end; fission of these by the diesterase would afford pyrimidine nucleoside 2',3'-phosphate–5'-phosphate, converted under the conditions of isolation to the 2'(or 3'),5'-diphosphate. RNA rigorously freed from ribonuclease gave very much smaller quantities of the diphosphates, now including those derived from adenosine and guanosine; it is conceivable that these were derived from end groups of linear structures. Thus branching on sugar has no real experimental support, but there is no positive evidence establishing its absence.

The situation with respect to branching by incorporation of phosphotriester groupings is more clear cut. The original proposals that such groupings existed depended on electrometric titrations of yeast RNA which showed that the ratio of primary to secondary phosphoryl dissociation was in the region of 4:1. Assuming a high molecular weight, branching was necessary to provide sufficient terminal phosphate residues. With the provision in later years of much better samples of RNA, no appreciable amount of secondary phosphoryl dissociation could be detected[17,187,188]. More significant, however, is the fact that while trialkyl phosphates are reasonably stable, those with a vicinal hydroxyl group are exceptionally unstable[189]. Thus dimethyl uridine 3'-phosphate is hydrolysed at room temperature even at neutrality so that if an analogous grouping were present in native RNA it would not persist through the isolation procedure.

An experiment by Koshland, Simmons and Watson[190] provides evidence, within the limits of the method, that no triester groupings are present in a native RNA. Tobacco mosaic virus was dissociated in water enriched with ^{18}O. The liberated RNA, if it had contained labile triester linkages should have become labelled in the phosphate oxygen atoms. No such incorporation was observed. We conclude that no evidence exists, therefore, for either of the two types of branching types discussed. That such branching may exist in nucleic acids as yet unstudied from this point of view is still possible. Electron micrographs, particularly of tobacco mosaic virus RNA, are taken to give strong evidence for a linear structure[191].

(c) Deoxyribonucleic acids

The general structure of DNA presents less of a problem than that of RNA. There are only two hydroxyl groups on the nucleoside residues, those at C-3' and C-5', to which phosphate can be esterified. It has long been recognised that DNA molecules are polynucleotides of high molecular weight. Over the years isolation methods have improved enormously, and values of less than a million are rarely quoted for well prepared material; values of over $100 \cdot 10^6$ may well become commonplace[192]. Evidence will be presented which shows that DNA consists of a linear polynucleotide in which the nucleoside

59   60

residues are linked at the 3'- and 5'-positions by phosphodiester bonds, as in (59). There seems no way at present of determining whether every linkage is of this type in, for example, a molecule of $130 \cdot 10^6$ or for that matter of $10 \cdot 10^6$ molecular weight. Indeed Bernardi and Sadron have recently[193] described an enzyme from chicken erythrocytes which seems to break down DNA, of molecular weight $6 \cdot 10^6$ to units of $5 \cdot 10^5$. It is quite conceivable that a pyrophosphate linkage, for instance, occurs between every genetically distinct unit. The DNA molecule is relatively rigid (see p. 280 *et seq.*) and the nature of the folding which allows it to fit into small cellular structures has not been clarified. This might also be grounds for arguing that an infrequent but different type of linkage occurred. With these reservations in mind, we can discuss the major internucleotide linkages in DNA.

Levene and Jacobs observed that when DNA is hydrolysed with acid, di-phosphates of deoxycytidine and thymidine are among the products. Although the early claim was disputed it was verified by Dekker, Michelson and Todd[194], who isolated the two compounds from acid hydrolysates of herring sperm DNA and showed them to be identical with synthetic 3',5'-diphosphates of deoxycytidine and thymidine (60: R = cytosine and thymine residues).

The chemistry associated with this degradation will be discussed in detail later (p. 255) in connection with nucleotide sequence, but regardless of the hydrolytic mechanism it showed the involvement of the 3'- and 5'-positions in the deoxyribonucleosides, as internucleotide linkage points.

Chemical hydrolysis is not satisfactory as a means of obtaining mono-nucleotides from DNA. Base-catalysed hydrolysis does not reduce the molecule to small fragments, due to the stability of dialkyl phosphate anions; acid effects the cleavage of the labile purine N-glycosidic bonds much faster than the phosphate ester linkages are hydrolysed. However, Klein and Thannhauser, using an arsenate-inhibited intestinal phosphatase effected an enzymic hydrolysis and isolated four nucleotides. Later Volkin et al.[195] separated them by ion-exchange chromatography and their dephosphoryla-tion by 5'-nucleotidase showed that they were the 5'-phosphates of the common deoxyribonucleosides; 5-methyldeoxycytidine 5'-phosphate was also isolated[196]. The synthetic 5'-phosphates, referred to before, provided the necessary confirmation of structure. The hydrolysis by purified snake venom phosphodiesterase of deoxyribonuclease treated or native DNA led to virtually quantitative conversion to nucleoside 5'-phosphates[197]. T bac-teriophages do not give quantitative production of nucleoside 5'-phosphates under these conditions, but complete hydrolysis can be attained by use of a diesterase from E. coli[120]. Thus all or almost all of the internucleotide linkages must involve the 5'-position of a nucleoside residue. This evidence strongly supports a structure of type (59). In support of this, enzymes have been described which hydrolyse DNA to give nucleoside 3'-phosphates[158]. A micrococcal nuclease converts about 50% of the DNA into a mixture of the four nucleoside 3'-phosphates[198,199] the rest of the material being present as dinucleotides, due apparently to a combination of endo- and exo-nucleo-lytic activity combined with an inability of the enzyme to split oligonucleo-tides smaller than the dimers[200]. Structural studies[201] show that the dinucleotides are of the general type (61). Pancreatic deoxyribonuclease (DNAase I) gives very small amounts of mononucleotides; oligonucleotides are the major products and, in the case studied[202], are of type (62). The evidence taken together supports type (59) structures for DNA and is in-consistent with structures which contain C-5'−C-5' and C-3'−C-3' inter-nucleotide linkages as in (63). The question as to whether a DNA is to be considered a poly(nucleoside 5'-phosphate) (62) or a poly(nucleoside 3'-phosphate) (61) or a polynucleotide lacking a terminal phosphate residue cannot be answered because the end-group represents such a small proportion of the whole. The biosynthetic pathway appears to involve exclusively the deoxynucleoside 5'-triphosphates so that the first type considered is the more likely[203]. Finally we may note that electron micrographs show that DNA appears to be linear over great lengths[204].

4. Nucleotide sequence in nucleic acids

The conclusion reached in the preceding section was that both RNA and DNA consist of linear polynucleotides. As regards chemical structure, the remaining problem is one of defining the nucleotide sequence. In no case, yet, apart possibly from the RNA of tobacco mosaic virus, is there any certainty that a single molecular species has been isolated in a pure state, although rapid progress is being made (vide supra) in the separation of individual soluble RNA species. This being so, studies in this field have had the more limited aims, firstly, of establishing methods for sequence determination which are effective with individual oligonucleotides. These naturally include methods for stepwise degradation. Secondly the question of the overall degree of randomness in nucleotide distribution has been considered.

It may be worth pointing out, here, without further elaboration, that nucleotide sequence in regions of DNA molecules conceivably may be established by a combination of mutagenesis by specific reagents together with a fine-structure genetic analysis of the mutants. Alternatively, it may be possible to argue from the amino-acid sequence of a protein to the nucleotide sequence of the region of the nucleic acid which defined it, presuming that a unique coding relationship can be established. In the present Chapter, however, we confine ourselves to the chemical and enzymic aspects of nucleotide-sequence studies.

It is likely that sequence determination will rest ultimately on the specific fission of polynucleotides to yield oligonucleotides the structures of which are then elucidated. Since there are in general only four types of monomeric nucleotide units, the number of observations needed to reach a unique solution will be much larger than in the comparable problem of protein structure. It is fortunate that in soluble RNA—the most likely candidate for initial work on structure determination—there are, in addition to the normal bases, 5-ribosyluracil and a number of methylated bases, present in small amounts, which may materially aid sequence studies.

(a) Oligoribonucleotides: production

(i) Chemical hydrolysis

When RNA is hydrolysed at room temperature in alkali, products larger than mononucleotides can be discerned if the process is interrupted before completion. A study has been made of this aspect of RNA hydrolysis, and a number of dinucleotides including di-adenylic acid can be seen to persist for a considerable time in such solutions[153]. Witzel[205] has made a valuable study of the hydrolysis of many dinucleoside phosphates, not only by hydroxide ion, but by other hydrolytic agents and it is clear that the nature of the base affects markedly the rate of hydrolysis of the internucleotide linkage. ApA for example is hydrolysed two times more slowly than UpC, the least stable of those studied. Such a range of stability cannot provide specific cleavage of polynucleotide chains in its present form but further development does seem possible. Dimroth and Witzel[63] observe that yeast RNA, on hydrolysis with bismuth hydroxide at pH 4, yields a large number of products among which they identify and separate all of the possible 16 dinucleoside phosphates. These have the usual 3',5'-internucleotide linkage but are accompanied by very small amounts of the corresponding rearranged 2',5'-linked compounds.

(ii) Enzymic hydrolysis

The most completely studied oligoribonucleotides are those derived from pancreatic ribonuclease action on RNA. Complete hydrolysis, as mentioned earlier (p. 230), leads to a series of purine oligonucleotides terminated by a

64   65

pyrimidine nucleotide residue carrying a 3'-linked phosphate residue of the general form (64; $n = 0, 1, \ldots$).

A large number of these have been separated by ion-exchange, electrophoretic and paper-chromatographic methods. Many of them have been structurally defined (see p. 242). It is perhaps unfortunate that few have been isolated in substance but it seems clear that solutions of the pure individuals have in many cases been obtained. All of the dinucleotides and many of the tri- and tetra-nucleotides can be separated from each other[206-208].

Paper electrophoresis is a valuable adjunct since it allows the separation of the components of incompletely resolved peaks from the initial column fractionation. Staehlin[209] has made a careful study of the ε-values of pure oligonucleotides and has thus put the quantitative aspect on a firmer footing. Removal of the terminal phosphate residue can readily be effected by monoesterases purified from contaminating diesterase and the products (65) are then more amenable to fractionation. Little progress has yet been made in fractionating the higher oligonucleotides; the amounts are relatively small and the number of substances, including positional isomers, is likely to be large.

In addition to pancreatic ribonuclease a variety of other nuclease preparations have been, and continue to be described. For example two nucleases from takadiastase, RNAase T_1 and T_2, complement the pancreas enzyme. T_1 is specific for guanosine 3'-phosphate esters and the T_2 enzyme hydrolyses only adenosine 3'-phosphate esters[210-212]. Very little work on the characterisation and structural definition of oligonucleotides obtained by use of these and other nucleases has yet been described.

(iii) Synthesis

A further source of oligonucleotides is from synthesis. Biosynthetic methods largely due to Heppel and co-workers[213] have led to a considerable variety of types some of which are symbolised in (66–69). Corresponding dimers and also higher homologous polymers have also been characterised. Enzymes of the polynucleotide phosphorylase type[1], first described by Grunberg-Manago and Ochoa, convert ribonucleoside 5'-pyrophosphates into homopolymers. Mixtures of nucleoside 5'-pyrophosphates lead to

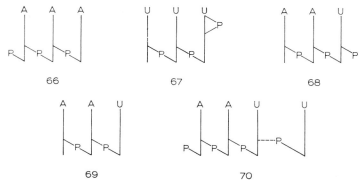

66   67   68

69   70

polymers containing the corresponding base type. These polymers can then be degraded enzymically to oligomers. The phosphorolytic activity of the enzyme on such polymers leads to products of type (66), since the enzyme acts more slowly on the lower oligomers and not at all on the dimer[214]. Ribonuclease fission of polyuridylic acid (poly-U) can lead to oligomers[213] of type (67) while its action on poly-AU gives substances[181] of type (68). Alternatively dinucleotides may be used as primers on which to build successive nucleotide residues, leading to polymers in which the end groups[215] may be defined. The removal of the terminal monoesterified phosphate is always readily effected by a phosphatase leading to products of the type (70). Steiner and Beers give a more extended discussion of these and other aspects of oligonucleotide production[1]. It is worth noting that the polyuridylic acids carrying Me, Cl, Br and I substituents on the 5-position of the uracil residues can be prepared[216,217]. Presumably nuclease hydrolysis could yield from them the corresponding unnatural oligomers.

By comparison chemical synthesis of oligoribonucleotides has not been so productive. This is essentially due to the difficulty experienced in protecting the 2'-position of nucleosides. The first synthesis in this series was in fact that of a 2',5'-linked compound, adenosine-2'-uridine 5'-phosphate, and relied on an intermediate used in the synthesis of adenosine 2'-phosphate (p. 218), the 2',5'-di-O-acetyladenosine 3'-(benzylphosphorochloridate), which was coupled with 2',3'-di-O-acetyluridine. Removal of the protecting groups then gave the desired product[154].

It is possible to protect the 2'-position by means of the acid-labile tetrahydropyranyl group. Khorana and co-workers[74, 218] have obtained 2'-O-tetrahydropyranyl-5'-O-trityluridine 3'-phosphate by a multistep synthesis. Coupling, by means of dicyclohexyl carbodiimide (DCC) to 2',3'-di-O-acetyluridine and removal of protecting groups gave the required uridine-

$$71 \qquad\qquad\qquad 72$$

3'-uridine 5'-phosphate (72). A much less tedious method of preparing the 2'-O-tetrahydropyranyl-5'-O-acetyl 3'-phosphate (71: R = acetyl) has been described by Smrt and Šorm[219]. The condensation of the latter intermediate with uridine 2',3'-phosphate provides a means of synthesis of di-uridylic acid[220].

Michelson has obtained polymers containing one or more monomer types with chain lengths up to twenty units, but in which both 2',5'- and 3',5'-

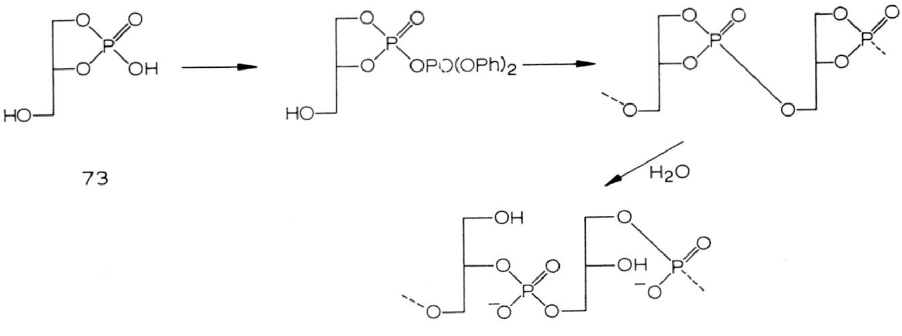

73

internucleotidic linkages are present. The process consists in the conversion of nucleoside 2′,3′-phosphates (73) by means, *inter alia*, of diphenyl phosphorochloridate, to reactive mixed anhydrides, which undergo polymerisation. Hydrolysis of the intermediate triester then gives the polynucleotide. Nuclease action on these polymers gives small oligonucleotides with the unnatural internucleotide linkage. The phosphorylation process can also be applied to the synthesis of dinucleoside phosphates[221].

(b) *Oligoribonucleotides: structure determination*

In essence, degradative structural studies on oligonucleotides amount to model experiments for polynucleotide structure. A number of methods have been devised which have been successfully applied to di- and tri-nucleotides.

(i) *Chemical and enzymic hydrolysis*

At the present time chemical and enzymic hydrolyses constitute the most frequently used techniques. In the first place it should be recalled that of all the diesterase type enzymes studied from this point of view, some hydrolyse esters of 3′- and the others, esters of 5′-nucleotides. None has been shown to split a 2′-nucleotide ester (see p. 233). Thus enzymic fission of an oligonucleotide is taken to indicate a 3′,5′-internucleotide linkage; in fact no exception to this linkage type has been observed among the naturally-derived compounds.

Alkaline hydrolysis products from (74) derived from a ribonuclease digest are in themselves definitive of the structure of the dinucleotide. Removal of the terminal phosphate, then venom diesterase or alkaline hydrolysis, gives confirmatory products as shown in the diagram[171].

The trinucleotide (75) from a ribonuclease digest has a 1:1:1 ratio of adenine, guanine and uracil on base analysis and yields the purine 2′- and 3′-nucleotides and uridine 3′-phosphate with base. The uridine residue is therefore terminal. Phosphatase yields the trinucleoside diphosphate (76) and the ratio of total phosphorus to orthophosphate released allows the molecular weight to be deduced. Snake venom diesterase on (76) affords guanosine and the 5'-phosphates of adenosine and uridine which completes the structure determination. The venom diesterase serves to differentiate (75) from the isomeric ApGpUp which is present in the same digest since conversion of the latter to ApGpU followed by diesterase treatment yields adenosine and the 5'-phosphates of guanosine and uridine[172]. Many examples of such degradations have been described[208, 212].

Oligonucleotides may be of the form (75) in which the terminal mono-esterified phosphate is in the 3'-position. Alternatively, they may carry a 5'-linked phosphate residue, as in (77). For example a series of such homo-oligomers are formed when polyadenylic acid is acted on by an enzyme from liver nuclei, as shown by Heppel, Ortiz and Ochoa[213]. The distinctive feature of their base hydrolysis which follows from the mechanism of the reaction is the production of adenosine from one terminus and adenosine 2',5'- and 3',5'-diphosphate from the other. The application of this type of end-group determination to RNA is of obvious importance since the nucleoside and the nucleoside diphosphate have very different electrophoretic mobilities from the mononucleotides that make up the bulk of the hydrolysate.

The above procedures are incapable in the majority of cases of defining the sequence in a tetra-nucleotide or higher oligomer. They can of course demonstrate the nature of both terminal residues but give no indication of the order of those internally situated. Exonucleases, *i.e.*, enzymes which cause degradation progressively from one or other end of a polynucleotide chain, could give the necessary information in a time course study. The spleen diesterase is such an enzyme and, certainly in the deoxy series has been shown to provide the necessary evidence, at least on a homopolymer[222]. The sequential action of phosphodiesterases having different specificities has clear application in this context[223]. Nevertheless chemical procedures for sequence determination are necessary. One such has been devised and will be discussed in some detail since it introduces a degradative reaction alternative to and more facile than hydrolysis.

(*ii*) *Elimination reaction*

Essentially, the fundamental problem in sequence determination is to discover methods of differentiating one internucleotide linkage from another. For stepwise degradation it is the terminal phosphodiester linkage which has to be differentiated. Brown, Fried and Todd[224], assuming that graded hydrolysis would not be expected to lead solely to removal of terminal residues, were led to consider elimination reactions such as those well known in esters of β-hydroxyl carbonyl compounds. They noted for example the extreme alkali-lability of glyceraldehyde 3-phosphate which gives orthophosphate and lactic acid, the latter presumably arising through pyruvaldehyde[64]. Another example is that of the easy and quantitative conversion of

$$^{2-}O_3PO\!-\!CH_2\!-\!C(OH)\cdot CHO \xrightarrow[\text{or OH}^-]{H+} HPO_4^{2-} + CH_2\!=\!C(OH)\cdot CHO$$
$$\qquad\qquad\qquad\Big|_H$$
$$\qquad\qquad\qquad\qquad\qquad\qquad\qquad\Big\downarrow OH^-$$
$$\qquad\qquad\qquad\qquad\qquad\qquad CH_3\!-\!CH(OH)\cdot COOH$$

glucose 3-phosphate to glucometasaccharinic acid by base[65]. These authors showed that the periodate oxidation product of adenosine 5'-phosphate underwent very easy although not quantitative elimination of phosphate at pH 10.5 in glycine buffer. Adenosine 5'-benzyl phosphate in the same way afforded benzyl phosphate and was in fact a close model for the terminal residue linked through its 5'-position in a polynucleotide (79). Polynucleotides terminating in a 3'-phosphate (78) could be converted to the latter by phosphatase action, as could the product (81) formed by the elimination of the terminal residue in the periodate-oxidised intermediate (80).

The feasibility of applying the method to polynucleotides was demonstrated, independently, by Markham and Whitfeld[225, 226] who carried out the degradation on several di- and tri-nucleotides derived from RNA by ribonuclease action. In each case elimination of the terminal residue left a nucleotide carrying the monoesterified phosphate in the 3'-position, thus confirming the enzymic evidence that the purine nucleoside residues are also linked through the 3'-position.

More recently, other investigations have shown that the reaction is markedly catalysed by primary aliphatic amines, *e.g.* lysine, cyclohexylamine or methylamine and that, then, the reaction can be carried out at pH 6.5, and proceeds essentially quantitatively[227–230,254a]. Secondary amines, *e.g.* dimethylamine, are very much less effective[230] and this suggests that the reaction may involve acid catalysis, with a mechanism of the type shown. It is evidently a special example of the Barry degradation[231]. One observation, made in earlier work, that the base, either purine or pyrimidine, is liberated in the free state has not been confirmed in the recent experiments[229,230]. It is a matter of some importance because the dialdehyde grouping could provide a convenient site for reaction with a radio-active labelled reagent, thus allowing increased sensitivity in the identification of the eliminated residue.

In this connection, it has been shown by Dulbecco and Smith[232] that condensation of periodate-oxidised nucleoside 5′-phosphates with thiosemicarbazide occurs readily to give 1:1 addition products. It emerges that these compounds (82 or related structure) are stable in the range pH 2–8, neither phosphate nor base being eliminated. The reagent, therefore, has clear advantages for terminal-group and sequence analysis. To this end it was shown that [35S]thiosemicarbazide can be condensed with periodate-oxidised polynucleotides (*e.g.* biosynthetic polyAGUC) and that the product can then be treated with RNAase, liberating a variety of labelled oligomers.

(c) Ribonucleic acids

In the first place one may raise the question as to the degree of statistical randomness in the arrangement of nucleotides in a given RNA. In so far as it has been studied, the distribution would appear to be close to random. Thus using yeast and tobacco mosaic virus RNA, Staehlin[207, 209] has made a very careful quantitative study of the products of ribonuclease action and compared the results with the theoretical values[233] for the amounts of products, based on a random distribution. The mono- and di-nucleotides were present in approximately theoretical amounts. In the trinucleotides, however, marked differences were found. In particular isomeric trinucleotides, which in a random distribution would be expected to be present in equal amounts, deviated markedly. Thus AGC occurred 50% more frequently than GAC in yeast RNA; the opposite was true in TMV RNA. Miura and Egami using RNAase T₁ have studied the guanylic acid distribution in these two RNA's. They find that more –GpG– centres are present than calculated[234] (see also refs. 212, 223). It is evident, however, that there are no very marked peculiarities in the overall distribution of nucleotides in yeast and TMV ribonucleic acids. All 16 dinucleotides can be obtained from yeast RNA by acid hydrolysis[235]. This type of study can tell little about sequence in a high molecular weight RNA, but as Staehlin points out[236], when the tetra- and penta-nucleotide fractions from an individual soluble RNA are studied it is quite possible that at most a very few of these will be found, and their structures will have, thereby, the more significance. Thus for individual small molecular weight RNA's, the larger oligonucleotides fraction should depart markedly from a random mixture. In fact Holley and co-workers[237] have found that the column elution profiles for the RNAase digests of the transfer RNA's for alanine, valine and tyrosine show marked differences throughout[237].

So far as the high molecular weight RNA's are concerned there is little more that can be said at present. Only in the case of highly purified TMV RNA has an end group study been made. This careful study reveals that no terminal monoesterified phosphate is released on alkaline hydrolysis (showing incidentally that there is no contamination from s-RNA) but the nucleoside released (approx. 1 mol/mol RNA) is adenosine. Thus the partial structure (83; $n \sim 6500$) can be drawn[52,238].

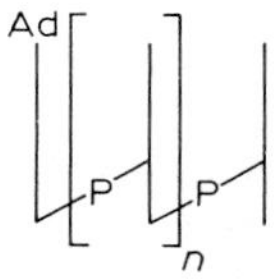

83

We consider now in more detail recent studies on soluble (transfer) RNA since sequence studies are likely to be much more productive with these substances.

The enormous volume of experimental work which has been devoted to soluble RNA in recent years has had to do with the initial stages of protein biosynthesis. This work and the related chemical studies on s-RNA have been reviewed by Hoagland[239], Zamecnik[240], Berg[241] and Cohen and Gros[242]. The following is a résumé of the chemical conclusions arising from these studies. The isolation of s-RNA has been mentioned already (p. 211); the measured molecular weights are consistent with chain lengths of 75–100 nucleotides[241,243]. The base ratios differ from those of the ribosomal fraction in that an equivalence between 6-aminopurine and 6-ketopyrimidine and between 6-ketopurine and 6-aminopyrimidine is found and, probably in consequence, a high degree of internal hydrogen bonding is observed[241, 244]. The following chart shows some of the chemical and enzymic reactions which are relevant to the structure of these nucleic acids.

In the first place s-RNA can be inactivated enzymically by pyrophosphorolysis and reactivated by incubation with ATP and CTP. Using ^{14}C-labelled substrates, the radioactivity incorporation pattern is consistent with the addition of the terminal group −pCpCpA. Incubation with CTP alone, then alkaline hydrolysis results in activity being recovered half as cytidine 2'(3')-phosphate and half as cytidine; all activity being recovered as cytidine

2′(3′)-phosphate if ATP has also been added to the system[245,246]. Alkaline hydrolysis of such activated s-RNA (84) affords essentially one mole of adenosine and one mole of guanosine diphosphate, the latter coming from the other terminus[247-249]. There is evidence in some cases for a —pUpUpG terminal trinucleotide structure (alternative to the —pCpCpA sequence) but further confirmatory study is necessary[250,251].

The s-RNA carrying the terminal CCA sequence (84) is active in amino-acid transfer. Incubation with an amino acid, ATP, and the requisite enzyme fractions leads to incorporation of the amino acid in the s-RNA. It appears that there is essentially one s-RNA species for each amino acid although cross reaction has been demonstrated[241,252]. The amino acid can be removed at pH 9.3 without destruction of the s-RNA. While the amino acid is attached, the material is stable to periodate. Removal of the amino acid, then periodate treatment destroys transfer activity[245]. These experiments argue in favour of the attachment of the amino acid at the 2′(or 3′)-position of the terminal adenosine residue as in (85). This view is substantiated by the observation that RNAase treatment of a ^{14}C-labelled aminoacyl s-RNA liberated a 2′(or 3′)-aminoacyl adenosine[253]. Although earlier speculation had centred around acyl phosphate structures and the rather rapid hydrox-amic acid formation with hydroxylamine gave some support, there is much evidence available that a suitably placed hydroxyl group can accelerate this reaction which is in any case faster with α-amino acid esters than with normal esters[254]. Whether the aminoacyl ester is reactive enough to take part in the immediate process of peptide bond formation is not clear, but a certain stability is probably necessary since, in the study of protein synthesis in cell-free systems, the process may be interrupted during ribosome isolation, and then carried to completion *in vitro*.

Yu and Zamecnik[254a] have shown the feasibility of applying the periodate—

cyclohexylamine elimination reaction to the stepwise degradation of s-RNA from the adenosine terminus. Recently a method has been devised for label-ling[254b] the terminus carrying the monoesterified 5′-phosphate (85a). Conversion to a phosphoramidate with [^{14}C]aniline using diisopropyl-carbodiimide gives the labelled s-RNA (85b) whence enzymic hydrolysis can yield the labelled terminal residue or oligonucleotides containing it. Guanosine is apparently not the sole terminal nucleoside residue. Some studies have been announced in preliminary form[241, 255] on the nucleotide sequences next to the −CCA terminal residues, in unfractionated s-RNA. Thus for example the fourth residue in the chain (i.e. X in 84) is mainly adenosine (68%) and less frequently guanosine (24%). The demonstration depends on pyrophosphorylysing s-RNA (a), incubating with ^{32}P-labelled CTP (b) and then hydrolysing with alkali (c).

85a   85b

(a) RNA—pXpCpCpA $\xrightarrow{\text{PP}}$ RNA—pX + ATP + 2 CTP

(b) RNA—pX + C^{32}PPP $\xrightarrow{-\text{PP}}$ RNA—pX^{32}pC^{32}pC

(c) RNA—pX^{32}pC^{32}pC $\xrightarrow{\text{OH}}$ X^{32}p + C^{32}p + C

Alternatively RNAase degradation can show the percentage of pyrimidine nucleotide in the 5th position, i.e. next to pX. This seems to be very large. Again RNAase T$_1$ which splits the chain only at guanylic acid residues (but not at the methylated residues) can give more extended information[241,256]. These methods can be applied to a particular amino acid-activating s-RNA by incorporating that amino acid, as a protecting group, periodate-oxidising the rest of the s-RNA and then going through the ^{32}P-labelling process (above); in this case only the specific s-RNA should become labelled[241,255]. Clearly this is an extremely tedious process and the recent developments in s-RNA fractionation should lead to materials on which degradative proce-dures can be applied directly.

Fractionation of s-RNA from a variety of sources has been receiving intensive study recently (see ref. 257 for literature) and it seems quite certain now that success can be achieved in the isolation of individual molecular species. The very surprising fact emerges that fractionation can be effected much more readily than would reasonably have been expected from the rather uniform size. It is probable that differences in nucleotide sequence can markedly affect secondary structure on which the physical fractionation methods depend[237] (see however ref. 257a).

Physical methods studied include counter-current distribution[257], column chromatography[258,260] and differential precipitation[31]. Chemical methods depend for their specificity on the presence of the amino acid corresponding to the transfer RNA being selected for. Thus, passage of a solution of s-RNA carrying its complement of amino acids through a column of diazotised polystyrene results in linkage of the tyrosyl- and histidinyl-s-RNA to the resin by diazo-coupling, whence they can be recovered after elution of the other s-RNA molecules[44,261]. The alternative approach, initiated by Zamecnik and co-workers[262], depends on clearing all amino acids from the s-RNA, enzyme-catalysed addition of a particular amino acid (valine), periodate oxidation which converts all RNA molecules other than valine-s-RNA to terminal dialdehydes. Subsequently the dialdehydes can be coupled to a hydroxynaphthoic acid hydrazide (cf. refs. 231, 232), then reaction with tetrazotised benzidine; the dye residue thus introduced alters the properties of the s-RNA (86; R = dye residue) so that separation from the valine s-RNA can be effected. Alternatively[263,264] an acyl hydrazide resin is used to remove all periodate-oxidised s-RNA molecules (86; R = resin). Over 70% purity has been achieved by combining countercurrent distribution[263] or a column-chromatographic method[265] with the chemical coupling methods. The countercurrent method by itself[257] appears to be capable of achieving a high degree of purity in several amino-acid specific transfer RNA's; it would appear that materials of a purity sufficient for structural studies are now available.

86

(d) Oligodeoxyribonucleotides: production and structure determination

The very high molecular weights of most DNA preparations make it unlikely that sequence determination by direct chemical methods will be carried out in the near future. Even the small DNA molecule present[266] in the bacterio-phage ϕX174 has a molecular weight of about $1.7 \cdot 10^6$, a size at which end group assay might just be feasible. The DNA of this 'phage, too, is single-stranded and hence end group assay would have some meaning but for the fact that the molecule seems to be in the form of a ring. In the complementary double-stranded, anti-parallel arrangement which is the norm, even end-group analyses would be difficult to interpret. However, studies of oligo-nucleotides derived enzymically and chemically have been carried out with more limited objectives.

As mentioned earlier, venom phosphodiesterase reduces DNA quantitatively to deoxynucleoside 5'-phosphates. There are a number of nucleases which produce mono-, di-, tri- and higher oligonucleotides, the precise specificity of which have not yet been defined. With them it is possible to produce a variety of oligodeoxyribonucleotides, but, as with the ribo analogues, very few have been isolated in substance.

Pancreatic deoxyribonuclease (DNAase I) produces oligomers carrying a 5'-phosphate residue, as shown by Sinsheimer and others[267,268]. The structure of a dinucleotide containing for example cytosine and adenine can be defined unambiguously by enzymic methods, e.g.

$$d(\text{pXpY}) \xrightarrow[\text{diesterase}]{\text{venom}} (d)\text{pX and } (d)\text{pY}$$

$$\downarrow \text{phosphatase}$$

$$d(\text{XpY}) \xrightarrow[\text{diesterase}]{\text{venom}} \text{X} + (d)\text{pY}$$

Such methods can obviously define trinucleotide sequences as well. Little or no study has been made of larger fragments.

The deoxyribonuclease from spleen[269] or thymus[270] (DNAase II) yields oligomers carrying a terminal 3'-phosphate. In a typical dinucleotide ApCp, the sequence can be deduced in a way similar to that above. Venom diesterase

$$d(\text{ApCp}) \xrightarrow{\text{phosphatase}} (d)\text{ApC} \xrightarrow[\text{diesterase}]{\text{venom}} \text{A} + (d)\text{pC}$$

hydrolyses 3'-phosphate terminated chains extremely slowly but with high concentrations of enzyme definitive fission can be effected[269,271]:

$$d(\text{XpYpZp}) \xrightarrow[\text{diesterase}]{\text{venom}} \text{X} + \text{pY} + \text{pZp}$$

The oligonucleotides from spleen DNAase II action are hydrolysed by the spleen phosphodiesterase of Hilmoe[180] to nucleoside 3'-phosphates in high yield[269].

Another such enzyme is the micrococcal nuclease of Cunningham[176,198,199,272] which hydrolyses both DNA and other chemically or enzymically

produced polynucleotides. Again mono-, di- and tri-nucleotide products
have been identified each carrying a terminal 3'-phosphate.

By the action of these nucleases a very considerable variety of oligodeoxyribonucleotides can be obtained. Enzymic methods are suitable for
structural definition at least up to the level of trinucleotides. However, a
chemical method has been devised for stepwise degradation which may
be of considerable utility in extending the range to higher oligomers. Essentially the method is dependent on β-elimination. The 5'-hydroxyl group of
nucleosides may be selectively oxidised to a carboxyl group by platinum
catalysed aerial oxidation[273]. The oxidation is also effected by platinum and
hydrogen peroxide and, applied to dithymidine phosphate, gives (87; R =

87   88

thymidine 5'-residue). The latter with methanol and DCC gives the methyl
ester whence n-propylamine affords the amide (88). This with base leads[274]
to elimination of thymidine 5'-phosphate ($ROPO_3H_2$) (97%). The conditions
for the elimination reaction may be too vigorous for general use, but the
method has clear potentialities.

Alternative to enzymic hydrolysis, as a means of oligonucleotide preparation, chemical synthetic methods have been devised which have considerable flexibility. The extensive studies in this field of synthesis have
been adequately reviewed[74, 75, 275], but an indication of the methods is
given here. Most work has been done on thymidine derivatives. There are
greater problems in the deoxyadenosine and deoxycytidine series where the
use of groups to protect the amino functions are apparently obligatory.
Two approaches have been used, either (a) polymerisation of a nucleoside 3'-
or 5'-phosphate or (b) stepwise synthesis using suitably protected intermediates. In the first of these the nucleotide (e.g. thymidine 5'-phosphate)
is polymerised to yield a mixture of homopolymers (89; $n = 0 - 10$) which
can then be separated. Cyclic oligomers (90) constitute quantitatively important by-products, but these can to some extent be minimised by addition of a 3'-O-acetyl deoxyribonucleoside 5'-phosphate which can act as a
monofunctional chain terminator. However, cellulose anion exchange chromatography fortunately provides high resolving power, so that the individual
oligomers can be isolated. The condensing agent is generally dicyclohexyl

carbodiimide but other reagents (*e.g.* toluene sulphonyl chloride) which effect the conversion of the nucleoside phosphate into a mixed anhydride with another strong acid are also effective[276]. Nucleoside 3'-phosphates may also be polymerised. There is no indication that the present methods can be

$$pT \xrightarrow[\text{pyridine}]{\text{DCC}} pT[pT]_n pT + \overline{pT \ldots pT}$$
$$(89) \qquad\qquad (90)$$

made to give products which could be classed as high polymers. Fortunately biosynthetic methods are available now. A poly-AT in which the two nucleotide units alternate and a (poly-C + poly-G) in which the separate strands of the double helical system are homopolymers can be made[277].

Turning to stepwise synthesis in the oligodeoxyribonucleotide series, the first successful attempt utilised a phosphorochloridate route. In this the 3'-(benzylphosphorochloridate) derived from 5'-O-acetylthymidine is coupled with 3'-O-acetylthymidine. Removal of protecting groups then affords[278] the dinucleoside phosphate, (*d*)TpT. This route has not been further studied. Much greater emphasis has been placed on condensations involving nucleoside phosphates at the monoesterified level. Thus 5'-O-

tritylthymidine and $N,3'$-O-diacetyldeoxyadenosine 5'-phosphate with DCC give, after removal of protecting groups, the dinucleoside phosphate, ApT. Clearly this type of synthesis can be extended to higher oligonucleotides since the intermediate in the above condensation can be deacetylated (retaining the trityl group) and a further nucleotide introduced in the usual way[75].

The true oligonucleotides, *i.e.* those carrying a terminal monoesterified phosphate can be prepared by introducing a cyanoethyl phosphate residue (see p. 222) before or after the condensation reaction. The cyanoethyl residue can then be removed, finally, or at an earlier stage to leave the monoesterified phosphate residue[279]. By these and related methods a considerable number of oligonucleotides have been prepared, in reactions which afford acceptable yields of products.

(e) Nearest neighbour frequencies in DNA

It has been known for some time that very mild acid treatment of DNA leads to a product from which the purine bases have been stripped. A molecular weight of 15000 has, in one instance been recorded but the value may be much lower than this. This material, apurinic acid[280–282], has been the subject of several studies mainly because it affords the possibility of studying the distribution of pyrimidine nucleotide residues and hence an assessment of the randomness with which the bases are distributed. Apurinic acid (91) can be reduced ($-CHO$ to $-CH_2OH$) by sodium borohydride[282] and

91

92   93

treated[283] with mercaptans to give mercaptals (92). Apurinic acid itself is very labile to alkali, probably due to β-elimination reactions[284,285]. It appears that (92) undergoes decomposition via cyclic phosphates[286–288] utilising $C_{4'}$-OH. The products have been studied but it would appear to be too complex a system for quantitative study.

The most valuable results have come from a study of the products derived from further acid catalysed decomposition of apurinic acid. In practice DNA may be subjected to more vigorous hydrolytic conditions (see p. 237).

Shapiro and Chargaff[289-292] have made an intensive study of the products of this hydrolysis which are of the form pNp, pNpNp, pNpNpNp etc., where N represents a pyrimidine deoxyribonucleoside. Some hydrolysis of mono-esterified phosphate leading for example to dinucleoside phosphates, occurs in addition to partial degradation by glycoside linkage fission[289]. Losses of products by these processes can be assessed so that the products from the primary apurinic acid break-down can be put on a quantitative basis[292]. Their separation can be effected by ion-exchange chromatography[293]. As mentioned before the reaction is essentially one of elimination and it is clear that proportions of the various products reflect the amounts of pyrimidine nucleotide residues which are present in the DNA in groups of one, two, and so on, bounded on either side by purine nucleotides. Thus the fragment (91) would yield a nucleoside 3',5'-diphosphate.

Burton, following a study of the Dische reaction[294] has observed[295-297] that a much more specific cleavage can be effected if DNA is treated with 66% formic acid containing 2% of diphenylamine. The acid is sufficient only to cause apurinic acid formation, the diphenylamine (the best of several amines tested) then catalyses the elimination reaction[296], probably via an enamine derived from (93) (see p. 245). In addition to the pyrimidine-containing products, the phosphate residues originally between two purine nucleoside residues should appear as orthophosphate. Orthophosphate is in fact formed, amounts ranging from 24–25.5% being recorded. On the assumption of a Pu:Py ratio of 1.0 and a statistically random nucleotide sequence, the expected value is 25%. Moreover, taking the base analyses into account the predicted amounts of the nucleotide products are close to those actually found[297]. The conclusion can be drawn that each DNA differs from the others and from the randomly arranged polymer but no obviously consistent pattern is found. There is a slight bias in favour of polynucleotides containing three or more nucleotide residues; these correspond in calf thymus DNA to 61% instead of 50% pyrimidine residues in the random arrangement. However, there is no very obvious tendency for purine and pyrimidine nucleotide residues to be bunched together. The view that long stretches of pyrimidine nucleotides exist in DNA has been advanced by Shapiro and Chargaff but while these can be observed, they are, according to Burton, in fact present in approximately the expected amount, e.g. the hexanucleotide (CT$_5$) is present to the extent of 0.5% (calculated 0.35%). Shapiro and Chargaff also note that cytosine and the minor component 5-methylcytosine (in calf thymus and wheat germ DNA) do not exchange positions haphazardly, for example the relationship pCp/pMp = pCpCp/pMpCp holds in no case[292]. Their work also supports the observation that an extraordinarily large amount of the methylcytosine nucleotide comes next to deoxyguanylate[202, 298] as in the isolable dinucleotide pMpG (ref. 298).

References p. 262

In connection with nucleotide sequence, one further study should be mentioned. It concerns the study by Kornberg and co-workers[203, 277] of nearest neighbour frequencies in biosynthetic DNA. Since it is very clear that the constitution of the biosynthetic DNA is an accurate reflection of the structure of the primer DNA, the method gives a direct measure of the nearest neighbour frequencies in the native DNA. Briefly, biosynthesis is effected with the four deoxynucleoside 5′-triphosphates one of which is α-^{32}P-labelled. The biosynthetic DNA is then degraded quantitatively to nucleoside 3′-phosphates by a combination of micrococcal nuclease and spleen phosphodiesterase. The incorporation into the four mononucleotides is then a measure of the nearest neighbour frequencies.

$$(d)\ ATP^* \\ (d)\ GTP \\ (d)\ CTP \\ (d)\ TTP \Bigg\} \longrightarrow \ \ .\,.\,pGp\overset{*}{C}pApCpApTpGpApT \ldots$$

enzymic hydrolysis

$$.\,.\,Gp + \overset{*}{C}p + Ap + \overset{*}{C}p + Ap + Tp + \overset{*}{G}p + Ap \ldots\ldots$$

It is found that each biosynthetic DNA has a unique and non-random pattern of the sixteen nearest neighbour frequencies. The data allow the important demonstration that the nucleotide pattern involves both base-pairing of adenine to thymine and of guanine to cytosine between sister strands and "opposite polarity" of the two strands as proposed in the DNA model due to Watson and Crick[299]. Essentially this follows from the demonstration that the structures ApC and GpT, for example, occur with the same frequency. In parenthesis, we should note that this type of experiment is essentially of the same sort as that employed in the RNA series, in which ^{32}P-labelled nucleoside 5′-phosphates are incorporated and nucleoside 3′-phosphates are obtained by alkaline hydrolysis of the labelled RNA. Its use in detecting terminal incorporation has already been mentioned (p. 247). In another application, first by Astrachan and Volkin[300], a very small percentage of RNA undergoing rapid turnover can be detected, and its base content approximately established. The technique has found large application in the study[301-303] of messenger RNA.

5. Miscellaneous reactions on DNA

In this chapter, the conformations or secondary structural aspects of the nucleic acids have been mentioned only in passing. These matters are considered in detail in the following section dealing with the physical chemistry of the nucleic acids, in particular, the evidence relating to the double helical complementary base-paired structure for most isolated DNA's. Here, we deal briefly with a few of the reactions of nucleic acids, where it is important to consider the whole molecule rather than the individual nucleotides. One may make the general point that where reactions of the bases are concerned it is usual to find that the process is much slower with polynucleotides than with the free bases or mononucleotides; for this reason valuable information on the intactness of the native secondary structure can often be derived from rate studies.

There are two complementary aspects of the action of reagents on nucleic acids that are worth stressing. In the first, for an understanding of mutagenesis from the chemical standpoint there is need of a search for reagents with a very high specificity in their reaction with the residues making up the nucleic acid. Equally, elucidation of the chemistry of known mutagens is a worthy objective, for the same reason. In the second, the question of nucleotide sequence must require that, in addition to the methods mentioned in the previous section, a search for specific reagents be made which will allow the cleavage of polynucleotides at defined points or influence the enzymic cleavage in a specified way. Clearly these two interests may have much in common. But there is one major point of difference. To effect a point mutation, reaction at one base residue in the genetic material, DNA or RNA, is apparently all that is necessary. The evidence for a chemical change is the appearance of a mutant; the single-hit is judged by extrapolation from kinetic data. The chemical change itself is at present unobservable and in no case can the mutation be ascribed categorically to a particular reaction. In contrast, when reagents are being considered from the standpoint of elucidation of nucleotide sequence it is presumably important that the reaction be specific and quantitative.

We discuss here some of the reagents that have been considered from the above points of view, but omitting the important effects resulting from the irradiation of nucleic acids (see p. 172 and refs. 304, 305). It might be useful to note, very briefly, that on present views mutations can be divided into two classes. Those which are thought to result from a base-pair change A–T → G–C (a "transition")[306] are exemplified by mutations due to base analogues such as bromodeoxyuridine, nitrous acid and hydroxylamine. The other type, which appear to result from the addition or deletion of a base-pair are considered to include many spontaneous mutations as well as those due to proflavin and hydrazine[307]. Low pH, heat and some alkylating agents produce mutants in both classes[308].

Nitrous acid. Nitrous acid has a powerful inactivating effect on a variety of viruses[309]. It is mutagenic to tobacco mosaic virus, the action being on the RNA[310], and to bacteriophages. The probability is high that the effect is due to deamination. The adenine, cytosine and guanine residues undergo deamination at pH 4.3 at closely similar, slow rates[311]. Vielmetter and Schuster[312] find evidence from a study of T2 bacteriophage mutation induction and deamination rates as a function of pH that it is the deamination of adenine or hydroxymethylcytosine which is mutagenic while action on guanine residues may be lethal. The same considerations apply to TMV mutation[310].

Alkylating agents. Since these are of considerable interest in cancer therapy, a great deal of work has been devoted to their chemistry and to their biological effects.

The whole subject has recently been discussed in detail by Ross[313]. The substances include alkyl sulphates and sulphonates, diazomethane nitrogen and sulphur mustards, epoxides and ethylene imines.

Much discussion has centred round the question as to whether the phosphodiester internucleotidic linkages in nucleic acids are alkylated to the triester state. Although dialkyl phosphates would not be expected to be particularly nucleophilic, this reaction should occur. The result in the case of RNA would be to form a highly unstable position in the molecule where chain fission could occur (see p. 235). Greater stability would be expected for the triester grouping in DNA where there is no neighbouring hydroxyl group. Trialkyl phosphates are alkylating agents and it is possible that alkylation on phosphorus is succeeded by the transfer of the alkyl group to some other position in the molecule. Diazomethane would not be expected to effect alkylation of the internucleotide linkage to any great extent at neutrality where the anion is the only species present. Alkylation of the phosphate residues by nitrogen or sulphur mustards might well be reversible to a much greater extent than the same reaction with for example methyl sulphate. This follows from the well-known lability of systems of type (94); these are, in fact, quite analogous to the mustard from which they derived[314].

$$(R^1O)_2PO \cdot OCH_2 \cdot CH_2 \cdot NR_2 \ \rightarrow \ (R^1O)_2PO \cdot O^- \ + \ \overset{\overset{+}{N}R_2}{\overset{\diagup\diagdown}{CH_2-CH_2}}$$

$$(94)$$

Much evidence is available to show that alkylation by dimethyl sulphate, ethyl and methyl methanesulphonates, nitrogen mustards and diazomethane proceeds on ring nitrogen atoms. Alkylation of N-1 of the uracil residue by diazomethane is a very fast reaction[315]. N-1 methylation of uridine 3'-phosphate esters completely inhibits RNAase action[176] so that the possibility of eliminating certain cleavage points in the enzymic hydrolysis of RNA is a possibility. In this connection, the reversible addition and easy hydrolytic removal of a carbodiimide to the N-1 position of uracil derivatives has also been noted[316].

So far as RNA and DNA are concerned it seems clear that the 7-position of guanine and the 1-position of adenine are affected, the first being quantitatively the more important[317-319]. The cytosine ring can be alkylated on N-1 but this is generally slow compared with the other bases[315, 320].

The product in the case of guanine derivatives (95) is very prone to hydrolysis. Alkali opens the imidazolium ring system, which can then be followed by other irreversible changes. In (95; R = ribosyl) the glycosidic bond is cleaved in acidic media. In the case of deoxyribosides, or DNA, the cleavage of 7-alkylguanine (96) occurs at neutrality, and very rapidly under acid catatalysis. It is this reaction which may in fact represent the mutational event[321]. It is of interest that mutation can be effected in transforming principle and in bacteriophages by heat, and by lowering the pH. Depurina-

tion is the expected reaction here and this indeed can be observed[322]. It is, of course, possible that loss of the purine base will be followed by chain scission, by elimination, but this aspect of the alkylation reaction has not been clarified.

Formaldehyde. Formaldehyde inactivates viruses, by its action on the nucleic acid and not the protein component. It reacts reversibly with nucleotides, its main reaction being with adenine and cytosine residues, when an increase in optical density with a bathochromic shift in the wavelength of maximum absorption of ultraviolet light is observed[323]. The reaction is slower than that with the amino groups of amino acids and there is some evidence for 1:1 addition products[324, 325]. The structures of the adducts are not known. The addition may occur at N-1 or N-6. The former corresponds to the position of protonation, but in view of the pK_a depression of the amino groups in presence of formaldehyde, reaction at N-6 is indicated.

References p. 262

(N^1-methyladenosine is a stronger base than adenosine)[325,326]. In fact Staehlin has detected two types of bonding[324], both of which are reversible.

Formaldehyde does not react with native DNA, but it does so with heat-denaturated material. It is clear that the reaction is of value in studying the degree of hydrogen bonding in nucleic acids[327]. Reformation of hydrogen bonds is prevented in presence of formaldehyde[328].

Other inactivating agents discussed by Staehlin are glyoxal and kethoxal (β-ethoxy-α-ketobutyraldehyde)[329]. It appears that these react exclusively with guanine residues to give stable adducts, the chemistry of which have not been elucidated. How these reagents will affect the specificity of various nucleases is of some interest.

Hydrazine. As mentioned before (p. 219) hydrazine reacts with the pyrimidine but not the purine bases; cleavage of the heterocyclic ring occurs in each case to give a pyrazole derivative and a ureido sugar is presumed to remain. The substance is mutagenic and appears to give mutants of the acridine class[307,330]. Reaction with RNA and DNA leads to apyrimidinic acids, substances apparently complementary to the apurinic acids[331]. It should be possible to degrade these to purine polynucleotides but no loss of orthophosphate is noted following treatment with alkali[332]. The reagent has been used for degradation of diribonucleotides[333]. Nevertheless the specificity as between cytosine and uracil (or thymine) derivatives is low; hydroxyl-amine appears to have an advantage in this respect.

Hydroxylamine. This substance inactivates tobacco mosaic virus. It also induces mutations in bacteriophage, probably by causing $C \rightarrow T$ transitions[330, 330a].

Reaction with cytidine derivatives[334-336] is fastest at pH $\sim$ 6 and with uridine derivatives pH $\sim$ 10, with some degree of specificity. Reaction with DNA is very slow compared with the isolated nucleoside derivatives[336]. Present evidence suggests that reaction with uridine or uridylic acid causes ring fission with formation of the isoxazolone (97) and a ribose oxime, that is, it reacts quite analogously to hydrazine[334, 335]. Reaction with cytosine (98; R = H), cytidine, and deoxycytidine gives another type of product. At pH 6 or in anhydrous hydroxylamine (100) is formed by an initial addition to the 4,5-double bond to give (99) followed by an exchange reaction. 5-Substituted cytosine derivatives react analogously, but more slowly. Large changes in the ultraviolet and NMR spectra are observed, consistent with this formulation[336]. It seems likely that the exchange reaction can be prevented if the base is hydrogen-bonded in the nucleic acid macromolecule, so that subsequent hydrolysis may give a cytosine and not an N^6-hydroxycytosine derivative (101). Preliminary studies seem to show that RNAase action on RNA treated with hydroxylamine is partially inhibited[335].

REFERENCES

[1] R. F. Steiner and R. F. Beers, *Polynucleotides*, Elsevier, Amsterdam, 1961.
[2] P. D. Lawley, *Biochim. Biophys. Acta*, 21 (1956) 481.
[3] I. Tinoco, *J. Am. Chem. Soc.*, 82 (1960) 4785.
[4] E. Chargaff in *C. and D.**, Vol. I, p. 333.
[5] S. Zamenhof, *Progr. Biophys. Biophys. Chem.*, 6 (1956) 85.
[6] A. Gierer, *Progr. Biophys. Biophys. Chem.*, 10 (1960) 299.
[7] A. D. Kaiser, *J. Mol. Biol.*, 4 (1962) 275.
[8] C. L. Sadron, in *C. and D.**, Vol. III, p. 1.
[9] C. A. Thomas and K. I. Berns, *J. Mol. Biol.*, 3 (1961) 277.
[10] M. B. Hoagland in *C. and D.**, Vol. III, p. 349.
[11] H. Fraenkel-Conrat, B. Singer and A. Tsugita, *Virology*, 14 (1961) 54.
[12] L. F. Cavalieri, M. Rosoff and B. H. Rosenberg, *J. Am. Chem. Soc.*, 78 (1956) 5239.
[13] P. Doty, B. B. McGill and S. A. Rice, *Proc. Natl. Acad. Sci., U.S.*, 44 (1958) 432.
[14] L. F. Cavalieri, *J. Am. Chem. Soc.*, 79 (1957) 5319.
[15] I. Rubenstein, C. A. Thomas and A. D. Hershey, *Proc. Natl. Acad. Sci., U.S.*, 47 (1961) 1113.
[16] E. Chargaff in *C. and D.**, Vol. I, p. 307.
[17] D. O. Jordan, *The Chemistry of the Nucleic Acids*, Butterworth, London, 1960, p. 8.
[18] A. E. Mirsky and A. W. Pollister, *J. Gen. Physiol.*, 30 (1946) 101, 117.
[19] G. Frick, *Biochim. Biophys. Acta*, 13 (1954) 41.
[20] M. G. Sevag, D. B. Lackman and J. Smolens, *J. Biol. Chem.*, 124 (1938) 425.
[21] E. R. M. Kay, N. S. Simmons and A. L. Dounce, *J. Am. Chem. Soc.*, 74 (1952) 1724.
[22] J. Marmur, *J. Mol. Biol.*, 3 (1961) 208.
[23] K. S. Kirby, *Biochem. J.*, 66 (1957) 495; *Biochim. Biophys. Acta*, 47 (1960) 18.
[24] J. B. Fleischman, *J. Mol. Biol.*, 2 (1960) 226.
[25] V. L. Myers and J. Spizizen, *J. Biol. Chem.*, 210 (1954) 877.
[26] R. L. Sinsheimer, *J. Mol. Biol.*, 1 (1959) 43.
[27] D. Dunn and J. D. Smith, *Biochem. J.*, 68 (1958) 627.
[28] B. Magasanik in *C. and D.**, Vol. I, p. 373.
[28a] F. W. Allen, *Ribonucleoproteins and Ribonucleic Acids*, Elsevier, Amsterdam, 1962.
[29] A. M. Crestfield, K. C. Smith and F. W. Allen, *J. Biol. Chem.*, 216 (1957) 185.
[30] F. F. Davis and F. W. Allen, *J. Biol. Chem.*, 227 (1957) 907.
[31] G. L. Brown, Z. Kosinski and C. Carr, *Acides Ribonucléiques et Polyphosphates, Structure, Synthèse et Fonction*, Colloques Internationaux du C.N.R.S., Strasbourg, 1961 (C.N.R.S., Paris, 1962), p. 183.
[32] E. J. Ofengand, M. Dieckmann and P. Berg, *J. Biol. Chem.*, 236 (1961) 1741.
[33] K. S. Kirby, *Biochem. J.*, 64 (1956) 405.
[34] K. S. Kirby, *Biochim. Biophys. Acta*, 55 (1962) 545.
[35] A. Gierer and G. Schramm, *Z. Naturforsch.*, 11b (1956) 138.
[36] A. Gierer and G. Schramm, *Nature*, 177 (1956) 702.
[37] R. Haschemeyer, B. Singer and H. Fraenkel-Conrat, *Proc. Natl. Acad. Sci. U.S.*, 45 (1959) 313.
[38] R. Monier, M. L. Stephenson and P. C. Zamecnik, *Biochim. Biophys. Acta*, 43 (1960) 1.
[39] S. Kit, *Arch. Biochem. Biophys.*, 88 (1959) 1.
[40] C. G. Kurland, *J. Mol. Biol.*, 2 (1960) 83.
[41] R. Rolfe and M. Meselson, *Proc. Natl. Acad. Sci., U.S.*, 45 (1959) 1039.
[42] J. Marmur and P. Doty, *Nature*, 183 (1959) 1427.
[43] C. F. Crampton, R. Lipshitz and E. Chargaff, *J. Biol. Chem.*, 206 (1954) 499.
[44] G. L. Brown, A. V. W. Brown and J. Gordon, *Brookhaven Symp. Biol.*, 12 (1959) 47.
[45] A. Bendich, J. R. Fresco, H. S. Rosenkranz and S. M. Beiser, *J. Am. Chem. Soc.*, 77 (1955) 3671.

---

* E. Chargaff and J. N. Davidson (Eds.), *The Nucleic Acids*, 3 Vols., Academic Press, New York, 1955 and 1960.

[46] A. BENDICH, H. B. PAHL, G. C. KORNGOLD, H. S. ROSENKRANTZ AND J. R. FRESCO, *J. Am. Chem. Soc.*, 80 (1958) 3949.
[47] A. D. HERSHEY AND E. BURGI, *J. Mol. Biol.*, 2 (1960) 143.
[48] W. E. COHN in E. HEFTMANN (Ed.), *Chromatography*, Reinhold, New York, 1961, p. 554.
[49] D. F. BRADLEY AND A. RICH, *J. Am. Chem. Soc.*, 78 (1956) 5898.
[50] E. K. F. BAUTZ AND B. D. HALL, *Proc. Natl. Acad. Sci., U.S.*, 48 (1962) 400.
[51] K. S. KIRBY, *Biochim. Biophys. Acta*, 41 (1960) 338.
[52] H. FRAENKEL-CONRAT AND B. SINGER, *Biochemistry*, 1 (1962) 120.
[53] A. DESJOBERT, *Bull. Soc. Chim. France*, (1947) 809.
[54] C. A. BUNTON, D. R. LLEWELLYN, K. G. OLDHAM AND C. A. VERNON, *J. Chem. Soc.*, (1958) 3574.
[55] W. W. BUTCHER AND F. H. WESTHEIMER, *J. Am. Chem. Soc.*, 77 (1955) 2420.
[56] P. A. LEVENE AND L. A. BASS, *The Nucleic Acids*, The Chemical Catalog Co., New York, 1931.
[57] P. E. VERKADE, J. C. STOPPELENBURG AND W. D. COHEN, *Rec. Trav. Chim.*, 59 (1940) 886.
[58] E. CHARGAFF, *J. Biol. Chem.*, 145 (1942) 455.
[59] P. A. T. SWOBODA AND E. M. CROOK, *Biochem. J.*, 59 (1955) xxiv.
[60] E. BAMANN, F. FISCHLER AND H. TRAPMANN, *Biochem. Z.*, 325 (1951) 413.
[61] K. DIMROTH, H. WITZEL, W. HULSEN, AND H. MIRBACH, *Ann. Chem.*, 620 (1959) 94.
[62] W. W. BUTCHER AND F. H. WESTHEIMER, *J. Am. Chem. Soc.*, 77 (1955) 2420.
[63] K. DIMROTH AND H. WITZEL, *Ann. Chem.*, 620 (1959) 109.
[64] O. MEYERHOF AND K. LOHMANN, *Biochem. Z.*, 271 (1934) 89.
[65] D. M. BROWN, F. HAYES AND A. R. TODD, *Chem. Ber.*, 90 (1957) 936.
[66] J. BADDILEY in *C. and D.*[*], Vol. I, p. 160.
[67] J. BADDILEY AND A. R. TODD, *J. Chem. Soc.*, (1947) 648.
[68] B. LYTHGOE AND A. R. TODD, *Nature*, 155 (1945) 695.
[69] J. D SMITH, in *C. and D.*[*], Vol. I, p. 267.
[70] W. E. COHN, in *C. and D.*[*], Vol. I, p. 211.
[71] A. M. MICHELSON AND A. R. TODD, *J. Chem. Soc.*, (1949) 2476.
[72] R. W. CHAMBERS, J. G. MOFFATT AND H. G. KHORANA, *J. Am. Chem. Soc.*, 79 (1957) 3747.
[73] G. M. TENER, *J. Am. Chem. Soc.*, 83 (1961) 159.
[74] H. G. KHORANA, *Some Recent Developments in the Chemistry of Phosphate Esters of Biological Interest*, Wiley, New York, 1961.
[75] D. M. BROWN, in R. A. RAPHAEL (Ed.), *Progress in Organic Chemistry*, Vol. 3, Interscience, London, 1963, p. 75.
[76] H. STEUDEL AND E. PEISER, *Z. physiol. Chem.*, 120 (1922) 292.
[77] P. A. LEVENE, *J. Biol. Chem.*, 41 (1920) 1.
[78] P. A. LEVENE AND S. A. HARRIS, *J. Biol. Chem.*, 98 (1932) 9.
[79] P. A. LEVENE AND S. A. HARRIS, *J. Biol. Chem.*, 101 (1933) 419.
[80] R. S. TIPSON, *Advan. Carbohydrate Chem.*, 1 (1945) 193.
[81] J. M. GULLAND, *J. Chem. Soc.*, (1938) 1722.
[82] J. M. GULLAND, *J. Chem. Soc.*, (1944) 208.
[83] C. E. CARTER AND W. E. COHN, *Federation Proc.*, 8 (1949) 190 *et seq.*
[84] W. E. COHN, *J. Am. Chem. Soc.*, 72 (1950) 1471, 2811.
[85] H. S. LORING, N. G. LUTHY, H. W. BORTNER AND L. W. LEVY, *J. Am. Chem. Soc.*, 72 (1950) 2811.
[86] W. E. COHN, in D. E. GREEN (Ed.), *Currents in Biochemical Research*, Interscience, New York, 1956, p. 460.
[87] D. M. BROWN AND A. R. TODD, *J. Chem. Soc.*, (1952) 44.
[88] D. M. BROWN, D. I. MAGRATH AND A. R. TODD, *J. Chem. Soc.*, (1952) 2708.
[89] L. F. CAVALIERI, *J. Am. Chem. Soc.*, 74 (1952) 5804.

---

[*] E. CHARGAFF AND J. N. DAVIDSON (Eds.), *The Nucleic Acids*, 3 Vols., Academic Press, New York, 1955 and 1960.

[90] J. X. KHYM AND W. E. COHN, *J. Am. Chem. Soc.*, 76 (1954) 1818.
[91] D. M. BROWN, G. D. FASMAN, D. I. MAGRATH AND A. R. TODD, *J. Chem. Soc.*, (1954) 1448.
[92] D. M. BROWN, G. D. FASMAN, D. I. MAGRATH, A. R. TODD, W. COCHRAN AND M. M. WOOLFSON, *Nature*, 172 (1953) 1184.
[93] C. A. DEKKER AND H. G. KHORANA, *J. Am. Chem. Soc.*, 76 (1954) 3522.
[94] M. SMITH, J. G. MOFFATT AND H. G. KHORANA, *J. Am. Chem. Soc.*, 80 (1958) 6204.
[95] A. M. MICHELSON, *J. Chem. Soc.*, (1959) 3655.
[96] J. J. FOX, L. F. CAVALIERI AND N. CHANG, *J. Am. Chem. Soc.*, 75 (1953) 4315.
[97] H. S. LORING, M. L. HAMMELL, L. W. LEVY AND H. W. BORTNER, *J. Biol. Chem.*, 196 (1952) 807, 821.
[98] A. M. MICHELSON AND A. R. TODD, *J. Chem. Soc.*, (1954) 4575.
[99] D. M. BROWN, C. A. DEKKER AND A. R. TODD, *J. Chem. Soc.*, (1952) 2715.
[100] P. A. LEVENE AND L. W. BASS, *J. Biol. Chem.*, 71 (1927) 167.
[101] F. BARON AND D. M. BROWN, *J. Chem. Soc.*, (1955) 2855.
[102] W. E. COHN AND D. G. DOHERTY, *J. Am. Chem. Soc.*, 78 (1956) 2863.
[103] D. M. BROWN, A. R. TODD AND S. VARADARAJAN, *J. Chem. Soc.*, (1956) 2388.
[104] E. ALVER AND S. FURBERG, *Acta Chem. Scand.*, 13 (1959) 910.
[105] L. SHUSTER AND N. O. KAPLAN, *J. Biol. Chem.*, 201 (1953) 535.
[106] F. DAVIS AND F. W. ALLEN, *J. Biol. Chem.*, 227 (1957) 907.
[107] W. E. COHN, *J. Biol. Chem.*, 235 (1960) 1488.
[108] W. E. COHN, *Biochem. Prep.*, 8 (1961) 116.
[109] W. KLEIN AND S. J. THANNHAUSER, *Z. physiol. Chem.*, 231 (1935) 96.
[110] E. VOLKIN, J. X. KHYM AND W. E. COHN, *J. Am. Chem. Soc.*, 73 (1951) 1533.
[111] C. E. CARTER, *J. Am. Chem. Soc.*, 73 (1951) 1537.
[112] A. M. MICHELSON AND A. R. TODD, *J. Chem. Soc.*, (1953) 951.
[113] P. HORN, V. LUZZATI AND K. N. TRUEBLOOD, *Nature*, 183 (1959) 880.
[114] D. H. HAYES, A. M. MICHELSON AND A. R. TODD, *J. Chem. Soc.*, (1955) 808.
[115] W. ANDERSON, D. H. HAYES, A. M. MICHELSON AND A. R. TODD, *J. Chem. Soc.*, (1954) 1882.
[116] A. M. MICHELSON AND A. R. TODD, *J. Chem. Soc.*, (1954) 34.
[117] L. CUNNINGHAM, *J. Am. Chem. Soc.*, 80 (1958) 2546.
[118] W. E. COHN, *J. Am. Chem. Soc.*, 73 (1951) 1539.
[119] L. L. WEED AND T. A. COURTENAY, *J. Biol. Chem.*, 206 (1954) 735.
[120] I. R. LEHMAN AND E. A. PRATT, *J. Biol. Chem.*, 235 (1960) 3254.
[121] G. STREISINGER AND J. WEIGLE, *Proc. Natl. Acad. Sci., U.S.*, 42 (1956) 504.
[122] G. STREISINGER, F. MUKAI AND S. W. KIM, *Carnegie Inst. Wash. Year Book*, 58 (1959) 432.
[123] S. KUNO AND I. R. LEHMAN, *J. Biol. Chem.*, 237 (1962) 1266.
[124] P. A. LEVENE AND H. S. SIMMS, *J. Biol. Chem.*, 65 (1925) 519; 70 (1926) 327.
[125] A. R. PEACOCKE, *Chem. Soc. (London) Spec. Publ.*, No. 8 (1957) 163.
[126] D. M. BROWN AND A. R. TODD, in *C. and D.* *, Vol. I, p. 409.
[127] G. SCHMIDT AND S. J. THANNHAUSER, *J. Biol. Chem.*, 161 (1945) 83.
[128] A. FONÓ, *Arkiv Kemi Mineral. Geol.*, 24A, No. 33 (1947) 14, 15.
[129] J. CAVALIER, *Compt. rend.*, 127 (1898) 114.
[130] C. A. BUNTON, M. M. MHELA, K. G. OLDHAM AND C. A. VERNON, *J. Chem. Soc.*, (1960) 3293.
[131] J. KUMAMOTO AND F. H. WESTHEIMER, *J. Am. Chem. Soc.*, 77 (1955) 2515.
[132] J. EIGNER, H. BOEDTKER AND G. MICHAELS, *Biochim. Biophys. Acta*, 51 (1961) 165.
[133] O. BAILLY AND J. GAUMÉ, *Bull. Soc. Chim. France*, 2 (1935) 354; 3 (1936) 1396.
[134] E. BAER AND M. KATES, *J. Biol. Chem.*, 175 (1948) 79; 185 (1950) 615.
[135] D. M. BROWN AND A. R. TODD, *J. Chem. Soc.*, (1952) 52.
[136] D. M. BROWN AND A. R. TODD, *J. Chem. Soc.*, (1953) 2040.
[137] D. M. BROWN, G. E. HALL AND H. M. HIGSON, *J. Chem. Soc.*, (1959) 3547.

---

* E. CHARGAFF AND J. N. DAVIDSON (Eds.), *The Nucleic Acids*, 3 Vols., Academic Press, New York, 1955 and 1960.

[138] R. MARKHAM AND J. D. SMITH, *Biochem. J.*, 52 (1952) 552.
[139] D. LIPKIN AND P. T. TALBERT, *Chem. Ind. (London)*, (1955) 143.
[140] D. LIPKIN, P. T. TALBERT AND M. COHN, *J. Am. Chem. Soc.*, 76 (1954) 2871.
[141] D. M. BROWN, D. I. MAGRATH, A. H. NEILSON AND A. R. TODD, *Nature*, 177 (1956) 1124.
[142] R. B. MERRIFIELD AND D. W. WOOLEY, *J. Biol. Chem.*, 197 (1952) 521.
[143] H. WITZEL, *Ann. Chem.*, 620 (1959) 122.
[144] J. KUMAMOTO, J. R. COX AND F. H. WESTHEIMER, *J. Am. Chem. Soc.*, 78 (1956) 4858.
[145] J. R. COX, R. E. WALL AND F. H. WESTHEIMER, *Chem. Ind. (London)*, (1959) 929.
[146] D. LIPKIN, J. S. DIXON AND P. T. TALBERT, *J. Am. Chem. Soc.*, 83 (1961) 4772.
[147] G. R. BARKER, M. D. MONTAGUE, R. J. MOSS AND M. A. PARSONS, *J. Chem. Soc.*, (1957) 3786.
[148] C. A. DEKKER AND H. G. KHORANA, *J. Am. Chem. Soc.*, 76 (1954) 3522.
[149] G. M. TENER AND H. G. KHORANA, *J. Am. Chem. Soc.*, 77 (1955) 5349.
[150] A. F. TURNER AND H. G. KHORANA, *J. Am. Chem. Soc.*, 81 (1959) 4651.
[151] J. D. SMITH AND D. B. DUNN, *Biochim. Biophys. Acta*, 31 (1959) 573.
[152] D. T. ELMORE AND A. R. TODD, *J. Chem. Soc.*, (1952) 3681.
[153] B. G. LANE AND G. C. BUTLER, *Biochim. Biophys. Acta*, 33 (1959) 281.
[154] A. M. MICHELSON, L. SZABO AND A. R. TODD, *J. Chem. Soc.*, (1956) 1546.
[155] J. M. GULLAND AND E. M. JACKSON, *J. Chem. Soc.*, (1938) 1492.
[156] W. E. COHN AND E. VOLKIN, *Nature*, 167 (1951) 483.
[157] W. E. COHN AND E. VOLKIN, *J. Biol. Chem.*, 203 (1953) 319.
[158] L. A. HEPPEL AND J. C. RABINOWITZ, *Ann. Rev. Biochem.*, 27 (1948) 613.
[159] M. GRUNBERG-MANAGO, P. J. ORTIZ AND S. OCHOA, *Biochim. Biophys. Acta*, 20 (1956) 269.
[160] M. KUNITZ, *J. Gen. Physiol.*, 24 (1940) 15.
[161] C. L. ANFINSEN AND F. H. WHITE, in P. D. BOYER, H. LARDY AND K. MYRBÄCK (Eds.), *The Enzymes*, Vol. 5, Academic Press, New York, 1961, p. 85.
[162] F. W. ALLEN AND J. J. EILER, *J. Biol. Chem.*, 137 (1941) 757.
[163] S. WEINER, E. L. DUGGAN AND F. W. ALLEN, *J. Biol. Chem.*, 185 (1950) 163.
[164] J. E. BACHER AND F. W. ALLEN, *J. Biol. Chem.*, 183 (1950) 633.
[165] G. SCHMIDT, R. CUBILES, B. M. SWARTZ AND S. J. THANNHAUSER, *J. Biol. Chem.*, 170 (1947) 759.
[166] B. MAGASANIK AND E. CHARGAFF, *Biochim. Biophys. Acta*, 7 (1951) 396.
[167] G. SCHMIDT, R. CUBILES AND S. J. THANNHAUSER, *J. Cellular Comp. Physiol.*, 38 Suppl. 1 (1951) 61.
[168] G. SCHMIDT, R. CUBILES, N. ZÖLLNER, L. HECHT, N. STRICKLER, K. SERAIDARIAN, M. SERAIDARIAN AND S. J. THANNHAUSER, *J. Biol. Chem.*, 192 (1951) 715.
[169] R. MARKHAM AND J. D. SMITH, *Nature*, 168 (1951) 406.
[170] R. MARKHAM AND J. D. SMITH, *Biochem. J.*, 52 (1952) 552.
[171] R. MARKHAM AND J. D. SMITH, *Biochem. J.*, 52 (1952) 558.
[172] R. MARKHAM AND J. D. SMITH, *Biochem. J.*, 52 (1952) 565.
[173] E. VOLKIN AND W. E. COHN, *J. Biol. Chem.*, 205 (1953) 767.
[174] H. CHANTRENNE, K. LINDERSTRØM-LANG AND L. VANDENDRIESSCHE, *Nature*, 159 (1947) 877.
[175] L. VANDENDRIESSCHE, *Acta Chem. Scand.*, 7 (1953) 699.
[176] C. A. DEKKER, *Ann. Rev. Biochem.*, 29 (1960) 453.
[177] L. A. HEPPEL AND J. C. RABINOWITZ, *Ann. Rev. Biochem.*, 27 (1958) 613.
[178] L. A. HEPPEL, R. MARKHAM AND R. J. HILMOE, *Nature*, 171 (1953) 1152.
[179] D. M. BROWN, L. A. HEPPEL AND R. J. HILMOE, *J. Chem. Soc.*, (1954) 40.
[180] R. J. HILMOE, *Biochem. Prep.*, 8 (1961) 105.
[181] L. A. HEPPEL, P. J. ORTIZ AND S. OCHOA, *J. Biol. Chem.*, 229 (1957) 695.
[182] K. SATO-ASANO, *J. Biochem. (Tokyo)*, 46 (1959) 31.
[183] S. TAKEMURA AND M. MIYAZAKI, *J. Biochem. (Tokyo)*, 46 (1959) 1281.
[184] A. S. ANDERSON, G. R. BARKER, J. M. GULLAND AND M. V. LOCK, *J. Chem. Soc.*, (1952) 369.
[185] D. M. BROWN, D. I. MAGRATH AND A. R. TODD, *J. Chem. Soc.*, (1954) 1442.
[186] A. M. CRESTFIELD AND F. W. ALLEN, *J. Biol. Chem.*, 219 (1956) 103.

[187] W. E. Fletcher, J. M. Gulland and D. O. Jordan, *J. Chem. Soc.*, (1944) 33.
[188] R. A. Cox, A. S. Jones, G. E. Marsh and A. R. Peacocke, *Biochim. Biophys. Acta*, 21 (1956) 576.
[189] D. M. Brown, D. I. Magrath and A. R. Todd, *J. Chem. Soc.*, (1955) 4396.
[190] D. E. Koshland, N. S. Simmons and J. D. Watson, *J. Am. Chem. Soc.*, 80 (1958) 105.
[191] R. G. Hart, *Proc. Natl. Acad. Sci., U.S.*, 41 (1955) 261.
[192] E. Burgi and A. D. Hershey, *J. Mol. Biol.*, 4 (1962) 313.
[193] G. Bernardi and C. Sadron, *Nature*, 191 (1961) 809.
[194] C. A. Dekker, A. M. Michelson and A. R. Todd, *J. Chem. Soc.*, (1953) 947.
[195] E. Volkin, J. X. Khym and W. E. Cohn, *J. Am. Chem. Soc.*, 73 (1951) 1533.
[196] W. E. Cohn, *J. Am. Chem. Soc.*, 72 (1950) 2811.
[197] R. L. Sinsheimer, *Science*, 120 (1954) 551.
[198] L. Cunningham, B. W. Catlin and M. Privat de Garihle, *J. Am. Chem. Soc.*, 78 (1956) 4642.
[199] L. Cunningham, *Ann. N.Y. Acad. Sci.*, 81 (1959) 788.
[200] M. L. Dirksen and C. A. Dekker, *Biochem. Biophys. Res. Commun.*, 2 (1960) 147.
[201] M. Privat de Garilhe, L. Cunningham, U. Laurila and M. Laskowski, *J. Biol. Chem.*, 224 (1957) 751.
[202] R. L. Sinsheimer, *J. Biol. Chem.*, 208 (1954) 445; 215 (1955) 579.
[203] A. Kornberg, *Science*, 131 (1960) 1503.
[204] M. Beer, *J. Mol. Biol.*, 3 (1961) 263.
[205] H. Witzel, *Ann. Chem.*, 635 (1960) 182.
[206] G. W. Rushizky and C. A. Knight, *Proc. Natl. Acad. Sci., U.S.*, 46 (1960) 945.
[207] M. Staehlin, *Biochim. Biophys. Acta*, 49 (1961) 11.
[208] M. Staehlin, *Biochim. Biophys. Acta*, 49 (1961) 27.
[209] M. Staehlin, *Biochim. Biophys. Acta*, 49 (1961) 20.
[210] K. Sato-Ansano and F. Egami, *Nature*, 185 (1960) 462.
[211] K. Ansano and F. Egami, *J. Biochem. (Tokyo)*, 50 (1960) 467.
[212] G. W. Rushizky and H. A. Sober, *J. Biol. Chem.*, 237 (1962) 834.
[213] L. A. Heppel, P. J. Ortiz and S. Ochoa, *J. Biol. Chem.*, 229 (1957) 679.
[214] M. F. Singer, *J. Biol. Chem.*, 232 (1958) 211.
[215] M. F. Singer, L. A. Heppel and R. J. Hilmoe, *Biochim. Biophys. Acta*, 26 (1957) 447; *J. Biol. Chem.*, 235 (1960) 738, 751.
[216] B. E. Griffin, A. R. Todd and A. Rich, *Proc. Natl. Acad. Sci., U.S.*, 44 (1958) 1123.
[217] A. M. Michelson, J. Dondon and M. Grunberg-Manago, *Biochim. Biophys. Acta*, 55 (1962) 529.
[218] M. Smith, D. H. Rammler, L. H. Goldberg and H. G. Khorana, *J. Am. Chem. Soc.*, 84 (1962) 430.
[219] J. Smrt and F. Šorm, *Collection Czech. Chem. Commun.*, 27 (1962) 86.
[220] D. M. Brown and E. Rosenberg, unpublished work (1962).
[221] A. M. Michelson, *J. Chem. Soc.*, (1959) 1371; (1962) 979.
[222] W. E. Razzell and H. G. Khorana, *J. Biol. Chem.*, 234 (1959) 2114.
[223] K. K. Reddi, *Biochim. Biophys. Acta*, 42 (1960) 365.
[224] D. M. Brown, M. Fried and A. R. Todd, *Chem. Ind. (London)*, (1953) 352; *J. Chem. Soc.*, (1955) 2206.
[225] P. R. Whitfeld and R. Markham, *Nature*, 171 (1953) 1151.
[226] P. R. Whitfeld, *Biochem. J.*, 58 (1954) 390.
[227] M. Ogur and J. D. Small, *J. Biol. Chem.*, 235 (1960) PC 60.
[228] S. Hakamori, *Proc. 8th Symp. on Nucleic Acids, Kyoto, Japan*, (1959) 16.
[229] J. X. Khym and W. E. Cohn, *J. Biol. Chem.*, 236 (1961) PC 9; *Acides Ribonucléiques et Polyphosphates, Structure, Synthèse et Fonction*, Colloques Internationaux du C.N.R.S., Strasbourg, 1961 (C.N.R.S., Paris, 1962).
[230] D. M. Brown and A. P. Read, unpublished observations.
[231] V. C. Barry and P. W. D. Mitchell, *J. Chem. Soc.*, (1953) 3610, 3631.
[232] R. Dulbecco and J. D. Smith, *Biochim. Biophys. Acta*, 39 (1960) 358.
[233] A. S. Jones, M. Stacey and B. E. Watson, *J. Chem. Soc.*, (1957) 2454.
[234] K. Miura and F. Egami, *Biochim. Biophys. Acta*, 44 (1960) 378.
[235] W. E. Cohn and R. Markham, *Biochem. J.*, 62 (1956) 17 P.

[236] M. STAEHLIN, *Acides Ribonucléiques et Polyphosphates, Structure, Synthèse et Fonction*, Colloques Internationaux du C.N.R.S., Strasbourg, 1961 (C.N.R.S., Paris, 1962), p. 249.

[237] R. W. HOLLEY, J. APGAR, S. H. MERRILL AND P. L. ZUBKOFF, *J. Am. Chem. Soc.*, 83 (1961) 4861.

[238] T. SUGIYAMA AND H. FRAENKEL-CONRAT, *Proc. Natl. Acad. Sci., U.S.*, 47 (1961) 1393.

[239] M. B. HOAGLAND, in *C. and D.* *, Vol. III, p. 349.

[240] P. C. ZAMECNIK, *Harvey Lectures*, Ser. 54 (1960) 256; Jubilee Lecture, *Biochem. J.*, 85 (1962) 257.

[241] P. BERG, *Ann. Rev. Biochem.*, 30 (1961) 293.

[242] G. N. COHEN AND F. GROS, *Ann. Rev. Biochem.*, 29 (1960) 525.

[243] R. MONIER, M. L. STEPHENSON AND P. C. ZAMECNIK, *Biochim. Biophys. Acta*, 43 (1960) 1.

[244] G. L. BROWN AND G. ZUBAY, *J. Mol. Biol.*, 2 (1960) 287.

[245] L. I. HECHT, M. L. STEPHENSON AND P. C. ZAMECNIK, *Proc. Natl. Acad. Sci., U.S.*, 45 (1959) 505.

[246] J. PREISS, M. DIECKMANN AND P. BERG, *J. Biol. Chem.*, 236 (1961) 1748.

[247] E. HERBERT AND E. S. CANELLAKIS, *Biochim. Biophys. Acta*, 42 (1960)363.

[248] M. F. SINGER AND G. L. CANTONI, *Biochim. Biophys. Acta*, 39 (1960) 182.

[249] Z. ZILLIG, D. SCHACHTSCHABEL AND W. KRONE, *Z. physiol. Chem.*, 318 (1960) 100.

[250] E. S. CANELLAKIS, *Biochim. Biophys. Acta*, 23 (1957) 217; 25 (1957) 217.

[251] E. HARBERS AND C. HEIDELBERGER, *Biochim. Biophys. Acta*, 35 (1959) 381.

[252] P. BERG, F. H. BERGMANN, E. J. OFENGAND AND M. DIECKMANN, *J. Biol. Chem.*, 236 (1961) 1726.

[253] H. G. ZACHAU, G. ACS AND F. LIPMANN, *Proc. Natl. Acad. Sci., U.S.*, 44 (1958) 67.

[254] H. G. ZACHAU, *Chem. Ber.*, 93 (1960) 1822, 1830.

[254a] C.-T. YU AND P. C. ZAMECNIK, *Biochim. Biophys. Acta*, 45 (1960) 148.

[254b] R. K. RALPH, R. J. YOUNG AND H. G. KHORANA, *J. Am. Chem. Soc.*, 84 (1962) 1490.

[255] P. BERG AND U. LAGERKVIST, *Acides Ribonucléiques et Polyphosphates, Structure, Synthèse et Fonction*, Colloques Internationaux du C.N.R.S., Strasbourg, 1961 (C.N.R.S., Paris, 1962), p. 259.

[256] K. S. MCCULLY AND G. L. CANTONI, *Biochim. Biophys. Acta*, 51 (1961) 190.

[257] J. APGAR, R. W. HOLLEY AND S. M. MERRILL, *J. Biol. Chem.*, 237 (1952) 796.

[257a] M. SPENCER, W. FULLER, M. H. F. WILKINS AND G. L. BROWN, *Nature*, 194 (1962) 1014.

[258] K. C. SMITH, E. CORDES AND R. S. SCHWEET, *Biochim. Biophys. Acta*, 33 (1959) 286.

[259] M. L. STEPHENSON AND P. C. ZAMECNIK, *Proc. Natl. Acad. Sci., U.S.*, 47 (1961) 1627.

[260] G. HARTMANN AND U. COY, *Biochim. Biophys. Acta*, 47 (1961) 612.

[261] G. L. BROWN, in Microbial Genetics, *Symp. Soc. Gen. Microbiol.*, 10 (1960) 208.

[262] P. C. ZAMECNIK, M. L. STEPHENSON AND J. F. SCOTT, *Proc. Natl. Acad. Sci., U.S.*, 46 (1960) 811.

[263] H. G. ZACHAU, M. TODA, W. B. LAWSON AND M. SCHWEIGER, *Biochim. Biophys. Acta*, 53 (1961) 221.

[264] H. VON PORTATIUS, P. DOTY AND M. L. STEPHENSON, *J. Am. Chem. Soc.*, 83 (1961) 3351.

[265] M. L. STEPHENSON AND P. C. ZAMECNIK, *Biochem. Biophys. Res. Commun.*, 7 (1962) 91.

[266] R. L. SINSHEIMER, *J. Mol. Biol.*, 1 (1959) 37, 43.

[267] R. L. SINSHEIMER, *J. Biol. Chem.*, 215 (1955) 579.

[268] M. PRIVAT DE GARIHLE, L. CUNNINGHAM, U. LAURILA AND M. LASKOWSKI, *J. Biol. Chem.*, 224 (1957) 751.

[269] J. F. KOERNER AND R. L. SINSHEIMER, *J. Biol. Chem.*, 228 (1957) 1049.

[270] U. LAURILA AND M. LASKOWSKI, *J. Biol. Chem.*, 228 (1957) 49.

[271] F. FELIX, J. L. POTTER AND M. LASKOWSKI, *J. Biol. Chem.*, 235 (1960) 1150.

---

* E. CHARGAFF AND J. N. DAVIDSON (Eds.), *The Nucleic Acids*, 3 Vols., Academic Press, New York, 1955 and 1960.

[272] M. ALEXANDER, L. A. HEPPEL AND J. HURWITZ, *J. Biol. Chem.*, 236 (1961) 3014.
[273] G. P. MOSS, C. B. REESE, K. SCHOFIELD, R. SHAPIRO AND A. R. TODD, *J. Chem. Soc.*, (1963) 1149.
[274] J. P. VIZSOLYI AND G. M. TENER, *Chem. Ind. (London)*, (1962) 263.
[275] H. G. KHORANA in *C. and D.**, Vol. III, p. 105.
[276] H. G. KHORANA, J. P. VIZSOLYI AND R. K. RALPH, *J. Am. Chem. Soc.*, 84 (1962) 414.
[277] J. JOSSE, A. D. KAISER AND A. KORNBERG, *J. Biol. Chem.*, 236 (1961) 864.
[278] A. M. MICHELSON AND A. R. TODD, *J. Chem. Soc.*, (1955) 2632.
[279] G. WEIMANN AND H. G. KHORANA, *J. Am. Chem. Soc.*, 84 (1962) 419.
[280] C. TAMM, M. E. HODES AND E. CHARGAFF, *J. Biol. Chem.*, 195 (1952) 49.
[281] S. G. LALAND, *Acta Chem. Scand.*, 8 (1954) 449.
[282] E. HURLEU, S. G. LALAND, R. A. COX AND A. R. PEACOCKE, *Acta Chem. Scand.*, 10 (1956) 793.
[283] A. S. JONES AND D. S. LETHAM, *J. Chem. Soc.*, (1956) 2573.
[284] C. TAMM, H. S. SHAPIRO, R. LIPSHITZ AND E. CHARGAFF, *J. Biol. Chem.*, 203 (1953) 673.
[285] D. M. BROWN AND A. R. TODD, *Ann. Rev. Biochem.*, 24 (1955) 311.
[286] A. S. JONES, D. S. LETHAM AND M. STACEY, *J. Chem. Soc.*, (1956) 2579, 2584.
[287] A. S. JONES, M. STACEY AND B. E. WATSON, *J. Chem. Soc.*, (1957) 2454.
[288] A. S. JONES AND M. STACEY, *Chem. Soc. (London), Spec. Publ.* No. 8 (1957) 129.
[289] H. S. SHAPIRO AND E. CHARGAFF, *Biochim. Biophys. Acta*, 26 (1957) 596.
[290] H. S. SHAPIRO AND E. CHARGAFF, *Biochim. Biophys. Acta*, 26 (1957) 608.
[291] H. S. SHAPIRO AND E. CHARGAFF, *Biochim. Biophys. Acta*, 39 (1960) 62.
[292] H. S. SHAPIRO AND E. CHARGAFF, *Biochim. Biophys. Acta*, 39 (1960) 68.
[293] W. E. COHN AND E. VOLKIN, *Biochim. Biophys. Acta*, 24 (1957) 359.
[294] K. BURTON, *Biochem. J.*, 62 (1956) 315.
[295] K. BURTON AND G. B. PETERSON, *Biochim. Biophys. Acta*, 26 (1957) 667.
[296] K. BURTON AND G. B. PETERSON, *Biochem. J.*, 75 (1960) 17.
[297] K. BURTON, *Biochem. J.*, 77 (1960) 547.
[298] J. D. SMITH AND R. MARKHAM, *Nature*, 170 (1952) 120.
[299] J. D. WATSON AND F. H. C. CRICK, *Nature*, 171 (1953) 737.
[300] L. ASTRACHAN AND E. VOLKIN, *Biochim. Biophys. Acta*, 29 (1958) 536.
[301] M. YCAS AND W. S. VINCENT, *Proc. Natl. Acad. Sci., U.S.*, 46 (1960) 804.
[302] M. NOMURA, B. D. HALL AND S. SPIEGELMAN, *J. Mol. Biol.*, 2 (1960) 305.
[303] M. V. SIMPSON, *Ann. Rev. Biochem.*, 31 (1962) 333.
[304] D. SHUGAR, in *C. and D**., Vol. III, p. 39.
[305] M. I. SIMON AND H. VAN VINAKIS, *Federation Proc.*, 21 (1962) 374.
[306] E. FREESE, *Proc. Natl. Acad. Sci., U.S.*, 45 (1959) 622.
[307] S. BRENNER, L. BARNETT, F. H. C. CRICK AND A. ORGEL, *J. Mol. Biol.*, 3 (1961) 121.
[308] E. B. FREESE, *Proc. Natl. Acad. Sci., U.S.*, 47 (1961) 540.
[309] H. SCHUSTER in *C. and D.**, Vol. III, p. 245.
[310] H. G. WITMANN, *Naturwiss.*, 48 (1961) 729.
[311] H. SCHUSTER AND G. SCHRAMM, *Z. Naturforsch.*, 13b (1958) 697.
[312] W. VIELMETTER AND H. SCHUSTER, *Biochem. Biophys. Res. Commun.*, 2 (1960) 324.
[313] W. C. J. ROSS, *Biological Alkylating Agents*, Butterworth, London, 1962.
[314] D. M. BROWN AND G. O. OSBORNE, *J. Chem. Soc.*, (1957) 2590.
[315] P. T. GILHAM, *J. Am. Chem. Soc.*, 84 (1962) 687.
[316] J. A. HAINES, C. B. REESE AND A. R. TODD, *J. Chem. Soc.*, (1962) 5281.
[317] P. D. LAWLEY, *Proc. Chem. Soc.*, (1957) 290; *Biochim. Biophys. Acta*, 26 (1957) 450
[318] B. REINER AND S. ZAMENHOF, *J. Biol. Chem.*, 228 (1957) 475.
[319] P. BROOKES AND P. D. LAWLEY, *J. Chem. Soc.*, (1960) 539.
[320] P. BROOKES AND P. D. LAWLEY, *J. Chem. Soc.*, (1962) 1348.
[321] E. BAUTZ AND E. FREESE, *Proc. Natl. Acad. Sci., U.S.*, 46 (1960) 1585.
[322] S. GREER AND S. ZAMENHOF, *J Mol. Biol.*, 4 (1962) 123.

---

* E. CHARGAFF AND J. N. DAVIDSON (Eds.), *The Nucleic Acids*, 3 Vols., Academic Press, New York, 1955 and 1960.

[323] H. FRAENKEL-CONRAT, *Biochim. Biophys. Acta*, 15 (1954) 307.

[324] M. STAEHLIN, *Biochim. Biophys. Acta*, 29 (1958) 410.

[325] D. E. HOARD, *Biochim. Biophys. Acta*, 40 (1960) 62.

[326] R. F. BEERS AND R. F. STEINER, *Nature*, 179 (1957) 1076.

[327] R. HASELKORN AND P. DOTY, *J. Biol. Chem.*, 236 (1961) 2738.

[328] D. STOLLAR AND L. GROSSMAN, *J. Mol. Biol.*, 4 (1962) 31.

[329] M. STAEHLIN, *Biochim. Biophys. Acta*, 31 (1959) 448.

[330] E. FREESE, E. BAUTZ AND E. B. FREESE, *Proc. Natl. Acad. Sci., U.S.*, 47 (1961) 845.

[330a] S. P. CHAMPE AND S. BENZER, *Proc. Natl. Acad. Sci., U.S.*, 48 (1962) 532.

[331] S. TAKEMURA, *J. Biochem. (Tokyo)*, 44 (1957) 321; *Biochim. Biophys. Acta*, 29 (1958) 447.

[332] D. M. BROWN, H. PAULUS AND P. SCHELL, unpublished observations.

[333] H. WITZEL, *Ann. Chem.*, 620 (1959) 122.

[334] H. SCHUSTER, *J. Mol. Biol.*, 3 (1961)

[335] D. W. VERWOERD, H. KOHLHAGE AND W. ZILLIG, *Nature*, 192 (1961) 1038.

[336] D. M. BROWN AND P. SCHELL, *J. Mol. Biol.*, 3 (1961) 709, and unpublished observations.

Physical Properties of the Nucleic Acids

Section a

The Three-Dimensional Configuration of the DNA Molecule

M. H. F. WILKINS

*Medical Research Council, Biophysics Research Unit,
King's College, London (Great Britain)*

1. Relation to genetic replication and mutation

The properties of DNA solutions show that DNA consists of long thread-like molecules. In the electron microscope these appear of uniform diameter ($\sim$ 20 Å) along their length. While chemical studies show that the molecules consist of polynucleotide chains, information concerning the configuration of the chains is mainly obtained from X-ray diffraction studies of fibres of DNA.

DNA molecules from all sources[1] have the same structure. This is the Watson–Crick structure consisting of two polynucleotide chains[2]. (The only exception so far found is the single-chain DNA from the bacteriophage φX174). Both chains have a right-handed helical form (Figs. 1, 2 and 3) and are twisted round an axis passing centrally along the length of the molecule. As a result one chain is twisted around the other. Apart from differences of nucleotide sequence, the two chains are identical except that the sequence of atoms along one chain, *e.g.* C_4–C_5–O–P–O–C_3, is opposite in direction in the two chains. The two chains are linked together by hydrogen bonds between the bases (Fig. 4). The hydrogen-bonded bases form base-pairs; there are only two of these and their geometry has special features which are of importance in relation to the structure and function of the molecule. First, the distance between the glycosidic bonds is the same in both pairs. Second, the angle between the glycosidic bond direction

Fig. 1. Photograph of a model of part of a DNA molecule in the *B* configuration. Each atom is represented by a sphere, or part of a sphere, with radius equal to the Van der Waals radius of the atom. Oxygen atoms are large white spheres, hydrogen atoms are small grey spheres. The wide and narrow helical grooves separating the two phosphate ester chains in the molecule can be seen. The view of the model corresponds to the drawing in Fig. 2.

and the the line joining the C-1 atoms (at the ends of the bonds) is the same in each pair and is the same for all four nucleotides. As a result the glycosidic bond of any nucleotide is arranged identically in relation to the helix axis of the molecule, this axis being at X (Fig. 4). Hence the configuration of the

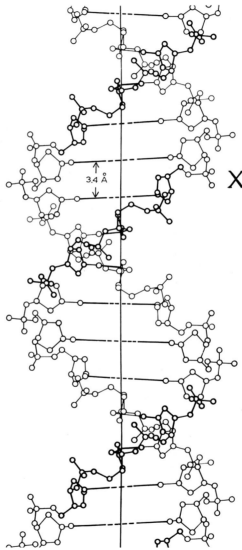

3.4 Å

X

Fig. 2. Projection of the B configuration of the DNA molecule. This corresponds to the view of the model in Fig. 1.

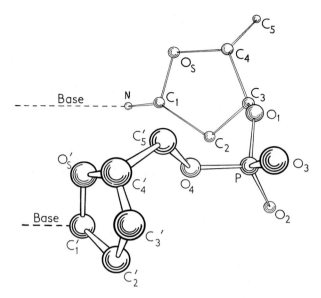

Fig. 3. Detail of the phosphate-ester chain in DNA showing two deoxyribose rings and a phosphate group. Atoms nearer the viewer are drawn larger. The arrangement is that shown at X in Fig. 2.

deoxyribose and phosphate part of the nucleotide can be exactly the same irrespective of which base is present in the nucleotide. As a result an exactly regular helical configuration is formed. There are a great many ways of hydrogen bonding bases in pairs but there are very few systems in which the glycosidic links, for all four bases, have equivalent position and direction. Approximate equivalence is given by pairings other than the Watson–Crick scheme (Fig. 4), but experimental evidence is in favour of the Watson–Crick pairing in DNA.

The sequence of bases along one polynucleotide chain is believed to contain the genetic information passed from one generation to the next. The base-pairing does not restrict this sequence but it requires the sequence in one chain in the molecule to be complementary to that in the other. It appears that, during replication of a DNA molecule, each chain acts as a template on which a second chain is built up and, as a result, two new double-chain molecules are formed, each identical with the parent molecule[3]. A necessary step in replication is the separation of the two chains in the parent molecule. Because the two chains are wound round each other and the length of the molecules is large, the separation involves considerable unwinding—one chain must, for each turn of the helix, make one complete rotation relative to the other. The parent chains remain intact during replication and, as a result, both daughter molecules after one duplication contain one parental chain and one new chain.

A mutation may take place when during replication the base-pairing

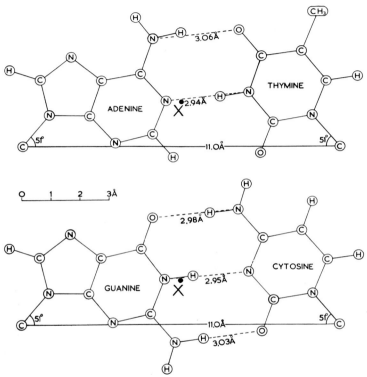

Fig. 4. Watson–Crick hydrogen bonding (after Spencer) in base-pairs in DNA. X shows the position of the helix axis in the DNA molecule in the B configuration.

rule fails to operate at one point in the chain and an error is produced in the copy of the base sequence. The base-pair formed in error may be efficiently hydrogen-bonded but, because the dimensions of the pair are incorrect, a local irregularity will be introduced into the helical structure. Mutation rates indicate that the probability of such an error per replication is extremely small. Hence the base-pairing mechanism must be highly specific. The specificity apparently arises as follows. Hydrogen bonding *per se* is relatively unspecific but the geometry of the hydrogen bonds in DNA is highly specific in as much as it permits the configuration of every nucleotide to be the same in the helical molecule. Hence, if during replication an enzyme holds a nucleotide pair in the correct configuration, adenine can pair only with thymine and guanine only with cytosine. Experiments on *in vitro* synthesis of DNA support the Watson–Crick hypothesis of replication and tracer experiments show that during replication the molecules split in half and the halves are conserved.

2. Stereochemical details of the DNA molecules

The helical molecule of DNA in its commonly observed *B* configuration (that found *in vivo*) contains 10 nucleotide pairs per turn of the helix (Fig. 2). The pairs are spaced 3.4 Å apart along the axis of the molecule. Hence there is one turn of the helix every 34 Å—the pitch length. The bases are planar and stacked on one another in Van der Waals contact roughly perpendicular to the helix axis. Since the hydrogen bonds from NH and NH_2 groups must lie near to the plane of the base, the base pairs are roughly planar. The deoxyribose ring is slightly puckered (like cyclopentane). Steric hindrance takes place when the sugar ring is rotated about the glycosidic link and as a result the ring lies roughly perpendicular to the base-pair. The phosphate-ester chain is stretched almost to its maximum extent and phosphate groups are about 7 Å apart along the helix. (Projected on the helix axis the separation is 3.4 Å for all parts of the nucleotide). The phosphorus atom is about 9.6 Å from the axis and the average overall diameter of the molecule is about 20 Å. The two polynucleotide chains are separated by two helical grooves on the surface of the molecule. One groove is wider than the other (Fig. 1) and contains space to accommodate groups attached to the C-5 atom of pyrimidines, *e.g.* the methyl group in methylcytosine, bromine in bromouracil, and glucose in T2 bacteriophage DNA.

3. X-ray diffraction studies of DNA

At high concentrations in water DNA forms viscous gels from which fibres of diameter 1–100 μ may be drawn. The shearing forces in this process cause the DNA molecules to be oriented roughly parallel to the length of the fibre. Because the molecules have a regular structure DNA, like many linear polymers, is able to form microcrystals. In these the molecules are packed regularly in three dimensions. There are also amorphous regions in the fibre where molecules are tangled and arranged irregularly. DNA molecules are so long that one part of the molecule may be in an amorphous region and another part in a crystalline region. The fibres are suitable objects for X-ray diffraction analysis[4]. A finely collimated beam of monochromatic X-rays is passed through the fibre roughly at right angles to its length. The X-rays are scattered at any point with amplitude proportional to the

References p. 279

electron density at the point. Because the structure is periodic, the amplitude, for a suitable angle of diffraction, is reinforced by the amplitude from corresponding points throughout the crystal. Strong diffraction, therefore, takes place at such angles and the X-ray diffraction photograph consists of

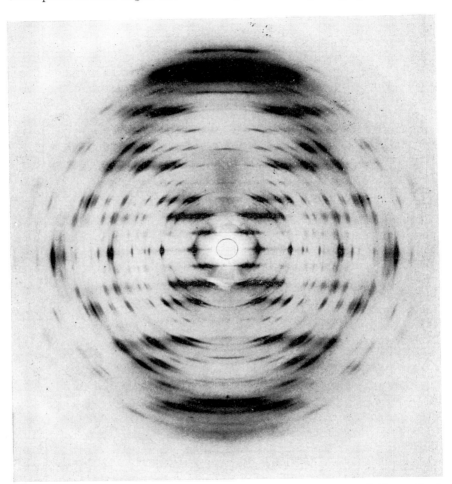

Fig. 5. X-ray diffraction photograph of microcrystalline fibre of the lithium salt of DNA in *B* configuration.

sharp spots (Fig. 5). The intensities of the spots can be measured and compared with intensities calculated from a molecular model. The positions of the spots show how the molecules are packed.

The DNA helix is somewhat flexible and can adopt various slightly different but distinct configurations, each of which may be identified from the corresponding diffraction pattern. The B configuration is found *in vivo* when DNA is bound to protamine or histone. It is given by all alkali metal salts of DNA at high relative humidity ($\sim 90\%$) when the fibres contain about 50% by weight of water. The axes of the molecules are then about 26 Å apart. The arrangement of the molecules is not exact and, as a result, the diffraction pattern is somewhat diffuse. On reducing the relative humidity to 66%, the water content drops to about 25% and the molecules are on the average about 21 Å apart. If the lithium salt of DNA (LiDNA) is used and if there is $\sim 3\%$ LiCl in the fibres, crystallisation takes place in the B configuration. In this configuration the planes of the bases are almost exactly at right angles to the helix axis. At lower humidities, or at 66% relative humidity if chloride is absent, LiDNA adopts the C configuration in which the bases are tilted about 5° so that a line along the length of the base-pair is inclined at 85° to the helix axis. The configuration of any one nucleotide is very similar to that in B but the position of the nucleotides in the helix is somewhat different. There are $9\frac{1}{3}$ nucleotides per turn of the helix and the nucleotides are spaced 3.3 Å along the helix axis. The Na, K and Rb salts of DNA adopt the A configuration at 75% relative humidity. This crystalline form is independent of the presence of salts. The bases are tilted 20° in the opposite direction to that in C (Fig. 6) and the configuration of the nucleotides is different from that in B and C. When fibres of DNA are dried, the regular structure collapses but is recovered on rehydration.

4. Flexibility of the DNA molecule

X-ray diffraction studies show that the DNA helix can adopt varying forms depending on the water content of the DNA and the tension on the fibre. Furthermore, fibres of DNA may be stretched reversibly so that the helix is extended by at least 50%. The extended molecules have an irregular structure in which the bases are tilted at about 45° to their length. The flexibility of DNA molecules indicates how they may be accommodated in their natural sites (*e.g.* in bacteriophage) that are smaller than the length of the molecules. The molecules could be bent, either sharply at points where the helical structure is interrupted, or continuously into a radius, probably as small as 300 Å, without disruption of the helical structure.

5. The configuration of RNA molecules

All types of RNA lack the well-defined periodic structure of DNA. As a result RNA gives rather diffuse X-ray diffraction patterns[5]. These patterns

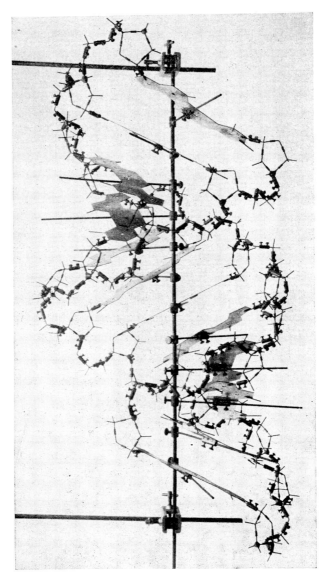

Fig. 6. Model of the *A* configuration of DNA. The base-pairs are represented by metal plates and tilted 20° from perpendicular to the helix axis. Atoms in the phosphate-ester chain are represented by wires along valency bonds; centres of atoms are at the intersections of the wires.

have a general form like DNA patterns. Study of the X-ray data and solution properties of RNA makes it appear very likely that isolated RNA has in part a double-helix structure like DNA. The double helix may be formed by one chain folded back on itself. It may be that the helical structure is confined to those parts of the molecule where complementary base sequences permit efficient hydrogen bonding. An alternative possibility is that the whole molecule is helical, the hydrogen bonds forming irregularly wherever proton donor and acceptor groups meet. The resultant base-pairs would on the average have less than two hydrogen bonds per pair and the chain configuration would be irregular though helical on the average. Molecular model building shows that the DNA configuration does not require much distortion to include, without steric hindrance, the hydroxyl group of the ribose. In ribosomes evidence suggests that RNA has a double-helical structure. This is not true *in vivo* for all forms of RNA for it is known that RNA in tobacco mosaic virus exists as an extended single chain[6]. (Recent X-ray study[7] shows that RNA molecules contain helical regions like the *A* configuration of DNA.)

6. Molecular configuration of synthetic polynucleotides

Ribopolynucleotides synthesised *in vitro* can form helical structures that bear a general resemblance to DNA molecules[8]. When polyuridylic and adenylic acids are mixed in solution the chains twist round one another and the bases pair with the same hydrogen bonds as in DNA. Polyadenylic acid forms a double helix in which the sequences of atoms in both chains are, unlike those in DNA, in the same direction. The propensity of bases to hydrogen-bond together gives rise to many two-chain and three-chain helical structures. Synthetic deoxyribopolynucleotides also give structures like DNA.

REFERENCES

[1] L. D. HAMILTON, R. K. BARCLAY, M. H. F. WILKINS, G. L. BROWN, H. R. WILSON, D. A. MARVIN, H. EPHRUSSI-TAYLOR AND N. S. SIMMONS, *J. Biophys. Biochem. Cytol.*, 5 (1959) 397.
[2] J. D. WATSON AND F. H. C. CRICK, *Nature*, 171 (1953) 737.
[3] J. D. WATSON AND F. H. C. CRICK, *Nature*, 171 (1953) 964.
[4] R. LANGRIDGE, H. R. WILSON, C. W. HOOPER, M. H. F. WILKINS AND L. D. HAMILTON, *J. Mol. Biol.*, 2 (1960) 19, 38.
[5] A. RICH AND J. D. WATSON, *Proc. Natl. Acad. Sci. U.S.*, 40 (1954) 759.
[6] R. E. FRANKLIN, D. L. D. CASPAR AND A. KLUG, in *Problems and Progress in Plant Pathology, 1908–1958*, University of Wisconsin Press, 1958.
[7] M. SPENCER, W. FULLER, M. H. F. WILKINS AND G. L. BROWN, *Nature*, 194 (1962) 1014.
[8] A. RICH, in R. E. ZIRKLE (Ed.), *Symposium on Molecular Biology*, University of Chicago Press, 1959, p. 47.

Chapter IV

Physical Properties of the Nucleic Acids

Section b

Solution Properties

JAMES D. COOMBES

Physics Department, King's College, London (Great Britain)

1. Deoxyribonucleic acid (DNA)

Early studies of the physical chemistry of DNA in solution often gave conflicting and puzzling results. As these studies progressed, however, it became clear that much of this was due to the peculiar sensitivity of the molecule to the environmental conditions to which it was exposed during the isolation procedures. Thus, alterations of the pH, salt concentration or temperature of the aqueous media used were found to induce abrupt and irreversible changes in viscosity, ultraviolet absorption and intensity of scattered light. By analogy with similar effects observed with protein solutions, the term *denaturation* was used to describe these effects.

Recent years have witnessed the continual refinement of isolation procedure in which the intracellular nucleic acid is obtained free of associated protein and with the secondary structure (pattern of hydrogen bonds) intact, that is in the *native* state. Important in these advances have been the X-ray structure determination of DNA (described above) and studies of bacterial transforming principle (DNA), both of which have indicated the correspondence of structure between isolated DNA and the biologically active DNA present in the cell (see article by D. M. Brown, Chapter III b, p. 158). In spite of these refinements, however, one is always dealing with molecules that may be damaged to an extent which, though small, is unknown.

For characterisation of the DNA molecule in solution it is essential that measurements of physical properties be made at a concentration sufficiently low to exclude any interference effects; *i.e.*, to study the isolated molecules.

This is a general problem in high polymer chemistry, for due to the large *effective volume* of these molecules this concentration is extremely low. It is overcome by making measurements at higher concentrations and then extrapolating to *infinite dilution*. In the case of DNA, however, the effective volume is so large that even the concentration range over which extrapolation is possible (below 0.01 % w/v) severely limits the techniques that may be employed. Osmotic pressure, and diffusion or sedimentation procedures involving schlieren optics, are excluded. The most useful methods are the scattering of light (and low-angle X-rays), and the hydrodynamic methods of viscosity, sedimentation velocity (employing ultraviolet absorption optics), or orientation birefringence induced by an electric or hydrodynamic field.

Before discussion of these techniques, it should be emphasised that most samples of DNA do not contain identical molecules, but are heterogeneous. The most commonly considered heterogeneities are molecular weight[1] and base-composition[2,3], it being assumed that the secondary structures (double-helix or random coil) are identical in a homologous sample. Thus, any complete description of DNA would include information on the distribution of sizes and composition throughout the sample.

(a) Size and shape of DNA

The size of the DNA molecule remains uncertain within fairly narrow limits due to the unknown extent of damage incurred in preparation. If too rigorous methods of isolation are employed (*e.g.*, stirring)[4], the observed molecular weight will be low, and if protein removal is incomplete, then aggregation will lead to an erroneously high value. With these provisos, it seems probable that the normal molecular weight range for DNA is a few millions (*e.g.*, calf thymus $8 \cdot 10^6$, *E. coli* $10 \cdot 10^6$). In the case of some viruses it may differ considerably from this: for example, the two bacterial coliphages T2 and φX174 have DNA of molecular weight 45 million and 1.7 million, respectively[5,6]. In spite of these difficulties, the state of native DNA in dilute solution is fairly well understood in terms of the Watson–Crick double-helix model[7].

Early studies of the effect of salt concentration on viscosity[8] (the electroviscous effect) indicated that, in contradistinction to normal polyelectrolyte molecules, DNA solutions showed only a very small increase in viscosity on lowering the salt concentration in the medium. This indicated an unusual rigidity which strongly suggested that the molecule could not be a randomly coiled single-chain polyelectrolyte. Further evidence that a secondary structure was present in the native molecule came from titration behaviour[9], in which a hysteresis effect was observed; that is, in titrating from neutral pH to acid or alkaline pH and then reversing the titration, the curves were non-superimposable. This clearly indicated that the molecules contained non-titrable acidic and basic groups which were only revealed by exposure to extremes of pH and suggested that H-bonding between acidic and basic groups was involved in the secondary structure.

In the light of these observations, we will now consider the various light scattering studies of DNA, from which the most complete information has come. Briefly (see article by Sadron, Vol. 3, p. 265, for more details), the method involves determination of I_θ, the intensity of light scattered from a small volume of solution at an angle θ to the incident beam, in excess of that scattered by the pure solvent. It may be shown that this is related to the molecular weight by the following relation

$$\frac{Kc}{I_\theta} = \frac{1}{M_w} + 2\,Bc$$

where K is a measurable constant involving optical and instrumental factors, B is the second virial coefficient, c the concentration, and M_w the weight average molecular weight. Thus, the method provides a value of M_w, the molecular weight. For particles larger than about 1/20 the wave length of the light used (often 436 mμ), and including DNA, destructive interference from light scattered by various parts of the molecule gives rise to a decrease in intensity of scattered light, in which case the relation becomes

$$\frac{Kc}{I_\theta} = \frac{1}{M_w \cdot P(\theta)} + 2\,Bc$$

where $P(\theta)$ is equal to one at $\theta = 0$ and is less than one at all other angles. Thus, to obtain M_w, the molecular weight, it is essential to extrapolate to zero angle $(P(\theta) = 1)$ as well as zero concentration. (The procedure for carrying out this double extrapolation, the Zimm plot, is explained in the article by Sadron, Vol. 3, p. 265). However, the angular dependence of $P(\theta)$ provides information on the shape of the particle, since it may be shown that

$$P(\theta) = 1 - \frac{h^2 \rho^2}{3}$$

where $h = 4\pi \sin{(\theta/2)}/\lambda$, λ being the wave length of the light used (in the solution) and ρ the radius of gyration of the macromolecule. The dimensions of simple geometrical forms are directly obtainable from ρ; for instance, the length of a rod is $12^{\frac{1}{2}}\rho$, the root mean square end-to-end distance of a randomly coiled polymer is $6^{\frac{1}{2}}\rho$.[*]

As an example, a sample of calf thymus DNA was found to have a molecular weight 7.7 million, and a radius of gyration of 3,000 Å. A hard sphere of the same molecular weight and density would have a radius of gyration of only 92 Å. Similarly, on the random-coil model the radius of gyration is equivalent to a root mean square end-to-end separation of 7,650 Å ($6^{\frac{1}{2}}\rho$). However, for the molecular weight and the linear density on the Watson–Crick model of 200 mass units/Å we can calculate a contour length of 39,600 Å for this polymer, *i.e.* only five times the observed end-to-end separation. For a randomly coiled polymer, the ratio is typically of the order of 100 : 1, so that the data are entirely inconsistent with this model.

That DNA cannot be described by either the random-coil or the sphere model is borne out by other physical properties. The extremely high viscosity (72 dl/g) for the sample discussed above is to be compared with the expected values of 0.014 dl/g and approximately 4 dl/g on the hard-sphere and random-coil models, respectively. Similarly, the sedimentation constant observed (21 S) is about 1/3 that expected from studies of randomly coiled polymers. As mentioned earlier, the lack of ionic strength dependence militates further against this model.

In view of the exclusion of the random-coil and sphere models by hydro-dynamic methods, and the acceptance of the Watson–Crick model, it is pertinent to consider the rigid-rod model for DNA in solution. The light scattering reciprocal envelope $(Kc/I_\theta \, v \cdot \sin^2 \theta/2)$ of DNA exhibits a pronounced downward curvature, indicative of a highly extended structure (excluding the alternative possibility that it is due to extreme polydispersity of the sample). On comparing the data with that expected for the two possible alternatives, the rigid rod and the gently coiled worm-like coil, it is found that the latter is preferred and gives a linear density in good agreement with that predicted by the Watson–Crick model.

Further evidence that DNA is intermediate in nature between a random coil and a rigid rod comes from studies of *sonicates* of DNA, *i.e.* a homologous series of polymer samples of varying molecular weight prepared by exposing DNA solutions to ultrasonic waves for various times[10]. The following relations were observed:

$$s_0 = 0.063 \, M_w^{0.37}$$
$$[\eta] = 1.45 \cdot 10^{-6} \, M_w^{1.12}$$
$$\rho = 2.7 \cdot 10^{-9} \, M_w^{0.58}$$

[*] It should be mentioned that due to practical difficulties measurements cannot be made at angles less than $\theta = 20°$. For very large particles, θ is such that $h^2\rho^2$ is appreciable in comparison to 1, so that more terms should be included in the expression for $P(\theta)$. Simply, this means that the extrapolation to $\theta = 0$ is not unambiguous, introducing an uncertainty into both M_w and ρ.

References p. 288

in which s_0 is the sedimentation constant connected to water at 20°, $[\eta]$ the intrinsic viscosity, and ρ the radius of gyration.

The exponents occurring within these relations may be compared with those predicted on the basis of various models (Table I).

TABLE I

MOLECULAR WEIGHT EXPONENTS

	a_s	a_n	a_ρ
Native DNA	0.37	1.12	0.58
Random coil (theory)	0.33–0.5	0.5–1.0	0.5
Rigid rod (theory)	0.2	1.70	1.0
Denatured DNA	0.35	0.91	—
RNA	0.49	0.53	—

a_s, a_n and a_ρ are the exponents occurring in the relations $s_o = K_s M_w^{a_s}$, $[\eta] = K_n M_w^{a_n}$ and $\rho = K_\rho M_w^{a_\rho}$

These relations provide a routine method of estimating the molecular weight of native DNA samples. For an unknown sample, however, the preferred method is to use the well known Flory–Maldelkern relation:

$$M = \left(\frac{s_o [\eta]^{\frac{1}{3}} \eta_o N}{\beta (1 - \bar{v}d)} \right)^{\frac{3}{2}}$$

in wich ρ_o is the viscosity of the solvent, $\bar{v}$ and d the partial specific volume and density of the polymer and solvent, N the Avogadro number, and β a slowly varying function depending on the axial ratio and lying between $2.21 \cdot 10^6$ for spheres and $3.50 \cdot 10^6$ for infinite axial ratio. In summary the physical chemistry of DNA suggests that in solution it behaves as a highly extended *worm-like* molecule, possessing the Watson-Crick double helical structure. The thread-like character may be seen by considering a typical DNA molecule of molecular weight 8 million. This would have a fully extended length of 40,000 Å, and a diameter of only 20 Å. A model the thickness of a normal pencil would have a length of 14 m!

Recently an exception to the above discussion has been observed. The small coliphage φX174 possesses DNA which behaves as a single-stranded polynucleotide chain exhibiting the expected properties of low viscosity with marked ionic strength dependence[6].

(b) Denaturation

As was mentioned earlier, various treatments, such as heating and extremes of pH, result in loss of the secondary structure of the *native* DNA, *i.e.*

denaturation. These changes do not involve primary covalent chemical bonds, but are due to destruction of H-bonding between the bases of the two polynucleotide chains. Denaturation is readily detected by a fall in viscosity, or specific optical rotation, but most conveniently by an increase in the ultraviolet extinction coefficient of about 40% (hyperchromic effect) over the native value of 213 at 260 mμ, the region of maximum absorption[*]. Since the H-bonds involved are periodic they are destroyed in a cooperative manner similar to the melting of a crystal and, in the case of DNA, due to the large number of bonds involved, the transition is very sharp, occurring over a range of a few degrees or a few tenths of a pH unit. Furthermore, the removal of ionised salts from the solution has the effect of lowering the temperature at which denaturation occurs due to decreased shielding of the charged phosphate groups. This effect is sufficient such that in the absence of salt, denaturation occurs at room temperature.

The temperature at which denaturation occurs on heating has also been found to depend upon the base composition of the DNA sample (*i.e.*, $(A+T)/(G+C)$ ratio)[2]. Due to the higher thermal stability of the G–C bond, on raising the temperature, molecules of a low G + C content denature first so that at any point during the denaturation process the sample consists of denatured DNA of low G + C content, and native DNA of a higher G + C content. Measurement of the temperature range over which a given sample is denatured, therefore, provides an indication of the heterogeneity of *composition* of the individual molecules composing the sample[**]. Thus it was found, as might be expected, that the thermal transition of viral DNA was much sharper than that from an animal source. The varying compositional heterogeneity of various DNA's was confirmed by the completely different technique of density gradient ultracentrifugation[11]. In this technique low-speed centrifugation of a salt solution results in the formation of a stable concentration gradient, *i.e.* equilibrium density gradient, in the ultracentrifuge cell. DNA present in the salt solution migrates to a position in the cell of equivalent density. Since the density of DNA also depends on the G + C content[3, 12], the band width of the DNA in the cell is an independent measure of the compositional heterogeneity of the sample.

The product of thermal denaturation has led to some controversy. Early reports that the molecular weight was halved have not been confirmed and recent reinvestigation of the problem has shown[13] that under conditions

---

[*] The hyperchromic effect is due to a rearrangement of the electron density distribution within the bases, accompanying the *unstacking* of the bases following the destruction of H-bonding.
[**] This heterogeneity was early indicated by experiments involving chromatographic separation of DNA into fractions having differing base ratios.

normally employed non-specific aggregation of the denatured DNA takes place. However, if the heating is carried out in a medium of low salt concentration, and with a low concentration of DNA, the molecular weight of the DNA is indeed halved, the separated single-stranded polynucleotide chains then undergoing thermal degradation (*i.e.* destruction of covalent bonds within the chain). The product was shown to behave as a single polyelectrolyte chain (see Table I), but due to residual intra-molecular H-bonding between the bases was more compact than the random coil.

Surprisingly, it has been found possible in a few favourable cases to *renature* DNA in which the strands have been separated by heat denaturation[13, 14]. In the case of bacterial and viral DNA, where the sample contains few species of molecules, *in vitro* recombination of separated strands may occur, and in the case of transforming principle, full biological activity regained.

(c) Degradation

The breakage of covalent bonds within the DNA molecule with subsequent decrease in molecular weight may be brought about by various procedures which give rise to two products:

(*1*) Limited enzymic digestion, treatment with ultrasonic waves, and shearing give rise to a product in which a substantial part of the secondary structure of native DNA is retained. Enzymic digestion with DNAase involves the isolated random scission of a single chain. Due to the duplex nature of DNA the molecular weight does not fall until two scissions in opposite chains come into juxtaposition. This results in an autocatalytic effect, the molecular weight falling more and more rapidly as degradation proceeds.

(*2*) The second class of procedures includes heating and exposure to extremes of pH. Here the initial effect is destruction of the secondary structure, followed by hydrolysis of phosphoester bonds, and the liberation of bases.

2. Ribonucleic acid (RNA)

RNA samples may be classified for convenience in a manner partly dependent on their origin and postulated function, and partly on their molecular size. Soluble or *transfer* RNA of low molecular weight ($M \sim 16,000$), is found distributed throughout the animal and bacterial cells, and is believed to be responsible for the transfer of amino acids to the site of protein synthesis in the cell. Particulate or *microsomal* RNA of higher molecular weight (samples of 0.6 and 1.1 million have been isolated) is found in the microsome fraction of cell debris, and is believed to direct the sequence of amino acids during synthesis. Finally, one may consider the RNA present in some viruses, and believed to correspond to DNA in that it carries the viral genetic information. In this case the molecular weight is often in the same range as DNA (*e.g.* tobacco mosaic virus (TMV) RNA has a molecular weight of 2 million).

The physical chemistry of these RNA's in solution is less well understood than that of DNA, partly because of the fewer investigations carried out. Mainly, however, it is due to the greater instability of RNA solutions, and the lower molecular weights observed, which makes distinction between the various possible models by physico-chemical measurements more difficult (*e.g.* in light scattering, the particle-scattering factors for all geometrical models become identically equal to 1 as the molecular size decreases).

Despite these difficulties, however, the main features are clear[15, 16]. All the RNA's examined in solution had properties quite unlike those of DNA. The viscosity was much lower than that for DNA of an equivalent molecular weight, indicating a more compact molecule. Furthermore, in contrast to DNA, the viscosity was markedly dependent on ionic strength, the effect being completely reversible. These studies were consistent only with a model in which RNA behaved as a randomly coiled single polynucleotide chain in aqueous solution. More recent studies have shown that, like DNA, RNA exhibits a marked hyperchromic effect on heating or exposure to extremes of pH. The magnitude of the effect, although less than that observed for DNA, was such as to indicate that about 50% of the bases were hydrogen-bonded in neutral salt solution. Furthermore, the temperature at which these changes in ultraviolet absorption occurred was dependent on the base ratio of the RNA in a manner reminiscent of that in DNA. In contrast, however, the changes were much less abrupt than those with DNA and were completely reversible, suggesting that only short lengths of adjacent nucleotides were involved.

Evidence that the secondary structure was helical in nature came from the parallel changes observed in the specific optical rotation, which again resembled those found in DNA. As a result of these observations, the most recent models of RNA involve a single polynucleotide chain which is doubled up in such a way that short regions of anti-parallel double helical regions are linked with randomly coiled chains of non-bonded bases[17].

Observations that similar hyperchromic changes are observed in micro-somes from *E. coli* suggest that such a structure obtains in the bacterial cell. In the case of TMV, although the isolated RNA in solution exhibits the secondary structure described above, when present in the virus it is a fully extended single polynucleotide chain and no base-pairing is possible.

ADDENDUM

Recent work has shown that currently employed isolation procedures for DNA seriously degrade the sample. Thus the coliphage T2 contains a single DNA molecule of molecular weight 120 million[18, 19] and not 45 million as quoted. Even more remarkable, the bacterium *E. coli*, which behaves genetically as if possessing a single linkage group, has been found to contain a single DNA molecule[20]. Doubtless molecular weight estimates for DNA from other sources will be drastically revised in the light of these studies.

An additional RNA species, *messenger RNA*, has been discovered[21]. This RNA, which in bacteria undergoes rapid turnover, is responsible for the transfer of genetic information from DNA to the sites of protein synthesis, the ribosomes (microsomal particles). The RNA normally present in ribosomes does not undergo turnover, and is believed to be devoid of genetic importance.

REVIEW ARTICLES

[1] A. R. PEACOCKE, Structure and Physical Chemistry of Nucleic Acids, *Progr. in Biophys.*, 10 (1959) 55.

[2] K. V. SHOOTER, Physical Chemistry of DNA, *Progr. in Biophys.*, 8 (1957) 309.

[3] C. SADRON, DNA's as Macromolecules, in E. CHARGAFF AND J. N. DAVIDSON (Eds.), *The Nucleic Acids*, Vol. 3, Academic Press, New York, 1960, p. 1.

[4] D. O. JORDAN, The Physical Properties of Nucleic Acids, in E. CHARGAFF AND J. N. DAVIDSON (Eds.), *The Nucleic Acids*, Vol. 1, Academic Press, New York, 1955, p. 447.

[5] E. P. GEIDUSCHEK AND A. HOLZER, Application of Light Scattering to Biological Systems: DNA and Muscle Proteins, *Advances in Biol. and Med. Phys.*, 6 (1958) 432.

REFERENCES

[1] J. A.V. BUTLER, *Proc. 4th Intern. Congr. Biochem.,Vol. IX*, Pergamon, London, 1959, p. 77.

[2] J. MARMUR AND P. DOTY, *Nature*, 183 (1959) 1427.

[3] N. SUEOKA, J. MARMUR AND P. DOTY, *Nature*, 183 (1959) 1429.

[4] P. F. DAVIDSON, *Proc. Natl. Acad. Sci. U.S.*, 45 (1959) 1560.

[5] C. LEVINTHAL AND C. A. THOMAS, *Chemical Basis of Heredity*, Johns Hopkins University Press, 1958.

[6] R. L. SINSHEIMER, *J. Mol. Biol.*, 1 (1957) 43.

[7] J. D. WATSON AND F. H. C. CRICK, *Nature*, 171 (1953) 737.

[8] B. E. CONWAY AND J. A. V. BUTLER, *J. Polymer Sci.*, 12 (1954) 199.

[9] J. M. GULLAND, D. O. JORDAN AND H. F. W. TAYLOR, *J. Chem. Soc.*, (1947) 1131.

[10] P. DOTY, R. B. McGILL AND S. A. RICE, *Proc. Natl. Acad. Sci. U.S.*, 44 (1958) 432.

[11] M. MESELSON, F. W. STAHL AND J. VINOGRAD, *Proc. Natl. Acad. Sci. U.S.*, 43 (1957) 581.

[12] R. ROLFE AND M. MESELSON, *Proc. Natl. Acad. Sci. U.S.*, 45 (1959) 1039.

[13] P. DOTY, J. MARMUR, J. EIGNER AND C. SCHILDKRAUT, *Proc. Natl. Acad. Sci. U.S.*, 46 (1960) 461.

[14] J. MARMUR AND D. LANE, *Proc. Natl. Acad. Sci. U.S.*, 46 (1960) 453.

[15] U. Z. LITTAUER AND H. EISENBERG, *Biochim. Biophys. Acta*, 32 (1959) 320.

[16] P. DOTY, H. BOEDTKER, J. R. FRESCO, R. HASELKORN AND M. LITT, *Proc. Natl. Acad. Sci. U.S.*, 45 (1959) 482.

[17] J. FRESCO, B. M. ALBERTS AND P. DOTY, *Nature*, 188 (1960) 98.

[18] E. BURGI AND A. D. HERSHEY, *J. Mol. Biol.*, 3 (1961) 458.

[19] J. CAIRNS, *J. Mol. Biol.*, 3 (1961) 756.

[20] J. CAIRNS, *J. Mol. Biol.*, 4 (1962) 407.

[21] S. BRENNER, F. JACOB AND M. MESELSON, *Nature*, 190 (1961) 576.

Chapter IV

Physical Properties of the Nucleic Acids

Section c

Spectroscopic Properties

G. R. WILKINSON

Physics Department, King's College, London (Great Britain)

As with the other physical properties of DNA it is necessary in considering its spectroscopic properties to distinguish between crystalline material with varying water content and material in solution, and also between *native* DNA and material which is denatured in some way. Spectroscopic studies are concerned with the investigation of the transitions induced by electromagnetic radiation between the allowed vibrational and electronic energy levels and between the magnetic energy levels which arise when unpaired electrons and nuclei with spin $I \geqslant 0$ are placed in a magnetic field. With oriented microcrystalline specimens of DNA the anisotropy of the absorption may be obtained using polarized electromagnetic radiation and hence more useful information can be obtained in this way about DNA than the less regular RNA.

1. The infrared spectrum

The infrared absorption spectrum of a crystalline film of a few microns thick of the lithium salt of DNA at 98% relative humidity (D_2O as well as H_2O) is shown in Fig. 1a,b (the spectrum of NaDNA is essentially identical with that of LiDNA). Many of the absorption bands may be assigned to the vibration of specific atomic groups. Thus the band in the 1650 cm^{-1} region is essentially due to the in plane vibrations within the purine and pyrimidine bases and consequently the maximum absorption occurs when the electric vector of the infrared radiation is perpendicular to the polymer axis. We define the dichroic ratio as the ratio of the absorption with the electric vector of the radiation perpendicular to the polymer axis to the

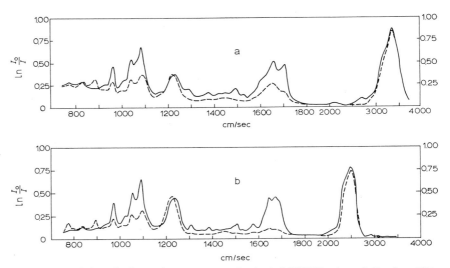

Fig. 1a. The infrared absorption spectrum of oriented LiDNA at a relative humidity of 86 % (H₂O) recorded using polarized radiation. ———— electric vector ⊥ʳ to fibre axis; ----- electric vector //ᴸ to fibre axis.
Fig. 1b. The infrared absorption spectrum of partially deuterated LiDNA at a relative humidity of 86 % (D₂O) recorded using polarized radiation. ———— electric vector ⊥ʳ to fibre axis; ----- electric vector //ᴸ to fibre axis.

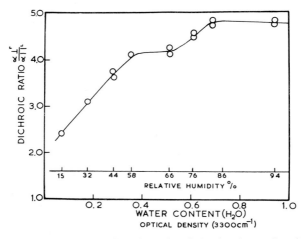

Fig. 2. The variation of the dichroic ratio of the in plane vibrations of the bases (1650 cm⁻¹) with water content. The scale at the bottom shows both the relative humidity of the atmosphere to which the sample was exposed as well as the water content. The latter was measured by determining the intensity of the H₂O band in the 3300 cm⁻¹ region.

absorption at the same frequency with the electric vector parallel to the axis. The variation in the observed dichroic ratio at 1650 cm^{-1} when the oriented crystalline film is exposed to different relative humidities is shown in Fig. 2. As water is removed the bases tilt and the angle calculated for the tilt is about 15° at ~ 70% RH in fair agreement with the value previously obtained by X-ray diffraction analysis of the A structure which exists at that humidity. Other bands such as those in the 3300–3400 cm^{-1} region may be assigned to N–H and O–H stretching vibrations. On deuteration these bands disappear and are replaced by others in the 2500 cm^{-1} region. The C–H groups do not exchange their protons on exposure to heavy water and consequently their vibrations in the 3000 cm^{-1} region are largely unchanged. The band at 1230 cm^{-1} is essentially due to the asymmetric stretching vibration of

the phosphate $P\underset{\diagdown O}{\overset{\diagup O}{}}$ group. The position of this band changes with the

water content of the specimen because of the removal of water molecules hydrogen-bonded to the oxygen atoms. In the 900–1100 cm^{-1} region the absorption is due to the vibration of the phosphate ester groups and to those of the sugar rings. The band at 894 cm^{-1}, which has a high parallel dichroism and is unaffected by exposure to D_2O, is an out of plane bending vibration of some of the C–H bonds in the bases.

The rate of deuteration of the labile protons when a crystalline DNA film is exposed to an atmosphere of D_2O is readily followed by observing the growth of the N–D and O–D absorption bands and the corresponding disappearance of the N–H and O–H bands. It is found that the exchange rate occurs at virtually the same rate as D_2O diffuses into the film. This clearly indicates that the hydrogen atoms in the hydrogen bonds between the base pairs are constantly being exchanged with the surrounding water protons.

2. The ultraviolet spectrum

Fig. 3 shows the ultraviolet absorption spectrum of a crystalline film about a quarter of a micron thick at a relative humidity of 90%. The ultraviolet absorption in the 30,000–40,000 cm^{-1} region is due to electronic transitions of both the $n \rightarrow \pi$ (weak) and $\pi \rightarrow \pi$ (strong) types. The latter are known to have transition moments in the planes of the bases and hence the maximum absorption occurs when the electric vector of the radiation is perpendicular to the polymer axis. The dichroic ratio of 4.7 to 1 obtained for these ultraviolet absorption bands agrees well with the values observed for the dichroic ratio of the infrared absorption band at 1650 cm^{-1} due to the excitation of the in plane vibrations of the bases.

The variation in the intensity of the ultraviolet absorption bands is of value in studying the configuration of DNA in solution. On breaking the twin helical structure—which is readily achieved by heating above about 80°—, the absorption at 37,700 cm^{-1} (2650 Å) increases by about 45%. This change in the intensity of the absorption is partly due to the breaking of hydrogen bonds which maintain the base pairs in essentially the same

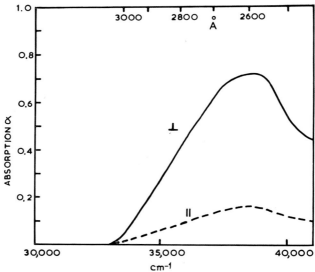

Fig. 3. The ultraviolet absorption spectrum of oriented DNA recorded with the electric vector of the radiation parallel and perpendicular to the polymer axis.

plane and their replacement by hydrogen bonds to water and also to the breakdown of the regular stacking of the base pairs one above the other.

The strong negative birefringence of oriented DNA results from the high in plane polarizability of the purine and pyrimidine bases. The difference in the refractive indices measured with the electric vector of visible light perpendicular and parallel to the fibre axis is 0.05.

3. Magnetic resonance studies

Preliminary nuclear magnetic resonance studies on DNA confirm that the water in immediate contact with the polyelectrolyte is much more strongly bound than that further away. It is unlikely that free radicals occur in appreciable numbers in pure DNA and hence the observation of an electron spin resonance spectrum requires the irradiation with U.V. rays, X-rays, γ-rays, electrons, etc., to produce the unpaired electrons.

4. RNA

The infrared spectrum of RNA and heat-denatured DNA are very similar. Efforts to produce highly oriented specimens of RNA which reveal either strong infrared or ultraviolet dichroism have not yet been successful. These observations support the view that RNA has a much less ordered structure than DNA.

REFERENCES

[1] E. Bradbury, W. C. Price and G. R. Wilkinson, *J. Mol. Biol.*, 3 (1961) 301.
[2] G. B. B. M. Sutherland and M. Tsuboi, *Proc. Roy. Soc. (London)*, A, 239 (1957) 446.

SUBJECT INDEX

PRINTED IN THE NETHERLANDS BY

DRUKKERIJ MEIJER – WORMERVEER AND AMSTERDAM